MARIJUANA

THE SECOND TRIP

MARIJUANA

THE SECOND TRIP

REVISED EDITION

EDWARD R. BLOOMQUIST, M.D.

Associate Clinical Professor of Anesthesiology
School of Medicine
University of Southern California

with a foreword by
William Cahn, District Attorney, Nassau County, New York

GLENCOE PRESS
A division of Benziger Bruce & Glencoe, Inc.
Beverly Hills, California
Collier-Macmillan Limited, London

To Carol Diane,
My lovely "Gigi"

Glencoe Press
A division of Benziger Bruce & Glencoe, Inc.
8701 Wilshire Boulevard
Beverly Hills, California 90211
Collier-Macmillan Canada, Ltd., Toronto, Canada

Library of Congress catalog card number: 75–171360

Second printing, 1972

contents

foreword

TIME AND TIME AGAIN, in my twenty-one years as Prosecutor, I have witnessed man's inhumanity to his fellow man. Every day, I have observed the injustices and cruelty men can inflict on each other. Yet, nothing is more painful and distressing to me than the growing tragedy of drug experimentation and abuse among our youth.

Not only have I witnessed the tragedy of these young people becoming involved in criminal activity, and the effect of such involvement on their future, and on their families and friends, but above all, I have seen the character-deforming effects of drug abuse and addiction upon our youth. I have seen the bodies and minds of once vibrant, intelligent, and creative young people destroyed, so that they become self-centered, withdrawn, and totally useless to themselves and society.

Not only as a District Attorney, but as a parent and concerned citizen, I am appalled and distressed by the waste of
these lives, and by the endless suffering that is the legacy of drug
abuse. As you have probably done, I have endeavored to educate myself in this problem, to seek out new solutions, to explore
with those who are seeking greater understanding of the problem and its causes. For I believe that much of the trouble is
traceable to our deficiencies of knowledge, and to the widespread distortion and neglect of relevant available information.

Among the most alarming developments in the drug scene
over the past few years is the dramatic acceleration in the use of
marijuana by our young people. Marijuana is the predominantly
abused drug of our youth. It has been their passport into the
drug culture, and is the fountainhead from which springs the
contagious infection of drug abuse and addiction.

Therefore, as President of the National District Attorneys'
Association, I have sought out experts from other disciplines to
educate us, to explore with us, to present to us their research and
opinions, and their proposals to combat the problem. For I believe that we in law enforcement must recognize that the problem of drug abuse encompasses a whole spectrum of disciplines,
from law enforcement to public health, from the educator to the
sociologist. Each of us has a vital stake in combating the loom-
ing menace of drug abuse which threatens our young people.
Above all, we in law enforcement must recognize that the meth-
odology of prosecution must be supplemented by the fullest
range of thought and informational resources from all disciplines.

Those of us who deal with the situation daily have observed
that many of our young people have been enticed into drug
abuse by false and misleading information, especially concerning marijuana. Both adults and young people have been confused and perplexed by the controversy over the dangers of
marijuana, and by the arguments of those who have advocated
its legalization.

In 1969, at the first National District Attorneys' Association
Institute on Drugs, Dr. Edward R. Bloomquist, in a factual and
scholarly lecture, tore aside the veil of confusion in his report
on the dangers of marijuana abuse and its effect on youth and
society. In his book, *Marijuana: The Second Trip,* Dr. Bloom-

quist continues his mission to educate us in the facts about marijuana, in terms each of us can understand.

This is one book about marijuana in which you will find answers to all your questions, a book that will aid you in exploring the whole range of the marijuana controversy. If you want to know the how, why, and where of the drug, reading this book is a must for you.

Dr. Bloomquist's book should be read by anyone who seeks a better understanding of marijuana, in order to prepare himself to meet the problems and controversy surrounding drug abuse. The book is a definitive work of integrity and scholarship. In easily-understood laymen's language, Dr. Bloomquist traces the history of marijuana from culture to culture, exploring the manner in which each society has sought to meet the problem. He surveys the drug scene, looking at types of users and the relationship of marijuana to other drugs. He explores the language of the marijuana world, and the research findings, from medical views on the drug's effect to the state of mind of the drug abuser. Dr. Bloomquist brings into focus and clinically analyzes the varied and controversial positions taken on marijuana, in a manner only possible for someone possessing his expertise in medicine and public health. Every facet of the marijuana problem is explored, whether it be in Vietnam, the emerging nations of Africa, or our own college campuses. The book also examines the laws restricting marijuana use, in this country and throughout the world, and the reasoning of the judges in reaching the major legal decisions on the drug.

Dr. Bloomquist presents his proposals for resolving the problem of how to deal with marijuana use. Whether one agrees or not, these proposals are novel and interesting, and show a deep compassion and understanding of the problems of the whole drug scene.

Dr. Bloomquist has performed an invaluable service in adding to our understanding, and in exploring and advancing new concepts and proposals to resolve the problem of marijuana abuse.

If we believe that education is the one effective weapon against ignorance, then reading this book will certainly dispel our ignorance about marijuana, and lead us toward a solution.

The drug problem is one of the great challenges of our time. It is a challenge to our social imagination and our sense of purpose. I am honored to introduce *Marijuana: The Second Trip.* I trust that you will find it as valuable, interesting, and informative as I have.

> — William Cahn
> District Attorney
> Nassau County, New York

May, 1971

acknowledgments

I WISH TO EXPRESS my grateful thanks for the assistance of Dr. Jared Tinklenberg, Assistant Professor of Psychiatry at Stanford University School of Medicine, for his careful review of the manuscript, and for the invaluable insights provided by those young people who have shared their experiences with me and helped me to bridge the "generation gap."

*Illustration of cannabis, or hemp, from the works of
Dioscorides, first century after Christ.*

SINGLE LEAF CAN
CONSIST OF THREE
TO ELEVEN LEAFLETS.
FIFTEEN HAVE BEEN
REPORTED.

9-30 m.

3 to 10 feet tall

Illustrations by Rudolph Freund

Illustration of cannabis, or hemp, from the International
Drug Abuse Manual, *twentieth century after Christ.*

(From *The International Drug Abuse Manual,* Published by Smith Kline
& French Laboratories, Philadelphia, Pennsylvania, © 1969. Reprinted by
permission.)

"It's the class of '60 back for its reunion, and their marijuana harvest!"

Grin and Bear It by Lichty. Courtesy of Publishers-Hall Syndicate,

from
cannabis
to
marijuana

Some call it evolution
And others call it God.
—WILLIAM CARRUTH

*I*T'S WHAT'S HAPPENING—marijuana, leading the list of the mind expanding drugs, the easiest to acquire, the cheapest, the most widely used and seemingly the safest. But what exactly is this particular drug? How does a person recognize marijuana or start to understand its effects?

Long before marijuana became something smoked by the boy next door, it was an easily propagated weed growing abundantly in subtropical and temperate climates. In the eighteenth century the great Swedish father of botanical classification, Carl von Linné (Linnaeus), gave marijuana the genus and species name of *Cannabis sativa L.* And so it is technically known today. Users refer to it as "pot," "Mary Jane," or "grass," or any one of a myriad of other names. For purposes of clarity, however, we shall refer to it as cannabis or marijuana.

Although the present controversy over cannabis is one concerning the *use* of a substance obtained from the cannabis plant, it is necessary to know something about the plant and its growth pattern if we are to understand the nature and activity of its product. Accordingly, in this first chapter we shall examine the botanical facts about cannabis, its growth and cultivation, the appearance of the plant in its growing state, the preparation of the characteristic product marijuana, some medical effects of marijuana use, and the pharmacology of cannabis. A tall order, to be sure, but necessary if we are to understand how a wild weed has become a symbol of the turned-on generation.

Cannabis is a unique and intriguing plant. At one time it was called the "green goddess" although this nickname had no relationship to the plant's color. Actually it described the greenish tinted extract-of-cannabis which owed its hue to the presence of an incidental adulterant, copper, that came from the metal vessels used to manufacture the medicinal.[1] Cannabis exists in a single species, and in this species in a large number of varieties which differ from one another in the quantity and potency of the resin they produce. Cannabis indica, for instance, contains the most potent resin of the varieties. This resin (which Americans usually call hashish) is five to six times more intoxicating than the resin of Cannabis americana, which grows in abundance in the United States.

The name *cannabis* is Latin for "hemp," or canelike plant, and denotes the genus of the hemp family of plants. *Sativa*, the species name, is Latin for "planted or sown," and denotes the nature of the plant's growth (from seed, not from perennial roots). The varieties of cannabis are usually named after their country of origin, i.e., mexicana, indica, etc. These varieties vary tremendously in the amount of psychoactive material they contain. These differences are largely conditioned by two factors: the genotypes (i.e., the ancestors) of the plants and the geographical location of plant growth. It is currently believed that two genotypes exist. One is a "drug" type that contains from one to five percent tetrahydrocannabinol (THC) content; the other is a "fiber" type which contains a high cannabidiol (CBD) content.[2] It is possible that cannabidiol may be a precursor of THC in the growing plant.[3]

The chemistry of marijuana is distinct, although pharmacologically it has some similarities to properties of the stimulant, sedative, analgesic, and psychotomimetic classes of drugs. Quoting various researchers, the recent HEW report to Congress makes several interesting observations.[4] Cannabis in high doses may precipitate effects similar in many ways to those of LSD, although acid is 160 times more potent as a psychotomimetic than is Delta-9-transtetrahydrocannabinol (THC) which is thought to be the most psychoactive chemical in cannabis. The strong hallucinogens (i.e., LSD and mescaline) effect some body changes not observed with the use of cannabis, i.e., an increased body temperature, an increased blood pressure, and dilated pupils. Cannabis, on the other hand, produces some findings not seen with acid, such as a sharply increased pulse rate and reddening of the eyes.

Cannabis intoxication tends to put most people to sleep whereas the intoxication of LSD causes wakefulness. Cannabis, therefore, especially in low doses, may behave somewhat as does alcohol. In fact, with low doses, subjects often experience difficulty differentiating the effects of alcohol from marijuana, although there is a difference. In the early time-action curve of marijuana intoxication there is central nervous system stimulation; only later does the biphasic nature of the experience become apparent and the user becomes relaxed and sleepy.[5] At higher levels, however, the marijuana high is easily distinguishable from alcoholic intoxication. As we shall see later, there are some definite differences between these two drugs.

Cannabis as a plant is more commonly known as hemp. As such it has a long history of commercial usefulness. Among industrial growers hemp is seldom thought of as a source of psychotoxins. Rather, it is commercially the source of red oil which is an ingredient of various paints, varnishes, and linoleum, while the plant itself serves as a basic substance for the production of twine, rope, bags, clothing, and certain papers.

Although the botanical terms place cannabis in the hemp genus, further classification is open to dispute. Some botanists insist that hemp belongs to the mulberry family, *Moraceae,* which also includes the sycamore. Others feel its uniqueness justifies establishing a separate single-member botanical family, which they term *Cannabinacae.*

As a matter of fact, no one other than Linneaus has thus far properly classified the chemical constituents of this plant, for as HEW notes, they "cannot be accurately classified without specifying dose level."[6] For this reason this author has campaigned for some time to have the plant and its chemicals classified for the thing they really are: Cannabis sativa L, including its naturally occurring and synthetically produced pharmacological substances. To call them anything else, or to attempt to classify the chemicals as stimulants, depressants, hallucinogens, or a combination of these as has been done in the past merely confuses the issue.

GROWTH AND CULTIVATION

Cannabis is an herbaceous annual, that is, a leafy plant with little or no woody parts, which grows for a season, dies down, then springs up again the following year from its own seed. The seed is essential, since cannabis will not regrow from last season's roots. Cannabis is dioecious; it requires both a male and a female plant to reproduce itself. Both sexes have flowering tops and both produce resin that has psychotropic (mind-affecting) properties. The various parts of the plant differ immensely in the amount of active principles they contain. The upper parts of the plant, i.e., the leaves and flowering tops, contain the most tetrahydrocannabinols. These are believed to be the main psychoactive chemicals contained in cannabis. The lower parts of the plant contain very little chemical. The clear, varnish-like resin produced by the flowering tops of the female plant contains from five to ten times more psychoactive ingredient than the leaves.[7]

The male and female cannabis plants look very much alike to the casual observer, but their reproductive functions become quite specific as the plants mature. When the male plant blossoms, it produces flowers that open wide, exposing pollen-laden stamens with their tiny life-bearing male anthers. The female also produces flowers that contain an inconspicuous pistil, or egg-bearing female flower, which patiently awaits the arrival of the pollen. The female plant must depend upon a properly directed wind to deliver the pollen. Other plants can rely on insects for the transportation of their pollen. Not cannabis. Insects usually refuse to have anything to do with this plant. So cannabis is quite literally propagated by the breeze. Once a capricious wind has wafted the pollen to the female, reproduction starts; mature seeds form and fall to the ground, and the cycle begins again.

The female of the species is the hardier of the two. Once it has served its reproductive purpose, the male dies. Under controlled agricultural circumstances the male does not even die naturally. Growers yank it out by the roots once pollination has occurred. In India, where cannabis cultivation has been highly developed, the male never gets the chance to pollinate the female—the plant is destroyed once it begins to show its sex. The Indians provide a "ganja" (marijuana) doctor who travels up and down the commercial fields trimming the lower branches of the female plants to better encourage resin production, while at the same time eliminating the male plants. Indians believe the female plants yield much better ganja if they are not fertilized.

Cannabis lives from spring to fall, then dies. Next spring it reappears from seeds that are unbelievably hardy. As long as the seeds can be protected by a soft covering of soil or leaves, cannabis will continue to spread as a wild weed. Under these conditions resin production tends to increase and its potency becomes much more marked. Cannabis does particularly well in areas where the soil is disturbed each year. Flooded plains provide an excellent medium for growth. Shady, stable areas will not permit the plant to reproduce itself, for cannabis thrives on soil instability. In general, it may be assumed that if thistle, milkweed, dandelion, and similar weed growths do well, cannabis will do even better.

Those interested in cultivating cannabis for industrial purposes are more concerned with plants grown in cold or temperate regions where the subsoil is moist and the rain is abundant. Plants growing in these areas are soft and fibrous and thus of greater commercial value. Hot, dry areas, on the other hand, produce brittle fibers in contrast to those that grow in cooler climates. Resin produced in arid countries is copious, heavy and sticky; its purpose is to protect the tender reproductive parts of the plants from the dehydrating rays of the sun. The stickier the resin the greater the intoxication potential, for this type of exudate has a much higher chemical content. Marijuana users, therefore, prefer a plant grown under circumstances unfavorable to the best commercial cannabis products.

Cannabis grows almost anywhere. It is a roadside flora in the southeastern United States; in the lowlands of the central United

States countless acres are covered with clusters of the plant. It will grow in almost any sort of soil, even where the nutrition is quite poor. Those who wish to grow it purposefully may do so on rooftops, in backyards, and in other unorthodox places. Two recently came to light in widely separated parts of the country: in Glendora, California, police found two twenty-year-old users trying to grow their supply in a local cemetery; and in Detroit, Michigan, authorities apprehended a known user trying to plant his garden in the center strip of the Willow Run Expressway! But the first prize for marijuana grown in obscure places goes to the variety noted by the *Marijuana Newsletter*[8] as "Manhattan Silver." This mythological plant was supposed to have originated from seeds flushed down the sewer by frightened users who were suddenly raided by police. Once the seeds reached the sewer, so the story goes, they germinated. Since they grew in darkness they produced a plant that was silver or white rather than green. Typical of fairy tales, this legendary plant was supposed to be especially potent.

Cannabis is so hardy and ubiquitous that anyone who wishes a supply of his own for tripping purposes faces little difficulty in securing it, other than having to guard against arrest. As John Rosevear,[9] who has written a step-by-step commentary describing the natural and artificial culture of the weed, has noted, "There are as many ways of growing marijuana as there are of growing corn." The Mexicans, for instance, merely poke a hole in the ground, dump in some seed, and wait for nature to take over. The seeds are so easy to grow that if a handful is tossed on the ground and pressed in with one's foot they will usually anchor and become plants. Since cannabis has few natural enemies, there is little to hinder its growth.

If insects are reticent to pollinate cannabis, they are even less prone to consume it for food. Thus cannabis is almost immune to attacks by locusts, grasshoppers, and similar pests. As for spiders, they may build their nests around the base of the plant, but they will usually not attack the plant itself. There are exceptions to this; researcher Vincent De Paul Lynch reports having lost several crops to cannabis-eating insects.[10]

Cannabis is usually resistant to weather change, although heavy frosts may kill it. It may also be choked out by heavy vines and other strong weeds. The only significant enemy the plant has is man, who has made various efforts to destroy it. In the thirties, when hysteria ran high against marijuana, WPA workers in New York were assigned to remove the offending growth from vacant lots in the Bronx, in Brooklyn, Queens, and Richmond. In the first seven months of 1936, forty tons of cannabis were pulled and destroyed from these four boroughs of New York City alone.[11] In 1935, New York City relief labor eliminated 170 tons of cannabis from 260 lots during a two-month period,[12] and in 1951, authorities in the same city destroyed 30,725 pounds of cannabis that grew in vacant lots.[13]

The campaign to destroy cannabis is and has always been an uneven battle; the plant can reproduce itself and grow faster than man can detect and uproot it. The plant's reproductive process is so insistent and hardy that very few requirements are necessary for its survival. Rosevear notes this when he gives explicit instructions on cannabis cultivation, whether in a hothouse or in natural field gardens. Cannabis, he assures his readers, generally takes care of itself once it has been given the chance to root. All one needs are minimal instructions for gardening, a little sunlight, water, tinfoil, earth, and one seed. "God," Rosevear intones, "will do the rest."[14]

RECOGNIZING CANNABIS

Once a person has seen the cannabis plant or smelled its resin or burning leaves, it is difficult to forget it. Cannabis even looks unusual. Its stalk is hollow, leafy, and four-cornered. It can become quite tall and may attain a height of some twenty feet, although ten feet seems to be the average. If uncrowded it will bush out with many branches. This is a disadvantage for one who wants to grow the plant for industrial purposes, since its fiber content is less if it grows uncrowded. It is an advantage to resin users, however, since sparse planting will increase the sap content. Cannabis smokers, therefore, try to keep their growing plants thinned down. Commercial producers, on the other hand, crowd them together.

The seeds are usually sown in May. The plants are harvested in September. When cannabis is full-grown its stalk may become three to four inches thick. Four ridges run lengthwise up this stalk with well-marked nodes or knots growing on it at four- to twenty-inch intervals. One of the more distinctive features of cannabis, if indeed the whole plant is not distinctive, is the appearance of its leaves. These are compound and consist of a number of smaller leaflets or lobules. The lobules are uneven in number, five to eleven being present in a single leaf. They are pointed at both ends like a slender canoe and are usually from two to six inches in length. The two proximal leaflets are always smaller than the rest of the grouping. The sides of the leaflets are serrated (sawtoothed) and pronounced ridges run diagonally from their center to the edges. The upper side of the leaflet is dark green, its underside being a lighter green. Long hairs run along the bottom of the leaflets; these couple back or reach out and retract toward the underside.

Plants containing a heavy resin content are sticky to the touch. The cannabis that grows in North Africa, for instance, will produce so much resin that at high noon the protective exudate may resemble dew.

Cannabis root structure is quite diversified. Usually there is a long tap root that is about one-tenth the length of the stalk. From this root small branches spread out to anchor the plant firmly in the earth. When the cannabis flowers, the resulting blossom appears as an irregular cluster of light yellowish green seeds. These egg-shaped seeds have encircling ridges with motley, lacy markings on their surfaces. Later, when they dry, the seeds will become brownish yellow, very hard in texture, and will exhibit sharp, definite ridges along the sides. On close examination they may seem identical. Their presence is one of the specific identifying features of the plant.

Cannabis remains green for long periods after it is cut. It may become brown as it ages but it does not resemble tobacco. When nonusers come into contact with cannabis it is either because someone shows it to them or because they inadvertently run across a supply or "stash." When so encountered, the leafy plants usually are bunched together in a plastic bag. In this condition cannabis is nondescript and may resemble any similarly stored weed. It differs from other weeds, however, in that it tends to retain its moisture, particularly if it is kept wrapped in plastic. Cannabis has a weedy, ropey, alfalfa-like odor that is intensified when it is ignited. When cannabis is lit it burns very hot and is easily extinguished. The odor is so distinctive that it is rarely forgotten. In addition, if one searches the "stash," typical seeds are almost always present.

Since the bushy, green cannabis plant is ornamental, it is not surprising that a number of innocent gardeners have been called to task by narcotics officers who inquired why marijuana plants had been included in the landscape. Such events may be dramatic and intense. The author recalls one instance when his commanding officer at a U.S. Air Force base was descended upon by alert agents who summarily chopped down a sixty-foot ornamental hedge the Colonel had been nuturing across the front of his lawn.

It is the resin of the cannabis plant, not the plant itself, that causes all the controversy. For in cannabis resin one finds potent psychotropics. This group of chemicals contains a number of related compounds: cannabinols, cannabidiols, cannabolic acid, and tetrahydrocannabinols. Synthetic forms of cannabis compounds were discovered in the 1940's. One, Synhexyl, was of particular interest because of its ability to produce euphoria. For a time it was used experimentally to combat the depression incident to withdrawal from opiates.

In 1942, H. J. Wollner and his associates isolated and identified a natural tetrahydrocannabinol.[15] This led to the current discovery of 1-$\triangle$-9 transtetrahydrocannabinol, also referred to by a different numbering system as 1-$\triangle$-1 transtetrahydrocannabinol or THC. Unfortunately, for the purpose of laboratory investigation, no compound seems to parallel the total effects of crude resin. Cannabis varies in its effectiveness from batch to batch both in potency and in the production of depressant, stimulant and euphoriant responses. Thus it is likely that several components with different biological properties may interact to produce the "typical" cannabis trip. This invariably makes it difficult to adequately evaluate cannabis in laboratory settings, a fact that recent studies, which will be discussed later, have frequently shown.

In the meantime, resin-laden cannabis leaves have become widely used and much discussed, so much so that an entire vocabulary has arisen to denote cannabis, especially among users. Many words are simply synonyms for cannabis, but they are tremendously varied and not necessarily linguistically related to each other. For the most part the words are street terms whose derivations may never be traced. The Latin term *cannabis* had a Greek origin (*kannabis*), whereas the English word *hemp* is derived from Middle English *hempe* and the earlier Old English form *henep* or *haenep*. Etymologically *hemp* and *cannabis* as words derive from the same obscure and unknown source, probably from the East. Marijuana (marahuana) may have arisen from the Mexican-Spanish *mariguana* or the Portuguese *mariguango,* both of which mean "intoxicant." On the other hand, it may have come from the Mexican-Spanish slang *Marijuana* (Mary Jane) or *Maria y Juana* (Mary and Jane), or even earlier from the Aztec *Milan-a-Huan* which the early Spanish conquerors could not pronounce and so enunciated *maria-juana* instead.

When English-speaking peoples refer to cannabis they usually employ the term *marijuana.* In these countries this term indicates a preparation made from the flowering or fruiting tops of the plant, preferably excluding seeds and stems, which are usually manicured out prior to smoking. If the smoker wants to save all of the substance, however, he may grind the entire plant in a pepper mill or similar apparatus.

If one talks about the cannabis plant per se, he may be referring to any variety of cannabis sativa. But if he specifically speaks of the isolated resin, crude or purified, he is referring to hashish or charas.

Charas is the pure resin extracted from the plant Cannabis indica. Americans refer to this substance as hashish. It is the most potent known existing pure form of naturally occurring cannabis resin and is from five to six times stronger in its psychotropic and psychotomimetic effects than the resin occurring in Cannabis americana. In ancient times, it is told, this resin was harvested by sending naked men through the fields to collect the substance on their skins. How much of this is fact and how much fancy is difficult to determine. In any event a more sophisticated modern industry presses the flower clusters between cheesecloth which absorbs and collects the resin.

In the Americas and England marijuana refers, as previously noted, to preparations made from the flowering tops and leaves of local cannabis plants, that is, Cannabis americana or mexicana. Many American users now tend to graduate in time from low resin-producing weeds to those containing higher potency resins, and in some instances, to other more powerful psychotropic agents if their use becomes more than casual. This has opened the illegal market to an increased demand for more potent cannabis products and a highly sophisticated industry is developing in order to supply varieties which differ in potency.

This, then, is cannabis, a unique plant that is in turn a weed, a commercial product, a sometimes medicinal drug, a "psychotropic" agent and, lately, the center of an intensely emotional controversy. Cannabis per se is a bit new to America in its role as a medium for socio-recreation and emotional release. To much of the rest of the world, however, the weed and its joys as well as its problems are an old, old story. To understand better what cannabis has meant in the past to other societies and other peoples, let us turn to the pages of history.

"*Peace pipe, my eye! Somebody here is smoking pot!*"

Grin and Bear It by Lichty. Courtesy of Publishers-Hall Syndicate

the
history
of the
weed

2

And God said, let the earth bring forth grass . . .
—GENESIS 1:11

*N*O ONE KNOWS WHERE it came from or, for
that matter, when man first discovered it, but cannabis was
probably known from the earliest of times. Even so, the plant
remains almost as much of a puzzle today as it was when man
first discovered he could use it to heighten perception and distort his concept of time, or as modern users say, to "trip" or
"turn on." Considering the important role cannabis has played
in the socioeconomic history of the world, the lack of information on the history of marijuana itself seems surprising. But,
then, cannabis contains amazing drugs than can make the impossible seem real and the real seem unnecessary.

How old is marijuana? An enthusiastic user may insist it is as
old as the earth, and it may well be. He may even refer to Genesis 1:11 (quoted above) to substantiate his contentions. For to

many marijuana has become a sacrament in a new religion that embraces a different kind of trinity: love, nonconformity, and anti-materialism. These users frequently fail to read on some sixty-two verses later in Genesis to the time when God showed Adam and Eve the exit from Paradise. "Cursed is the ground for thy sake," He said, "In sorrow shalt thou eat of it all the days of thy life: thorns also and thistles shall it bring forth to thee."

In many ways cannabis has been beneficial to humans. In earlier days man used the hemp plant as a source of rope and clothing and for the treatment, with varying degrees of success, of almost every imaginable illness. The full history of cannabis lies in its use as a commercial product, as well as in its current use as a social relaxant and/or a drug for escape from reality. Where students of psychopharmacology are concerned, it is cannabis the psychotropic, rather than cannabis the rope, that is of immediate interest. Marijuana's resin, then, not its fibre, is the subject of this chapter.

THE MYSTERIOUS ORIENT

History had to wait until the Chinese recorded the first adequate description of the hemp plant. Their writings indicate cannabis originated somewhere to the north of the Himalayan Mountains; but how it got there, or why, no one seems to know. The learned emperor Shen-Nung,[1] a surprisingly adept pharmacologist, was well aware that cannabis had medicinal effects. About the year 2737 B.C., when he wrote his book on pharmacology, he noted a number of still accurate observations concerning the hemp plant.

For centuries hemp remained the principal source of clothing for the Chinese, for this civilization failed to discover the practicality of using flax fiber. Why this is so is unknown. Perhaps, since they began with the hemp fiber and were satisfied with its product, they felt no need to develop an alternative. In any event, hemp was so commonly utilized that is was described in the Chinese treatise *Rh-Ya*,[2] compiled during the fifteenth century B.C. This work noted that hemp grew in both male and female forms and referred to it as *Ma*, a term that still has some colloquial usage.

During this period the Chinese developed an interesting folk custom. They took the hard hemp stalk and carved one end into the shape of a snake's head. When a Chinese became ill his friends or relatives would beat his bed with this "magic" totem, believing it had the power to dispel evil spirits. While the Chinese attributed supernatural powers to the hemp plant, they had little, if any, use for the peculiar resinous exudate that oozed from the attractive yellow-green flowering clusters. Chinese moralists of the time, watching the effects produced by the use of this resin in those wild youth of the era, concluded that this substance had no place in stable Chinese culture. Shortly, with proper warning to recalcitrant youths, the drug was labeled the "Liberator of Sin," and the use of the hemp plant or its resin as an escapist phenomenon forbidden to the Chinese.

Shen-Nung, however, was not opposed to utilizing cannabis in medicinal treatment. He prescribed it for beriberi, constipation, female weakness, gout, malaria, rheumatism, and, of all things, absent-mindedness! One particularly interesting medicinal use of hemp resin was recorded about 220 A.D. in the biography of the Chinese physician Hoa-Tho.[3] He mixed the resin with wine, termed it *Ma-Yo,* and employed it as an anesthetic for various surgical procedures. It must have been effective because later when the doctor queried his patients they insisted they felt no pain during surgery.

It is an interesting commentary on the variance of psychological response produced by the use of cannabis when employed by different civilizations that the placid Chinese for the most part did not appreciate its euphoria. Tranquil, smooth, languorous reveries from opium, yes. Technicolor fantasies from hemp exudate, absolutely no. The unpredictable reactions of hemp intoxication, sometimes stimulative, sometimes sedative, seemed alien to the nature of this culture, which preferred, when it chose to relax, to utilize a predictable drug that would afford it the chance to sleep and dream. Cannabis proved to be too labile for the stable Chinese, who chose as a nation to leave this drug and its sensory alterations to cultures more temperamentally suited to enjoy them.

THE SONG OF MOTHER INDIA

South and west of the Chinese lived a people who could well appreciate the effects of hemp intoxication. The land was India; its major religion, significantly, Hinduism. Cannabis was not indigenous to this area. More than likely it was taken there from somewhere in central Asia, perhaps by Iranian tribes. In the beginning hemp use was concentrated among the more contemplative members of Indian society who desired its effects to lessen the temptations and the noise of the external world. This group used the drug to place worshippers in an attitude of reverence by separating them from gross reality. In a short time, however, cannabis use became widespread. When it did, it was soon integrated into both the daily life and the religious activity of the people.

Unlike the Chinese, who cultivated hemp for its fibre, and who forbade its aberrant psychopharmacological use, the people of India specifically employed the resin of the plant for its mind-altering effects. Indeed, India perfected the use of cannabis for this purpose. Here, hemp culture became an agricultural science and its use an almost universal habit. For centuries, until recently when a governmentally sponsored program was begun to phase out the use of cannabis, nearly every system of Indian philosophy and religion was inextricably entwined with the use of Indian hemp products.

The Indians looked upon their hemp plant with eyes that teared with love. They nearly deified the drug products of the plant and developed a nomenclature for each major type: bhang, charas (hashish), and ganja. Native literature extolled cannabis and called it holy. "A guardian," an Indian philosopher wrote, "lives in the bhang leaf. . . . To see in a dream the leaves, plant, or water of bhang is lucky. . . . A longing for bhang foretells happiness. It cures dysentery and sunstroke, clears phlegm, quickens digestion, sharpens appetite, makes the tongue of the lisper plain, freshens the intellect and gives alertness to the body and gaiety to the mind. Such are the useful and needful ends for which in His goodness the Almighty made bhang. . . ."

The thought that someone might later come along and deprive the people of this magnificent experience caused native writers to predict terrible consequences that could follow such deprivation: "To forbid or even seriously restrict so holy and gracious an herb as the hemp would cause widespread suffering and annoyance and to large bands of worshipped ascetics deep-seated anger. It would rob the people of a solace in discomfort, of a cure in sickness, of a guardian whose gracious protection saves them from the attacks of evil influences. . . ." Surprisingly, this Indian writer concluded his eulogy of cannabis with an apology: "So grand a result, so tiny a sin."[4]

Cannabis users had good reason to fear their ecstatic state might be interrupted. Disapproval soon was expressed by Christian missionaries and other representatives of European culture who felt the use of the drug kept the people from being converted to Christianity. J. Campbell Oman, in his study of Indian mystics, commented: "It would be an interesting philosophical study to endeavor to trace the influence of these powerful narcotics (charas and bhang) on the minds and bodies of the itinerant monks who habitually use them. We may be sure that these hemp drugs, known since very early times in the East, are not irresponsible for some of its wild dreaming." Oman also noted that Christian missionaries were inclined to remark sarcastically: "A great number of Hindu saints live in a state of perpetual intoxication and call this stupefaction which arises from smoking intoxicating herbs, fixing the mind on God."[5]

The barrage of insults and protests from the anti-cannabis group failed to dent the enthusiasm of the masses, however, and they continued to make cannabis a part of their everyday lives. Despite growing pressure to eliminate cannabis use, it soon became known about the country as the "Happy Plant." Although the Indians were inclined to be preoccupied with the euphoric effects and contemplative aid offered by the use of cannabis, they were not unaware of some of its other potentialities. The *Susruta*[6], compiled sometime before 1000 B.C., not only mentioned the euphoria-producing capability of hemp, but also recommended its application for various diseases.

From the writing of the *Susruta* on, cannabis became increasingly mentioned in Indian literature. Some of these references contained dry humor. About the year 1500 A.D.[7], a story was transcribed concerning two rogues who were disturbing the peace by arguing over one of the "nymphs of the bazaar." At their trial the judge demanded they post bail. Complying, one of the defendants left his ganja bag as security. The judge not only accepted the offer, but as soon as the defendants were out of sight he used the ganja for his own enjoyment. Thus, in Indian literature and in song, cannabis was extravagantly lauded, and soon, yogis, ascetics, and heroes were reported to rely on its support prior to performing important feats.

Eventually the club of cannabis users began equating themselves with the gods. "No god or man," native writers eulogized,[8] "is as good as the religious drinker of bhang." Accepting this philosophy, the Indian people more and more incorporated the use of the drug as an integral part of their religious worship. Theology students were given bhang prior to studying the scriptures. Holy men at sacred places took it prior to centering their thoughts on eternity. Ascetics employed it to enable them to go days without food or water. For those caught in the euphoric grasp of hemp, the drug seemed to provide the answer to all problems. To the Indian, unlike the Chinese who had rejected it, bhang offered a much desired experience. As opium had found its position in the life of the Chinese who wished to escape serenely the pressures of reality, bhang became a staple in the emotional experience of the introspective Indian.

The use of the drug, however, was not without complications. Soon cannabis became so important to those dependent on its effects that legislators became fearful of the ultimate result. Despite these fears the government, after a careful study that revealed the use of the drug was so widespread attempts at its elimination seemed almost futile, begrudgingly issued a recommendation to the League of Nations in 1930 to the effect that it was neither practical nor advisable to attempt to exterminate the practice.[9] Some thirty years later the government had to come to grips with this problem again. This time it legislated against the use of cannabis. In so doing, the Indian government appears to have accepted the argument that cannabis use has deleterious social consequences and to have embraced the position, maintained by diverse investigators, that continued use of psychotropic drugs tends to eliminate the learned patterns of culture. So grand a result, so tiny a sin?

CANNABIS IN CLASSICAL ANTIQUITY

It was inevitable that once the knowledge of the effects of cannabis became known to the great nations of India and China, it would soon become known to other countries. West of India, in nearby Assyria, scholars were aware of a fascinating plant they referred to in 650 B.C. as *Azallu*. This plant could not only be used in spinning and in rope-making but also to dispel depression of the spirit. Cannabis had reached the Middle and Near East.

About the same time the Homeric poems told of a drug that eliminated all pain and anger. It was so effective that Helen, daughter of Zeus, was said to have used it to lull her anguish and sorrow. So powerful was the drug, the poet rhapsodized, that if one used it he would not feel sorrow even though his mother and father died, nor cry if he saw his brother or dear son slaughtered before him.[10]

Herodotus[11] reported during this period that the Scythians were growing a plant that was thicker and taller than flax and produced a seed that, when thrown on red-hot stones in an enclosed space, was believed to cleanse the body. (This was probably an erroneous assumption since "seeds" contain very little psychotropic agent.) This activity produced a steam which, he noted, was so remarkable that Grecian vapor baths could not surpass it. Once the Scythians were transported with this vapor, they would shout and scream in frenzy. Herodotus also remarked about a group of people living along the Araxes River who met together in groups, made a fire and threw a weed into the flames. "By inhaling the burning food that has been thrown on," he said, "they become intoxicated by the odor just as the Greeks do by wine; and the more food that is thrown on, the more intoxicated they become until they rise up to dance and betake themselves to singing." This same technique, interestingly, was described by Burton[12] as a method employed by African savages in the late nineteenth century.

The classical world offers additional commentary on the use of hemp. Pliny,[13] in the first century A.D., quotes the description of Democritus concerning the use of "Potamaugis" (pot?). This plant was probably hemp. Partaking of it produced a delirium. When it was taken internally with myrrh and wine it caused "all sorts of visionary forms" and precipitated "outbreaks of the most immoderate laughter." A few years later, Dioscorides[14] accurately described and illustrated the hemp plant (see front pages), commenting about its use in rope manufacturing and its curative power in cases of earache, edema, and assorted ills. Oddly, he failed to indicate it had any specific sedative or intoxicating properties. A century later the great physician Galen[15] reported the use of cannabis as a confectionery dessert which, when taken after meals with drinks, caused exciting pleasure, created much warmth and, if overindulged in, affected the head. He recommended its use for extinguishing flatus, curing earache, and other problems.

CANNABIS IN ARAB COUNTRIES

As time progressed, the use of hemp products increased, and the problem of its abuse spread geographically. It is improbable, however, that the plant was generally abused by the majority of the people who lived during the centuries just before and after the beginning of the Christian era, by which time it was well known in the eastern Mediterranean. More probably, as Walton[16] suggests, it was a folk custom practiced sporadically by various tribes in isolated localities. By 500 A.D., cannabis was being used throughout most of Europe except for the far West. Arabian physicians employed the drug for numerous ailments, including its administration as an aphrodisiac. About 950 A.D., an Arabian physician noted that the hemp that was used for rope-making could ease headaches. Concurrently, other Arabian writers complained that hashish drugs were enjoying too great a popularity, so much so that stories about the joyful effects of the drug had come to occupy a prominent place in Arabian literature. *The Tales of the Arabian Nights* recounted lurid accounts of the effects of hashish abuse. Undoubtedly these tales led more young Arabs to try the drug.

One of the early Arabian manuscripts relates the story of a Moslem priest who stood in the mosque exhorting his listeners to avoid the use of "beng" because it intoxicated the user and produced sleep. Soon he was transported by his harangue and began flailing his arms about to emphasize his point. This caused his robe to loosen. As it did, the priest's private source of beng, which he had wrapped in paper and tucked away in his gown, fell to the ground where his listeners could see it. Instead of losing his cool, the priest seized upon this unanticipated object lesson to strengthen his argument. "This is the enemy," he cried, "this demon of which I have told you; the force of my words has put it to flight; take care that in quitting me it does not hurl itself on one of you and possess you." Cowed by this outburst, no one in the audience dared to touch the paper full of beng. To be certain, however, the priest stood guard to protect his property.

As soon as the crowd dispersed, the priest recovered his precious package and retired to enjoy himself. He fooled, the translator noted, no one but himself.[17]

By the middle of the thirteenth century A.D., adverse conditions arose for Arabian hashish users. In 1251, the Garden of Cafour, near Cairo, notorious for the abuse of hashish by its fakirs, was destroyed. This destruction was viewed by contemporary writers as a "just punishment of God." These men also complained about the existence of another small colony in the Canton of Timbaliere. Here hashish was not only sold, its use by the inhabitants of the colony was almost universal. The drug was employed in Timbaliere, said the critics, by the most degenerate of people, libertines, and feebleminded individuals, who vied with each other to see who could outdo the others in use of the drug. This they did without shame, one scribe observed; yet cannabis use was not always so freely accepted, "for I have seen, myself, a time," he noted, "in which it [cannabis] was regarded as the vilest of filth and most revolting excrement."[18]

While denouncing the behavior of the hashish abusers, this social philosopher expressed even more concern about the ultimate effects of the use of the drug on people who might be tempted to abuse it in the future. "In truth," he said, "there is nothing which is more dangerous to the temperament. As it is known today by everybody in Egypt, in Syria, in the Irak and in the country of Roum, we believe we should speak of it in some detail." And speak they did. But to no avail, for the drug habit had caught the fancy of many, and they would not relinquish it.

THE LEGEND OF HASAN

One of the most fascinating stories to come out of the East involving the use of cannabis is that of a character known as Hasan-Ibn-Sabbah who, to the joy of his enemies, finally died in 1124 A.D.[19] The tale of Hasan has played a critical role in the current controversy over cannabis because the story has been repeated numerous times in an attempt to "prove" that cannabis use can cause violence and crime. Why so much emphasis should be placed on one event is difficult to say, except that having once entered the arena in the continuing marijuana debate, it became a target for both polarized sides.

The controversy began in 1937 when the then Commissioner of the Federal Bureau of Narcotics informed the United States House of Representatives that marijuana had led the followers of Hasan "to a delirious rage after its administration." Commissioner Harry J. Anslinger, an ardent foe of the use of cannabis, used the illustration to show that improper use of the weed by violence-prone individuals could result in erratic and hostile behavior. Unfortunately, in referring to this story, Anslinger opened a Pandora's box.

Much debate has since ensued over the story of Hasan which, simply, involved the alleged use of cannabis by a terrorist leader to influence teenage zealots to perform violent slaughter. Marco Polo related the episode in his adventures[20] and later Alexandre Dumas popularized it in his book *The Count of Monte Cristo*. Because of the socio-political issues involved in the implication that cannabis was used to encourage violence, some highly emotional verbiage has been directed toward the tale. Socio-psychiatrist Joel Fort asserts that the Hasan tale is abhorrent as it relates to the use of marijuana. "The most deeply imbedded, demonic, and perhaps least truthful of the tales linking illegal drugs to crime and violence," he says, "is the one linking marijuana with assassination."[21]

In 1966, sociologist Jerry Mandel turned his talent towards debunking the tale, ending up with some fascinating interpretations of history and the conclusion that hashish probably wasn't used by the assassins at all.[22] His dissertation was later picked up with enthusiasm by Stanford University Professor of Law John Kaplan, who seemingly began a one-man campaign in 1969 to discount much that had previously been said about cannabis that would in any way cast doubt on his thesis that the weed should be legalized in America.[23] A year later, Don M. Casto III, with the advice and assistance of Professor Kaplan, performed another scholastic autopsy on the assassins and their alleged use of marijuana.[24] Apparently there is no end to the energy to be spent on this fascinating topic.

The serious student of cannabis, however, has just cause to wonder what all these polemics are about. It's simply this. For years anti-cannabis forces have used the Hasan story to "prove" that smoking cannabis causes criminal and violent behavior. In return, pro-cannabis forces have laughed and sighed, groaned and fomented because of what they considered to be the inappropriate use of the moral, if any, of the story. Actually, the episode has a point; it is this: men have a remarkable propensity for getting sidetracked in discussing critical issues.

In the first edition of this book, this author included a brief resumé of the history of Hasan because of its general interest. As was true of the man who wrote the "Purple Cow," "I'm sorry, now, I wrote it."[25] Perhaps the simplest way of dismissing this noncritical issue is to refer to the last paragraph of Mr. Casto's article. After defending the assassins and assuming their violence was unrelated to the use of cannabis, he states, quite honestly, that his review does not prove "that marijuana is not causally related to acts of violence." He then offers some sage advice that hopefully may end this irrelevant debate over an almost unprovable issue. His review suggests, he says, "that those who seek to link marijuana use and aggressive behavior must look elsewhere for support." So, Hasan, wherever you are, rest in peace! Along with your debaters.

Let's digress for a moment from the past, which is hard to defend, and look in on the experience of a modern country where argument is less plausible because the participants are in many instances still alive. The country is Nigeria which recently underwent riots involving thousands of young hoodlums who assaulted each other and the police at a time when, according to local reports, the youths were high on cannabis. Since then, Nigeria has moved with vigor against the use of cannabis. In May, 1966, Nigerian police caught a British tourist and an American growing and smoking Cannabis indica. Both men were promptly sentenced to fifteen years' imprisonment.

Nigerian journalist Akin Davies[26] explained some of the reasons for his government's harsh action. Above all, they had to do with political dangers and the disruption of social stability, but they also reflected the Nigerian government's concern with the damaging effect on progress that cannabis addiction is believed by some to inflict. Davies explained the way in which cannabis seemed to have been used in Nigeria for political purposes: "The system works like this: An unscrupulous politician decides to build a private army. He goes around the country and finds unemployed young men who are not too intelligent and close to starvation. He sees to it that every day they each get food, pocket money, and a supply of marijuana (a luxury for a poor man). What they must do in return is to carry out his orders: beat up, kill, or kidnap political opponents, perhaps plunder or burn a house now and then. They are usually called the 'party stalwarts'."

This journalist points out that recent rioting in western Nigeria went on for three months. The army and police were unable to quell the rioting, and terrorists, using guns and locally manufactured flame-throwers, indiscriminately sprayed victims with burning petrol. They killed 567 people. The government's reaction to this chaos was to minimize the problem and deny that any significant number of people were killed. Faced with this political aloofness, the army, much to the joy of the people, moved in and took over.

"One of the first acts of the Military Government," Davies reports, "was to issue a decree making it punishable by death to grow marijuana, and by up to twenty years of prison for merely being in possession of it. This seems extremely excessive, but must be considered as a reaction to the misdeeds of the gangs of 'party stalwarts.' It is to be hoped that the law can be modified when a way is found to prevent politicians from forming such private armies. In the meantime, we Nigerians have to stop getting high for a while and develop our country."

THE DRUG ARRIVES IN AFRICA

About the thirteenth century the central Africans discovered the intoxicating experience afforded by breathing hemp vapors. Their technique was simple: they threw the weed on the fire, then stood around inhaling the smoke. Soon they became more sophisticated. Prostrating themselves on the ground, they poked hollow tubes toward the hot embers to acquire the smoke more directly. Later they elevated these fires to the tops of tall stumps so they could sit or stand while smoking. African Bushmen discovered they could modify the irritating effects of hemp smoke if they took a mouthful of water before they inhaled. In time even this technique was improved upon, and smokers used a hollow antelope horn partially filled with water and with the burning hemp placed on the larger open end. The smoke could then be "drunk."

Over the following centuries practices in cannabis use were modified and changed as the hemp habit traveled through various tribes. The habit remained new to some and unknown to others, however, a fact supported by Livingstone's comments[27] in the mid-nineteenth century that, while younger men of the upper Zambezi River tribes smoked cannabis, the older men were often unaware of its effects. Eventually, crude pipes were developed. The gourd, the coconut, and bamboo stems were employed to achieve the best effect. Finally, pottery-makers in North Africa stumbled upon the idea of making a water pipe to cool the smoke and remove some of its irritants. The hashish pipe thus came into being. This is still the most common means of cannabis consumption for the "kif" smokers of North Africa.

In Egypt cannabis use increased from the thirteenth century on. Eventually officials began to make desperate, albeit futile, attempts to eradicate it. By 1789, when Napoleon began his invasion of Egypt as a preliminary toward the conquest of British India, hashish abuse was so prevalent among Egyptian lower classes that the French legislated severe penalties for the sale or use of the drug. Napoleon was zealous in his attempts to eliminate Egyptian hashish dens, but his attempts were less than successful. He discovered, as have others before and after him, that once the cannabis camel enters the tent it is extremely difficult to get him to move out again. The situation Napoleon found in Egypt continues to this day and, according to recent press reports, the habitual use of marijuana in Egypt has reached alarming levels. In 1960 the Egyptian government issued the following statement on cannabis:

. . . the prepared product of [the] Cannabis sativa plant, while having very little useful medical use, is capable of profoundly disturbing the brain cells and inducing acts of violence, even murder; that it is in fact a fairly vicious and dangerous thing of no value whatever to humanity and deserving of nothing but the contempt of civilized people.[28]

Recently these sentiments were supported by Masters and Houston,[29] who claim that the use of cannabis still accounts for a high percentage of Arab worker absenteeism and for a large percentage of the mental illness in Egypt. Masters and Houston state that in both Indian and Moslem cultures, the social impact of the use of hemp has been enormous. This has been equally true of many African Negro cultures where the plant is worshipped and its use believed to bestow supernatural powers on the witch doctors.

CANNABIS IN EUROPE

Except for areas bordering directly on the Mediterranean, Europe per se did not experience the cannabis abuse problem until recent years. In the middle of the last century in Europe a number of scientific investigators suggested that the products of the plant might have beneficial medical qualities. Oddly, for those scientists who dared to probe the secrets of the hemp plant, cannabis seemed to carry its own private curse. Easterfield and Spivey, the first pioneers to hydrogenate and nitrate cannabinol, one of the active ingredients in hemp resin, were soon killed in separate laboratory explosions. O'Shaughnessy, who pressed for a medical evaluation of the resin, was killed in an accident while investigating the drug.[30]

In 1844, in Paris, the famous Club des Hachichins was established at the swank Hotel Pimodan. The specialty of this club was a sweetmeat, Dawamesc, which contained hashish. This dish was introduced to the romantic society of the day from Algeria, where it was frequently served as a delicacy. As a dessert it was eaten by many notables who came to the hotel to meet, eat, and become intoxicated by this strange drug.

Not all of those who frequented the club came to escape reality. Actually, interest in the drug, which eventually spread throughout the Bohemian elements of Paris, began with an idea fostered by Dr. Jacques Moreau. Moreau was a respected physician at the Hospital de Bicetre, whose staff had initiated reform in the treatment of the mentally ill. Moreau believed cannabis could be used therapeutically to manage the emotionally disturbed. It was Moreau who introduced the use of the drug to the impressionable twenty-four-year-old popular author Théophile Gautier. Gautier, intrigued more with the bizarre emotional effect of the drug than with its medical potential, established the Pimodan Hotel hashish club. The doctor and the young author remained good friends, despite the variance in their interest in hashish; so much so that when Moreau published his findings in 1845 on the use of hashish in the treatment of the mentally ill, he included a report by Gautier.[31]

Gautier, impressionable, artistic, creative, receptive, has given literature some of its most descriptive passages on the glories of hashish. A provocative author, he began his literary career by writing a novel, *Mademoiselle de Maupin,* in which he described the adventures of a transvestite. Gautier had his own ideas concerning social values, and expressed them vigorously in statements such as, "Enjoyment seems to me to be the end of life, and the only useful thing in the world."[32]

To Gautier and men like him, hashish offered a heady escape from the pressures of reality. But even with the influence of such eloquent advocates, the use of cannabis did not gain a significant foothold in western Europe until recent years. Then it was stimulated by American travelers and by the international press. As it has appeared in major cities of Europe, officials have labeled it "the American vice," considering it another cultural offering to Europe from the United States.

WELCOME TO AMERICA

Cannabis was known and used in the New World as a euphoria-producing agent when Columbus was attempting to prove the world was round. During the early sixteenth century, and possibly before, it seems to have been utilized in certain Aztec religious ceremonies. Montezuma II was known to partake of a strange postprandial tobacco that caused him to fall into a deep sleep. It is possible that this strange tobacco was cannabis, although historians are not altogether certain.

In the late sixteenth century an English decision to increase Britain's shipping fleet made hemp cultivation a vital necessity, for flax could not provide the long, flexible, strong ropes needed for sea duty; nor could it be satisfactorily used for caulking as could hemp rope once it had served its original purpose. England compounded its hemp supply problems at this time by becoming embroiled in a series of disagreements with the Dutch. This automatically curtailed the British supply of hemp, which came largely from the Dutch East Indies. To remedy this, England decided to utilize its New World colonies as a new hemp supply source. Thus, in 1611, near Jamestown, Virginia, cannabis was first purposely planted and grown in what is now known as the United States. Instructions were given the colonists by His

Majesty King James I, to increase hemp production. Apparently the colonists made every effort to comply. By 1630 hemp became a staple of the colonial clothing industry. Soon half the colonists' winter clothing, and most of their summer clothing, were woven from its fibre.

In the early revolutionary period of American history, hemp was second only to cotton as an important agricultural product. It is quite probable that Washington raised it on his estate at Mount Vernon, as did other gentlemen farmers. And as settlement of the West began, hemp accompanied the pioneers as a valued companion in the form of tough cloth which covered the wagons and shaded heads from the hot sun.

A century later, however, in 1770, steam power began to replace the sail on ships. About the same time, Eli Whitney invented his cotton gin. With the demand for hemp markedly decreased, its cultivation was abandoned in America. The remaining plants were allowed to go to seed and return to weed status. Slowly, borne by the wind, this seed spread across the United States where it flourished, waiting for the arrival of another generation who would find a use for it. It had to wait a long time—until the middle of our century.

Very little was written in early American literature concerning experimentation with cannabis. That which did appear aroused little interest. However, an important volume, *The Hasheesh Eater*, was published in 1857, written by an American educator named Fitz-Hugh Ludlow.[33] Ludlow began using cannabis products in his teens after he determined that the intrigue appearing in *Tales of the Arabian Nights* had been contrived under the influence of hashish. He started exploring the effects of this drug at age sixteen and continued until he left college to teach at Watertown, New York.

An imaginative youth, Ludlow was inspired by the earlier adventures of De Quincy, who lived to regret his excursions into the drug-induced unknown. Determined to see the same visions as had others who dared to travel the drug route, Ludlow tried various concoctions in an attempt to open the recesses of his mind. He quickly made friends with an apothecary in Poughkeepsie, New York, and soon adopted the shop as his "favorite lounging place." Since the need to regulate drugs was not as critical at the time, he had ready legal access to almost anything that appeared on his friend's shelves. One morning in the spring of 1854, he happened upon a vial which the pharmacist advised him was a preparation of East Indian Hemp, considered then to be a potent remedy for lockjaw.

Ludlow, being a serious student of drugs, recognized the olive-brown extract as the key to his search for the unknown. "This," he reasoned, "may unlock more than jaws." Putting his six cents on the counter he took his prize home for closer examination. His first experiment consisted of dropping ten grains which he had rolled into a pill. As is not infrequently the case—nothing happened. Undaunted, he decided to try again and for the next five days increased his dosage by five grains daily until he had reached an oral intake of twenty-five grains. At this point, feeling he was "absolutely unsusceptible" to hashish, he almost quit. But as a final try, he swallowed thirty grains. Nothing happened. Discouraged, he went to the home of a friend to visit and listen to music. About three hours passed from the time he swallowed the pill; he had eaten supper after arriving at his friend's home. Suddenly . . . WHAM! He began a wild, unbargained-for experience that in today's jargon would best be described as a "bummer."

"A shock, as of some unimagined vital force, shoots without warning through my entire frame, leaping to my fingers' ends, piercing my brain, startling me till I almost spring from my chair."[34] His first emotion was that of uncontrollable terror and he found himself fervently wishing he had not dropped the cannabis pill. An unusually high trip had occurred, and without a guide he had to travel the road alone. Time and space disintegrated; his personality became a sort of dual existence. With withering accuracy, he described the transient fragmentation of his ego as he noted that, "One part of me was whisked unresistingly along the track of this tremendous experience, the other sat looking down from a height upon its double, observing, reasoning and serenely weighing all the phenomena. . . ."

Uncoordinated, alarmed, unsure, he staggered out of the house and found "the view stretched endlessly away . . . I was doomed to pass through a merciless stretch of space." He stepped into the street and headed home, bumping into a pedestrian on the way. His senses distorted by the drug, he gazed into the face of the man and saw in the altered pattern of his visual perception a face that was "Horror unspeakable."

At this point he began to turn his observations inward and

concentrated on his body functions, tracing in particular the travel of his blood "along every inch of its progress. I knew when every valve opened and when it shut," he recalled in his memoires. His heart became a great fountain "whose jet played upward with loud vibrations . . . striking on the roof of my skull as on a gigantic dome [which then] fell back with a splash and echo into its reservoir." Appalled, he concluded that he was lost, "since judgment, which still sat unimpaired above my perverted senses, argued that congestion must take place in a few minutes, and close the drama with my death. . . ."

Today, marijuana pundits who prefer to believe the drug can do no harm might argue that someone had slipped Ludlow some acid. But no one had. Ludlow discovered, as others are now finding, that the "high" cannabis trip may, under certain circumstances, mimic many of the effects obtained by taking LSD.

Ludlow, determined to find the secret of the Arabian and Persian story tellers and hopefully aiming toward the literary career which he in time achieved, continued his experimentation with hashish. He called it the drug of the traveler, noting that "for the humble sum of six cents I might purchase an excursion all over the earth." Unfortunately he soon found that while the ticket for his trip was cheap, there was a significant drawback: the train seldom traveled according to desired schedule. The destinations were as unpredictable as was the sensory activity along the trip.

"The same dose of the same preparation of hashish will frequently produce diametrically opposite effects," he complained, as do many present-day counterparts. "I have taken at one time a pill of thirty grains, which hardly gave a perceptible phenomenon, and at another, when my dose had been half that quantity, I have suffered the agonies of a martyr or rejoiced in a perfect frenzy. So exceedingly variable are its results that, long before I abandoned the indulgence, I took each successive bolus with the consciousness that I was daring an uncertainty as tremendous as the equipoise between hell and heaven. Yet the fascination employed Hope as its advocate, and won the suit."

Ludlow's "bummers" and "bad trips" were formidable. His interest in the metaphysical, increased by an active imagination, was spurred by the unpredictable effects of the intense drug experience and put him into a state of terror. For a time he felt enslaved by his habit. This enslavement may have reflected a propensity to use drugs which can develop and remain an intensely annoying problem among those who are susceptible to the effects of marijuana.

As he matured, however, and his need for psychological experiences through drugs diminished, Ludlow established himself as an acceptable teacher and writer. Then, and apparently only then, did he dare to reveal his experimentation which, since it was quite legal at the time, had little or no negative effect. The media was not inclined to glorify the drug or the experience. There were no promarijuana television shows and today's version of the underground press was not thought of. Ludlow's observations were thus considered flights of fantasy and those who read his story apparently considered it a type of science fiction to be consumed, enjoyed and discarded.

Cannabis failed to elicit any significant popularity as a euphoriant in the United States until Mexican laborers began to bring their little bags of "mota" across the border in the early part of this century. The first significant endemic use of the drug in this country began in New Orleans. Once the practice caught hold it spread quickly. By 1926 New Orleans was saturated with cannabis users. Since the weed grew with facility, the supply was more than adequate for a time. Soon, however, river sailors took the habit from New Orleans and spread it up the Mississippi River. Four years later small groups of marijuana smokers could be found in almost all major cities of the United States.

In the thirties the demand for cannabis became so intense that Mexican laborers could not meet the market requirements. To forestall any shortage, shipments now began arriving from Havana, Tampico, and Vera Cruz. Marijuana importation became a full-time occupation with some, and the price jumped from an original ten dollars a kilo (2.2 pounds) to nearly fifty dollars.

By 1936 the government of the United States began to take a serious look at the increasing use of this drug. Unfortunately, irresponsible journalists became the loudest voices in this controversy and soon launched a series of myths which even today are used to argue against the use of marijuana. Whipped by yellow journalism, inflamed by ridiculous and untrue stories, the public panicked. A year later, in 1937, the government passed the Federal Marijuana Tax in an attempt to control the distribution and thus the abuse of the drug.

These laws have had a significant effect in controlling the use of cannabis. They have also become the center of a great deal of controversy, a point that will be discussed later. Users of the drug now faced the alternative of quitting or going underground. For the most part, hardcore users followed the second course.

For quite a long time, as Rosevear[35] noted, marijuana remained (as it still is) extremely popular among jazz musicians, a large number of whom are Negro. Since the use of cannabis seems to alleviate tensions and problems facing some minority groups, it was and is currently employed with high frequency by them. The drug's use was not limited to Negroes in the past, nor is it now, since the emotional problems which precipitated the desire for marijuana use and its effects have spread to other segments of our present population.

Until the fifties the use of cannabis in the United States remained relatively clandestine, a fact which raises some doubts about the arguments that law enforcement had little or no effect in controlling the "marijuana habit." In the last two decades, a serious change in attitude toward law in general and social mores in particular has led to a liberal stance among many Americans who do not use the drug. The fifties brought about a rise in civil rights activities and racial integration. The sixties witnessed the birth of the hippie counterculture. These social forces acted to mingle races and to integrate habit patterns as well as social trends. Because the use of marijuana was one of the habits deeply ingrained in certain segments of a number of minority groups, intrigue and experimentation with the drug increased, and Americans soon found themselves following the general course of history where marijuana smoking has been recorded as a part of the culture.

Marijuana use has traditionally been associated with unrest, emotional deprivation, and hedonism. These factors are currently on the rise in America, and as they become more deeply ingrained in the daily routine, it is to be expected that more and more people will be encouraged to experiment with a drug alleged to bring only pleasure and to have no ill effects. This allegation, however, is contradicted by history, a point that those who are urgently sponsoring the legalization of marijuana must consider. If marijuana is to be legalized, and the current trend seems to be in that direction, it would pay these advocates to study history well.

America is at a critical juncture where drug use is concerned. Suppose prohibition were still in effect, and today's debate were over alcohol, rather than marijuana. If we could compare any benefits of alcohol's legalization to the price of its effects on society, it is unlikely that prohibition would be ended. Alcohol became an integral part of our social, religious, and recreational activities before we were fully aware of the cost of permitting its use. Entrenched as it is today, we seem unable to remove it or to control its adverse effects. Other cultures have had an analogous experience with marijuana—enjoying the pleasure it provides on one hand, enduring its ill effects on the other. America, still in the pleasure stage, has yet to recognize the other side of the picture.

The history of marijuana use in American society could well be written in two chapters, as the drug's use has spread to wider and wider segments of our society. The first was a sad tale of misinformation and poorly-directed energy; no news on the drug was permitted to reach the public unless it was derogatory. Suppression was the name of the game. The public, less involved in a mad race to escape reality than people are now, was disinterested for the most part. The exception was the small minority who considered cannabis their key to relaxation.

The second chapter is almost a mirror image of the first. Today's trend is to say nothing but good about the drug, minimizing adverse reactions (which are on the increase), and misinterpreting the problems of the past. Permissiveness is the byword today. People should be allowed to "do their own thing" as long as they "never hurt nobody."

Perhaps. But history has taught that those who can safely use cannabis as a socio-relaxant traditionally refuse to permit it entrance into the vital framework of their lives. Such people usually follow one of two courses of action: they minimize the drug's use, or in time put it down because they recognize that uncontrolled use has the tendency to alter their motivation and achievement. Use of the drug by this group is usually insignificant because they remain in control. But there are others—who are certain the drug holds no negative effects for their lives, but who need a crutch, and find it in the subtle, smoothing, relaxing, amotivating wisps of cannabinol-containing marijuana smoke or the confections in which it can be included. These people can no more cope with marijuana than the alcoholic can cope with his drinking. These are the people who have filled the history of cannabis with bitter experiences. Three decades ago, America had a few of them. Today, they may well constitute a significant minority. This group will heavily influence the outcome of the third chapter, now in the making, of the history of cannabis in America. Whether our country will repeat the experiences of India, which is now trying to eliminate the use of the weed from its culture, or of the Near East and Africa, which permitted cannabis use to their regret, or emulate the example of China, which decided long ago that cannabis was not for them, remains to be seen.

*"Gloria will be down in a minute. Would you like some
pot or something while you wait?"*

the
world
of
marijuana

3

"You know, when you don't turn on, you don't know anybody else who does. When you do, then it seems you don't know anybody else who doesn't."
—MRS. GARNET BRENNAN
(*Life*, Nov. 17, 1967)

A DECADE AGO FEW PEOPLE mentioned cannabis. Those who did whispered about it in the same hushed tones they reserved for discussions of sex and venereal disease. Those were the days when nobody had any use for marijuana. Usually they would not even discuss it. During that period the noted pharmacologists Goodman and Gilman described the contemporary cannabis user. He was, they said, "usually twenty to thirty years of age, idle and lacking in initiative, with a history of repeated frustrations and deprivations, sexually maladjusted (often homosexual), who seeks distraction, escape, and sometimes conviviality by smoking the drug. He almost uniformly has major personality defects and is often psychopathic."[1]

There was nothing wrong with this description then. There is nothing wrong with it even now *as it relates to this particular group of cannabis users.* These were the users who invariably progressed to heroin; these were the sociopaths who routinely flowed in and out of police stations; these were the so-called "dope fiends" who took that "incarnation of evil"—marijuana. And marijuana, according to posters of the day, caused mental deficiency, crime, physical deterioration, addiction, and anything else poster writers happened to think of. But no one cared. Cannabis use was essentially confined to a very limited group of citizens. Most teenagers had other ways of rebelling against their elders and flouting adult laws. Only the truly delinquent used marijuana.

This caricature of the cannabis user became deeply ingrained and still persists even though the user picture has so drastically changed that the current edition of the Goodman and Gilman text no longer contains the old description. It just doesn't fit any more. Today's users are, for the most part, well-educated middle- and upper-class young people. The sudden realization that this is so has caught society by surprise and created grand confusion. A survey of the marijuana scene today is therefore in order.

THE RANGE OF USE

Overnight, it seems, cannabis has become the "in" thing to use; and overnight two sharply polarized camps have come into being for purposes of debating almost every issue pertinent to pot except, perhaps, its psychopharmacological and physical effects on the user. It is these camps that have given meaning to the marijuana revolution, and it is they who have devised a new game that has rapidly replaced monopoly in the American parlor.

The game, says writer Jerry Cohen, is called "Expert Witness."[2] The board is any stage that will tolerate the verbiage. The players include educators, physicians, police, theologians, criminologists, attorneys, and even professors of law. Said players line up on opposite sides of the board and joust among themselves while speaking knowledgeably about "grass," "joints," "roaches," and what have you. While youth ponders and experiments, some to their regret and distinct harm, the "experts" indulge in some of the worst put ons and put downs of each others' veracity the world has endured for many years.

These camps are so widely separated in viewpoint it is almost impossible for the authorities involved to sustain an intelligent debate. Pro-cannabis people are so certain the drug can serve as a cure-all for every cultural ill that they cannot see its potential for producing social harm. The more these men talk to users who experience no apparent complications from cannabis use (*or the more these men use it themselves*), the more certain they are that the whole cannabis problem is a sham and that the drug should be legally, morally, and socially approved.

In the other corner, weighing in with an impressive number of authorities, both qualified and unqualified, we find the anti-cannabis people. This group is so violently opposed to cannabis and so certain it is a diabolical underminer of everything holy, they become apoplectic at any suggestion the drug might not be as bad as it has been previously painted. These men are as sub-jective in their own way as the pro-cannabis clan. Caught be-tween these dissenting groups, we find the rest of the citizenry, who by now are getting a little dizzy and disgusted, not to say a bit confused, as they listen to all the undistilled verbiage that emanates from so many "authorities."

Just how common is cannabis use in America? Frankly, no-body knows. A few questionably valid statistics indicate the ex-tent of local problems; by piecing these together we can try to estimate the national use. Even so, it is currently inaccurate to say that any given percentage is valid for the country as a whole. This much we do know: cannabis use by American youth, and even by many not-so-young people, is on the increase. Next to alcohol, cannabis is the major drug of abuse among American youth. But pot may be losing its glamor. As "older children" hop onto the bandwagon (professors, doctors, theologians, and the like), it is getting to the point, as Dr. David Smith of Haight-Ashbury clinic fame has noted, that narcotics and hallucinogens may be losing some of their distinction as a young-adult hangup.[3]

Professionals on the sociological firing line who have to deal with the complications of cannabis abuse are almost obsessive in their determination to try to do something at least to keep the situation under control. This is particularly true of enforcement officers from the federal level on down. It is also true of organized medicine, which has had to take a stand through committee action on the cannabis situation. Most of these professionals have no axe to grind. The medical profession, for instance, cannot properly be accused, as police are often accused by the uninformed, of making a living by controlling the use of the drug.

Physicians are primarily interested in public health and safety as, incidentally, are the police. The medical associations' goal has been well documented by the stand taken by most doctors, many of whom have followed their own advice despite personal anguish, in advocating the cessation of the use of tobacco. Valid research (which the tobacco industry "can't find") indicates that youth who begin and continue to smoke tobacco are a fertile source of new patients for both surgeons and internists. Despite this economic boon the medical profession continues to try to change the public's smoking habits through education and example. For equally important public health reasons doctors again, with some outstanding exceptions, present a solid front against the abuse of pot.

One representative expert is Dr. Nathan B. Eddy, who has spent forty years working for the National Academy of Sciences on problems related to drug abuse. He is wholeheartedly against legalizing the use of cannabis. "The only use for marijuana is to achieve gratification," Dr. Eddy says. "Society cares enough about having alcohol available to pay the immense social and economic cost of having millions of people depending on it. If we are thinking clearly we will not make freely available yet another agent of abuse and magnify the costs we pay."[4]

Such warnings, however, are watered down by men within the profession, primarily those psychiatrists and sociologists who are well known for their permissive approach to life. These people repeatedly issue the glad tidings that "pot is here to stay," "pot is cool," and "pot can't possibly hurt you." For the most part, their observations seem based on wishful thinking and a desire to give people what they want despite the social cost.

One of the most vocal men seeking to change current laws is a socio-psychiatrist who argues: "If marijuana were not called terrible by society, everyone would find that it is a mild drug that has little effect except to stimulate the appetite, slow down the time sense and create mild euphoria. It will not transform an individual into a monster." He further assures the nation's youth: "It doesn't cause crime and doesn't lead to the use of stronger drugs, sexual excess or deviant conduct—nor is it likely to cause mental illness or automobile accidents."[5] Such permissive counsel sows confusion and may seriously contribute to the now large-scale problem of cannabis use in the United States.

Just how large is the problem? It is big enough so that at the nation's most prestigious educational institutions one can find cannabis with very little effort. Numerous statistics can be quoted to show twenty percent are "using" here and eighty percent are "using" there, but such statistics have now become almost meaningless. Experimentation has risen almost to a parallel with the increased reassurances on the part of some of the news media that "everybody is using pot." These statements are misleading. It is true a growing number of persons are experimenting with pot because their curiosity is whetted and because they are constantly and irresponsibly being reassured by some "experts" that the drug is completely safe. It is not true, however, that large numbers of Americans are "using" in the critical sense of the word. Casual, occasional trips cannot be properly classified as *use*, and such categorization is both inaccurate and misleading. The difference between the occasional user and the chronic abuser is tremendous; the abuser is motivated to employ the drug as a release with which to face or, more often, to escape, reality, while the casual user seeks fun and relaxation.

There was a time when one could place marijuana users in a fairly accurate framework, and within this framework correctly or incorrectly associate behavioral activity and attitudes with the use of the drug. No more! Contemporary use of marijuana has changed so dramatically that it has now crossed all ethnic, religious, geographical and social boundaries. It is not surprising therefore to find that groups once thought to be impervious to the attractiveness of the drug, or for that matter to drugs in general, are now becoming major experimenters and/or users.

Today it is no longer possible, as *Newsweek*[6] once noted, to categorize marijuana as the "magic grass" of the Negro ghetto, the jazz world, or more recently, the hippie community. Today it has entered the cultural patterns of the American middle class. "Marijuana," *Life* magazine says, "long a part of the bohemian scene in the United States, suddenly has become commonplace on college campuses, among intellectuals and suburbanites and, most worrisome of all, even among the subteenagers."[7] In other words, the scene has become ubiquitous and confused.

Three Types of Users

While it is not possible to depict accurately the marijuana user as a specific type of individual, it does seem that three major categories for drug abuse have been formed, based on use, activity, and motivation. We find first on the list a persistent group of antisocial misfits, the "lower-caste" group (i.e., uneducated, and usually unemployed and poorly motivated), who have from the beginning used the drug as an added chorus to an already established refrain of antiauthoritarianism, antidisciplinarianism, and antisocial activities. These are the users the police used to associate with the drug. This picture is so strongly retained by police that many law enforcement personnel still have difficulty recognizing that this group, once the only significant one, has now become the minority.

When this type of user employed marijuana in the past, he frequently found that it failed to provide the trip he really wanted. Seeking further (but not "led" to a specific drug, as the old steppingstone theory held), he in time found a soporific that erased the pressures of life. This user was not interested in exploring his mind or the universe; to the contrary, he wanted to blot them out. Heroin proved to be the drug of his choice because of its ability to "take over" and produce a vacant feeling of "nothingness." Heroin still achieves these goals efficiently, and it can be noted, sadly, that heroin use is on the upswing.

Group Two is peopled by an entirely different breed. The difference appears in their choice of drugs and in the reasons that cause them to use drugs. Whereas Group One was formed by "lower-caste trippers," Group Two, although it can enjoy tripping, is far more interested in the use of the drug for self-exploration, mind expansion, and socio-relaxation.

The upper-caste hippie belongs to Group Two, although he may stand apart from the rest of this segment by his adoption of obvious antisocial protest symbols. In addition to committed users, we find the intellectuals, pseudo-intellectuals, and religious and pseudo-religious people. This group tends to pursue a search for inner truth and inner peace. They share the common denominator of being dissatisfied, bored, curious, and in desperate need of finding something different to experience. When members of this group discover the effects of cannabis are becoming prosaic, they tend, along with the lower-caste hippie (who, in other ways belongs more to the first category), to progress to the use of stronger hallucinogens such as LSD, DMT, mescaline, and others.

The third group is the largest. It is composed primarily of average, curious, uninhibited people out for a lark. These youngsters are usually "chippers," that is, they play with the drug now and then as the mood directs them. Seldom if ever do they become "hung up" on the drug itself, although by proximity if nothing else they inherit some of the complications and disadvantages of using illegal drugs.

In a way, Group Three people might be described by the anecdote of the mother who took her child to the psychoanalyst each week for therapy, which consisted of the analyst's reading comic books aloud to the child. After an hour or so, the psychiatrist would dismiss the child, directing the mother to return for another session. Soon, the mother began to object to this procedure. "Just why do you do this sort of thing?" she demanded. "Madam," the analyst replied, "you fail to comprehend the problem. We've got to keep reading these comics to your son until we find out why he wants me to do it." The mother threw up her hands in disgust. "For heaven's sake," she said, "I can tell you that. He wants you to read to him because he enjoys the stories."

Although many reasons can be advanced for the growing number of people who are playing with cannabis, the simple fact (totally unacceptable to many adults) is that most young people are using it because they enjoy the effects they experience and the excitement that goes along with the act. They enjoy seeing adults turn pale with rage, impotent in their attempts to control the problem. Then, too, they enjoy playing with the effects of the drug.

Smoking cannabis is a modish way to get the attention of society and to watch one's parents go berserk. In fact, some youngsters possess the drug without any real plans to use it. One fifteen-year-old apprehended by police made this fact plain to his arresting officers: "Honest," he said, "I don't plan on smoking the stuff; I just keep it around as a status symbol." Of course this is not usually the case.

Many observations have been offered by various authorities about the users belonging to Group Three. Most of these opinions seem to be based on biased, subjective, unsubstantiated observations. Some adults assume these youths automatically become social misfits the minute they pick up a joint. Others promote the idea that no harm occurs to those who merely play with cannabis. Both arguments are wrong.

While youth is youth and each individual is an entity unto himself, several reasonably correct observations can be made about this group as a whole. First, they are not bad. They come from what are currently accepted as good homes. They may turn out to be Sam or Joe or Sally or Jane from across the street. They may even be our own children. Only a few of these youngsters will progress to the constant use of other dangerous drugs. In saying this, however, we must keep in mind that the potential for such progression is always there because of the ready availability of more dangerous drugs and the presence of peer-group pressure which constantly reassures newcomers. "Nothing can go wrong (except getting busted)," the novices are told, "because small amounts of these drugs can't hurt you."

Most Group Three users will emerge from their drug experience without any apparent harm either to themselves or to society. Unless they slip into the drug abuse pattern seen in Group One and Group Two, few will continue to abuse cannabis once the fad is over and the communications media find something more newsworthy.

In this author's experience a changing trend has been noted. The statistics which glowingly report that "everybody is turning on" fail to mention the large number of youths who are simultaneously turning off. There are numerous reasons for this. "I don't need it any more . . ." "I can't afford the waste of time . . ." "I'm getting too hung up on it and it's interfering with my school work (or job)." These and similar reasons are, in effect, creating a retreat from the pot-using community. Further, it has been noted in Los Angeles that as the hysteria has subsided a bit and rational education methods have been promoted, preteens and those early in their teens seem less intrigued by pot and drugs in general. Thus, while the cycle is far from reversing itself, the critical swing toward drug oblivion and abuse of drugs, including pot, seems to be slowing down in those areas where endemicity once was high. The shock wave of increasing use, however, may yet hit communities which up to now have been relatively drug free.

The Steppingstone Theory

While preteens and early teenagers seem to be reorienting their attitude toward drugs, their older brothers and sisters, (and in some cases uncles, aunts, fathers, and mothers) may not be as well off. For some, the drug problem has become progressively more harmful with casual use of mild drugs giving way to the abuse of more dangerous pharmaceutical products. This situation has reactivated an old controversy, namely the "steppingstone theory." The problem with this theory is that it has categorically stated that anyone using cannabis will inevitably end up using heroin. This is untrue. Numerous studies have discredited the steppingstone theory, but the idea seems to die slowly in the minds of older members of the community.

Unfortunately disavowing the steppingstone theory does not settle the issue. While pot use doesn't "lead" to the use of more dangerous drugs, it is *not* totally innocent, because the use of one pleasurable drug may reenforce the user's tendency to employ other drugs. The type of drug which becomes associated with pot use varies from culture to culture and from need to need. For a time it was popular to completely deny any association between heroin abuse and the smoking of pot. The moment society relaxed its attitude associating pot with more dangerous drugs, however, heroin began to reappear as an escapist drug for American youth. Pot's role in this recurrence may be indirect and controversial, but nevertheless it is involved. We would do well to take a closer look.

In the wake of heroin usage, or perhaps, associated with it, numerous other drugs have entered the scene which also offer heroin's "wipeout" effects. Among the more critical of these are drugs which are highly dangerous when abused. Cannabis is connected to these more dangerous drugs, not because it is a steppingstone in the sense that it takes the user by the hand and leads him on to other drugs, but because cannabis use is often an innocuous experience that is so surprisingly uneventful and uncomplicated it allays the drug-prone individual's concerns about trying stronger drugs. As Popoff noted,[8] the more often a person uses marijuana, the more positively he tends to rate his experience with the drug. This observation can be carried further. The more positively one relates to the marijuana trip the more defensive he becomes of it and the less critical he becomes of the drug scene as a whole. Thus, if one is inherently seeking a different or more varied psychopharmacological effect, he may well be encouraged to proceed from one drug experience to another.

The old concept that marijuana leads to the use of heroin or other drugs was poorly stated. It did not nor does not lead, per se, but it catalyzes the drug scene for many people by providing an initial, usually pleasant, experience; it was and is distributed among individuals who tend to encourage the use of other drugs. Marijuana in the '70's is not as often directly associated with the use of heroin. There is, however, a frequent relationship between the chronic use of cannabis and the use of LSD in some subcultures. In other groups, pot smoking seems to be linked with amphetamine abuse.

When Shick[9] and his associates interviewed 413 drug users in the Haight-Ashbury district during the fall of 1967, it was noted that the use of marijuana and amphetamines were often associated. In this group, where cannabis use was 96 percent prevalent, 34.1 percent had at least tried intravenous amphetamines and 21.3 percent were abusing the drug at the time of the study. Additionally, 75 percent had tried oral amphetamines.

These statistics should not encourage one to assume, however, that cannabis "led" to the use of amphetamines. Cannabis as always was instead a common-denominator drug with a group that was highly familiar with many dangerous drugs. Not only was the use of cannabis in this subculture almost universal, but 36 percent had tried cocaine, 55 percent had tried sedative drugs, and a fourth of the group had tried heroin (although only 8 youths were using the drug at the time of the study); 58 percent had tried smoking opium and 87 percent had tried LSD or a similar psychedelic drug. Additionally, 87 percent of the youths who used to consume alcohol now rejected hard liquor once they had become satisfied with pot.[10]

The significance of these findings is that while pot may be unfairly blamed as a "steppingstone" to other drugs, it is nevertheless a prime introductory drug, a satisfactory catalyst in the drug counterculture, and a reassuring factor in confirming the idea that drug use is not potentially dangerous. This is particularly true where progression to the use of LSD and comparable hallucinogens are concerned.

In Shick's study, "the habitual use of marijuana was signifi-

cantly more frequently associated with the abuse of the psychedelics than with the abuse of any other drug."[11] Cannabis was
used habitually by 85 percent of the psychedelic devotees, a percentage significantly higher than found in any other group of
abusers. Whether the use of cannabis preceded the use of acid
within this group is open to dispute, since marijuana was apparently used to modulate the psychedelic experience either as a
"downer" sedative, when the trip became too high, or as an
adjunctive drug employed to heighten the LSD experience. This
diametric difference in utilizing cannabis may be due to its biphasic nature, although this remains to be demonstrated.

Where amphetamine abuse is concerned, cannabis has also
played a role as a "downer" because speed users apparently employ the sedative effects of the drug in an attempt to control
"far out" highs. The problem is that the effects of marijuana are
not always reliable, although this point is often debated. Pot
users are all-forgiving of their drug and offer numerous excuses
for the presence of adverse reactions associated with pot's use,
all of which tend to exonerate the drug. Nevertheless marijuana
did not seem to offer proper sedative effects sufficiently well that
its use was totally accepted by speed freaks. Heroin, on the other
hand, can be depended upon to slow the trip and reduce the
high. It can also be depended upon to produce rapid and tena-
cious physical and psychological dependence. Just where pot
is involved in the progression to heroin here is open to heated
discussion, but one thing does seem pertinent: regardless of
personal biases, speed (intravenous methamphetamine) promotes the use of heroin. Speed also engenders the use of barbiturates which, in their own sick way, are more dangerous from
a physical and probably from a psychological standpoint than
is heroin.

While it is difficult to determine whether cannabis preceded
acid in the Haight-Ashbury subculture, the sequence is less debatable among a group of 14,748 diversified, sophisticated readers of the magazine *Psychology Today,* who answered a survey
on drugs made by the editors of the magazine prior to April,
1970.[12] When the tally was published, 63 percent of the respon-
dents had at least tried marijuana and 30 percent were using
it at least once a week at the time of the survey.

"The strongest relationship," the editors noted in reviewing
their findings, "is between marijuana and LSD use. Of those

who have *never* taken marijuana, 99 percent have *never* tried LSD. But 31 percent of the once a week marijuana users have tried LSD, and 77 percent of the daily marijuana users have tried LSD. The same trend exists with other hallucinogens." In other words, if one never uses pot, then statistically, the chances are that he won't try hallucinogenic drugs. If he does smoke pot, then the more he smokes the greater his chances are, statistically, that he will try stronger drugs. In recent months the most commonly used drug, following the use of pot, is a stronger hallucinogen. It is interesting, however, to note that as the drug scene matures heroin use is again rapidly becoming popular.

Where opiates were concerned only 14 percent of the daily marijuana users had taken them more than once or twice. Those in this study who had infrequently used cannabis, i.e., twice a month or less, essentially showed no tendency to use hard narcotics.[13]

Whether cannabis leads to more dangerous drugs, therefore, can become the subject of numerous debates and the cause of a great loss of time. While people debate, drug abuse goes on with the critical issue being not who is right but how one can reduce the devastation resulting from the drug abuse scene. Pot may enter where amphetamines are abused because it is potentially a "downer." If pot fails, heroin and barbiturates may take its place. Pot introduces users to and seemingly encourages their participation in the use of stronger psychedelics. At this point, heroin may re-enter the scene—for what, to some, may appear to be an unexpected reason.

"Sure I use heroin," a youth told this author. "Why not? I turned on and I tuned in and I saw. And what I saw scared the hell out of me and I had to turn it off. Smack does the job for me and while I may have other problems at least I've turned off the visions." Other youths give an additional reason. The ghettoes they have created in the city pads have become so oppressive they can no longer face the environment, even with drugs; thus they have turned to heroin to blot out the entire picture. This group must not be confused with the spiritually-oriented hallucinogenic users, the original hippies of the drug subculture, who long ago fled the city to seek a better understanding of themselves and their relationship to God, and who limit their drug intake to hallucinogenic substances, feeling no need for other drug experiences.

As we shall see in the next chapter, marijuana use and pot-oriented people vary intensely from one situation to another. Certain things, however, tend to hold them together in a loosely knit brotherhood. One of these elements is the jargon of the world itself. This colorful aspect of the world of marijuana deserves closer inspection.

THE LANGUAGE OF THE MARIJUANA WORLD

"The world of marijuana," Cohen says, "is a state within a state, a culture within a culture, and it is impossible to estimate its population."[14] This world has its own etiquette, its ethics, its pattern of survival, and its jargon. A knowledge of these factors is essential for an understanding of this subculture and the people who inhabit it. First, the jargon.

Cannabis (marijuana, marajuana, marihuana) has, as we have noted, numerous synonyms. The same holds true for the people who use it. The more common descriptive term for the user today is "head," in this case "pothead" or "weed head." He may also be called a "roach bender," "tea man," "weed hound," or numerous other terms that might be popular in a particular community of users at any given time. The word "head" is more versatile than other names since it can be used to denote any drug-taker; those who use LSD are termed "acid heads," opium users, "hop heads," and so forth.

The marijuana cigarette is probably blessed with as many nicknames as the weed itself. It is referred to as a "reefer," "rocket," "stick," "joint," or "weed." Once it has burned to a tiny butt it is known as a "roach." Because the tetrahydrocannabinols tend to accumulate in this small tip, roaches are prized by users. Such a reefer butt really looks like a cockroach and doubtless acquired its name from this resemblance. The association of the two inspired at least one song prior to the acid-rock days about a groovy cockroach who could not get through the day without using marijuana. You may have sung "La Cucaracha" without realizing its meaning.

With the entrance of the intellectual into the cannabis drug community, a caste system has evolved. Basically there are two castes, an upper and a lower. Each is characterized by the way the user enjoys his drug. The lower-caste user is totally unconcerned about the intellectual advantages of philosophizing and self-exploration which intrigue his educated counterpart. The lower-caste user simply "trips," that is, he experiences the bizarre effect of the drug for its own sake. The word *trip* can generally be defined as a psychological excursion produced by the intake of a drug or drugs, during which interval the individual enjoys, or endures, certain ideas and mental and sensory effects. Until recently, when the high school, college, and postgraduate crowd entered the drug arena, most cannabis users were lower-caste users, both as to their origins and as to their mode of use of the drug.

The upper caste today is populated by a group of people who seem to use marijuana as a transient interlude in their progress with the use of drugs. It is composed of intellectuals—students, professionals, artists, musicians, actors, and professors, who, for a while, take the drug to "maintain" and to explore themselves and the infinite. To "maintain" in this parlance is to defer the enjoyment of the pleasurable effects of the drug, and to utilize the experience to better understand one's inner self and rid oneself of his "hangups." This is not to imply that the upper-caste user does not "trip." He does. Not infrequently this is his principal goal at a given cannabis session. But whereas the upper-caste user will both trip and maintain, the lower-caste user seldom sees any benefit in maintaining per se. The latter considers cannabis primarily as fun or as a recreational or escapist thing to enjoy, without the complications of intellectual overtones. In recent months it has become increasingly common for pot devotees to use the drug not only for pleasure at social events where it is cool to smoke but, additionally, as a modifier to what might otherwise be a boring social evening.

A "hangup" in the world of cannabis, and in the world of hallucinogens in general, is a psychological problem that prevents one from arriving at the desired state of ultimate composure, or of "being cool." A hangup differs from a "hassle," another unpleasant experience, in that the hassle is usually an interpersonal squabble of varying intensity.

There are four states of being, with gray zones in between, which characterize the relationships of the user of cannabis to society in general and to his fellow users in particular. They are: "cool," "groovy," "hip," and "square."

At the bottom of the social ladder we find the square. The square is seldom if ever cool. He is "not with it," that is, he doesn't know "what's happening" (what's going on around him, particularly as it relates to the drug community). Worse, he probably doesn't realize his sad situation inasmuch as he is immersed in such activities as paying the rent, fixing the car, and raising a family. With rare exceptions, people over thirty-five are square.

A rung up the ladder we find the "hip." The hip individual is one who may or may not be out of the age group where "it's happening"; he may or may not take part in the action. But he knows "where it's at" (he is aware of the situation). The true hip is not only savvy but probably approves of the action. If he is a straight hip he knows but either ignores or disapproves of these drug activities. If, on the other hand, he casts a tolerant or friendly eye on the goings-on, he is a groovy hip or sometimes, groovy hippie. In any case, the hip is not to be confused with the Haight-Ashbury type of hippie who was a breed unto himself.

Near the top of the ladder we find the truly groovy individual. He is aware of the "scene" (the overall picture) as is the hippie, but he differs in that he delights in indulging in the action with the rest of the "cats" (users). Whereas the groovy cat is always hip, the hip individual may not be capable of grooving and he may or may not be cool. For, as we shall see, cool people may groove but groovy people may not necessarily reach the state of being cool. Not infrequently the groovy person fails to attain the cool state because of his hangups, the principal one being that he prefers to trip rather than to maintain.

The word *groove,* incidentally, may also be used to describe the ability of two or more people to communicate with seemingly total rapport. Thus, as two people sit and "rap" (express serious, usually personal thoughts, preferably without hypocritical overtones), they find themselves in such accord that they begin to "groove."

The cool individual is at the top of the heap. He "has it made" because he has conquered, at least in his own opinion, all his hangups. He not only knows what's happening but he knows where it's at. He can maintain or trip; he can groove or he can cool it. You ask him for an opinion and he lets you have it with no hassle or pretense. In user's parlance, he "lets it all hang out."

In a more conforming idiom, the cool individual is one who is capable of existing in reality because he understands himself and his problems. More important he understands the problems of his fellow human beings and accepts both the person and his hangups for what they are, without censure. If he departs from this condition of tolerance and acceptance and expresses himself without maintaining control over his emotions, he is said to have "blown his cool." If this happens, it is usually due to a resurgence of one of his hangups.

Parents will recognize that this terminology is also a part of many teenagers' vocabularies. It varies from place to place and individual to individual. Newer terms such as "clean," "righteous," "heavy," and others have come in to give competition to "cool." No one knows from one minute to the next what term will survive and what one will fold. As soon as the older generation begins to employ a current term, it loses its adolescent appeal and is rapidly discarded.

Degree of confusion in the use and study of this terminology increases in direct proportion to the squareness of the individual. At the moment it is contemporary teenage thinking to consider parents "square." Parents are supposed to lack the quality of universal tolerance which precludes their being truly cool, or inclines them toward "blowing" whatever little cool they might possess, when faced with their children's often erratic behavior. Most adults ignore and deplore this jargon. The lower-caste weed head uses it as part of his subcultural language. The high-caste weed head, however, and particularly the high-caste acid head, both employ and purposefully define these terms as they relate drug users to society.

GETTING AND SPENDING

Before one can turn on to cannabis he has to have a supply. There are basically four ways he can do this. He can grow cannabis himself, smuggle it over the border if he lives close to Mexico, acquire it from a user friend or group of users, or he can buy it.

Growing one's own for fun and profit is easy enough, since cannabis grows readily in any kind of soil. Thus the gardener with the blackest of thumbs can sow his seed in the spring and harvest it three months later. He cuts off the flowering tops, partially dries them in the sun or the oven, or he may take them to the laundromat, as did one enterprising young man, and toss them into the dryer (with the heat set at "Cotton"). Then he's ready to roll his own. The fact that more people do not grow their own supply is to be credited to the omnipresent police, who are ever on the lookout for the tall, ornamental weed. These men—commonly referred to as "fuzz," "the man," or "heat" by the cannabis crowd—are eagles at detecting marijuana growths of any size. As an example, in the summer of 1967 a young man leased a thirty-five-acre farm outside Washington, D.C., in suburban Virginia, and seeded one acre in cannabis. At current market prices his acre would have yielded him a return of something like a hundred thousand dollars. But before that could happen narcotics agents found the planting and arrested the grower. For good measure, the agents informed the grower he had planted his seed too late and frost would have killed the plants before they could have been harvested.[15]

If growing cannabis is hazardous, smuggling is worse. It is true that customs and narcotics agents cannot possibly catch all the cannabis that tumbles past the wide-open border gates between the United States and Mexico, but they make a sufficiently successful effort so that most people hesitate to take a risk that could send them to prison for as long as ten years. Moreover, many Mexican suppliers cheerfully turn in the occasional buyers, whom they won't see again anyway, and collect from customs agents a sum based on the value of the contraband. Even so, enough people make it through so that others are tempted to follow suit.

Constant borrowing from friends causes the usual kinds of friction. Some people are fortunate enough to be supplied without complaints by friends, lovers, or even parents. In Los Gatos, California, juvenile authorities encountered such a family of users. Truant officers called for help from narcotics agents when they sought an explanation for the continual absence from school of four children. The agents visited the home, a mountain cabin, inhabited by a thirty-eight-year-old father, his twenty-eight-year-old wife, and five children, aged four through fourteen. The father was kneeling in the rain on the front lawn, his eyes gazing skyward. "I can see the Resurrection taking place," he informed the officers. Inside, agents found the children, one of whom offered the information: "My Daddy puts LSD in my soda pop so we can turn on as a family." The wife added, "Sometimes the kids keep their own bags of grass." The nine-year-old volunteered that he had taken thirteen trips that week and was accustomed to sharing his supply with fellow students at school. During the booking of the parents on charges of possession of marijuana and contributing to the delinquency of minors, the police unearthed the information that two weeks previously the husband had shot his wife in the leg when he was "high" and had summarily taken care of the problem by digging the bullet out with his hunting knife. This family that smoked together did not stay together.[16]

If families don't supply it, young people occasionally can acquire it at "pot parties." Some pot shindigs have occurred under the very noses of innocent parents, such as a recent case in suburban Connecticut. There parents held a party for their daughter's seventeenth birthday, only to find a total of 170 teenagers overrunning the house and filling it with heavy smoke. While the adults remained ignorant of the nature of the smoke, police did not. They raided the party, booked the mother and some seventy young people in what was the largest raid to that date involving teenage drug users in the state of Connecticut.[17]

But it is generally agreed that the most common way of acquiring a "stash" (private supply) of marijuana is to "cop" (buy) it. It takes little effort to find a seller today, unless you happen to be over thirty-five or a newcomer to town. Sellers are suspicious of older buyers or persons obviously unacquainted with the area. But persistence will usually find a careless seller who is himself primarily a user. Careless sellers last only a short while. In time they usually sell to a narcotics agent and their peddling days are over. It takes some familiarity with an area and the presentation of the right attitude before the unknown buyer can make the necessary contacts to acquire his own marijuana.

An instance of the crude buyer was vividly brought to the attention of the author on a visit to the San Francisco's Haight-Ashbury district. A hippie who peddled underground newspapers claimed that a now-aging actress had just slipped him a five and asked where the "grass action" was, that is, the action of buying and selling cannabis. The hippie told her, "I don't know nobody that's holding" (anyone with a supply of marijuana). He pointed her out down the street where, with her two male escorts, she was still pressing her search for a "lid" (a supply sufficient to make two or three dozen reefers).

For many people the act of buying cannabis is more exciting than actually smoking it. They find a certain thrill in the game of "narco versus narks" (user versus narcotics agents). Normally they are looking only for small amounts of cannabis, or for "bag or box action," "lid or tin action," or occasionally "pound action." Such terms refer to the amount of marijuana being bought and sold at a given time. These volume measurements, confusing to the uninitiated but clear to the user, are usually constant throughout the United States. What varies is the price and the quality, which are determined by supply and demand, season, and source. Supply is dependent upon the season of the year (cannabis is most plentiful in the fall), locale (the nearer to the Mexican border, the cheaper it usually is), and the intensity of local police activity. As for the quality, some connections are more reputable than others. Part of this discrepancy is due to the honesty, or lack of it, of one's friendly dealer, but much is due to the complexity of the plant itself. "As we examine the drug in its various natural and synthetic forms," HEW told Congress in 1971,[18] "it becomes evident that the deceptively simple question posed is highly complex and marijuana is not a single, simple substance of uniform type. It consists of varying mixtures of different parts of the plant, Cannabis sativa, with psychoactive properties ranging from virtually nonexistent to decidedly hallucinogenic in its stronger forms and at high doses." Little wonder, then, that some users seem to receive no effect while others really "flip out."

In general, a bag or box is a small amount, usually enough to stuff into a penny matchbox. The price is from five to ten dollars, hence the terms nickel or dime bags. Sufficient cannabis is contained in this amount to make about eight skimpy cigarettes, or joints. The next size up is the lid or can. This is approximately an ounce and comes wrapped in a plastic bag or in an old tobacco can. Cans are of two sizes, short (loosely packed) and long (tightly packed). They vary in price from ten to thirty dollars, depending on local conditions. If one has "a half a C" ($50.00), he can buy a pound—which is sufficient weed that if he wants to repack it, he can make a thousand dollars' profit from his original investment.

There seems to be no set rule for wrapping marijuana for sale. Large quantities may come wrapped in newspaper or packed into attaché cases. In a recent diplomatic flurry, a foreign agent was caught bringing in a whole case full of cannabis under his arm. More recently a west coast priest was apprehended with two kilograms of grass carefully hidden under his cassock. Small quantities may be placed between the pages of a book, put into cigarette packages, or wherever human ingenuity contrives to conceal them.

A recent advertisement in a Los Angeles underground newspaper could revolutionize the whole picture. It offered two hundred factory-rolled, king-sized cigarette papers with the brand name and crest stamped in gold on each. "Mom will never know unless she smokes it," the ad read. "Turn your mother on! She'll think it's a carton of regular cigarettes. Simply fill with your brand. Gruvy for business meetings, church or your next coffee break. Society will think you have gone legit."[19]

As for sellers, they can be anybody from a teenager to a grandmother. Few people, however, sell cannabis as a profession. Most do it for the excitement, for a rapid intake of cash, or for a lark. Often, they decide to sell only as long as no stranger asks to buy from them, figuring that such an approach is a deadly sign of their being spotted by the "outside world" as sellers.

Much petty peddling is done by teenage users. In Van Nuys, California, police arrested a fifteen-year-old girl selling $2.00 worth to a girlfriend. The transaction took place in the girls' restroom during nutrition class.[20] In Salt Lake City, police apprehended a sixteen-year-old boy who was selling asthmatic tobacco and claiming it was cannabis. Some two hundred people had purchased from this boy, and they were so eager to have the drug that they did not know it was a deadly substitute. They got their high, although for some it was more than they bargained for. The substitute he gave them contained medicinals that are extremely toxic if used in large quantities. They were capable of producing a "high" complete with hallucinations and, for some, toxic psychoses. In fact, several deaths have now been reported throughout the nation as a result of the abuse of asthmatic tobacco.[21]

Not all who sell are users. One apparently troubled youth wrote a nationally syndicated religious columnist stating he had a friend who got his supply from a brother in the merchant marine, and was now making a tidy sum reselling it. He wrote the columnist inquiring if it would be proper to do this himself to earn money to go to college. "I'm trying to tell myself there is nothing wrong with this," he philosophized. "After all, I don't make those kids smoke the stuff. They do it of their own free will. Besides I have read it doesn't harm you."[22] Many others have read the same thing. With consistent reassurance from various communication media that the drug is harmless and laws controlling it stupid, they have decided that the psychedelic minority cannot be wrong, and so they try to pick up some extra money from those who are looking for a supply.

Though numerous cases of teenage sellers could be cited, none is more poignant than that recorded by *Los Angeles Times* reporter George Reasons[23] concerning Johnny, age sixteen, who had a going business established among his friends. "I tried pot a couple of times but I didn't like it," the youth told police. "There were others who did, though. They wanted pot. I had pot. I didn't twist anybody's arm. I didn't turn anybody on. I didn't drum up the action. They came to me. It was strictly business. I didn't try to sell to them. I don't think kids ought to use it."

Johnny was one of nineteen arrested in his school for peddling drugs, after police invested some four hundred man-hours of time to establish their case. The boy sold his joints to fellow students for a dollar each, a bit higher than the usual going rate. From this trade he managed to stash away about $700 before his arrest. John, who came from a respectable middle-class family, as did the other pushers, had a particular reason for wanting the cash: "I got interested in auto racing a few months ago," he explained. "I had started saving my profits to buy a car."

John was so discreet in setting up his sales that school authorities had no idea their halls were frequently the scenes of drug contacts. Because of his caution he sold no drugs at school, preferring to make deliveries off campus. That police ever discovered the situation was due primarily to a break that occurred during an investigation of a minor traffic violation. The arrested juvenile, once he began talking, was a veritable fountain of information. He told police all he knew about narcotics operations in his school and offered to introduce a young deputy undercover man to the proper people.

Once the deputy managed to work his way in, he discovered these young peddlers worked primarily out of a drive-in hamburger stand and a local bowling alley. Not content with selling cannabis, they peddled everything from pep pills to hard narcotics. Teenagers came from all over the county to buy from them. Each of these pushers—seven under age eighteen, eleven barely past that age—worked together, sold to the same customers, yet maintained their separate business operations. Parents were astounded after the arrests. A police officer told Reasons: "With present laws, we can't stamp out the problem. All we can expect to do is control it to the best of our ability."

Though petty pushers of cannabis tend to limit their sales activities to a few friends or known customers, some sellers mimic the big time. These people deal in kilos (a little over two pounds) bought with a ritual reminiscent of the days of Al Capone. The large purchases are then divided for greater profits to be made from individual sales. Such deals are usually made by a contact introducing a potential buyer and seller. Only first names are used, and no questions asked as to source of supply or the way it was brought in. The purchase is made either by putting the money in front (presale payment) or on credit, if the customer is well known. Delivery is then set for some future date. On the day of pickup, the buyer is notified of the drop, told to be there at a given time, and the deal is completed.

Most of the larger sales are made at night, either in a home or in the back of an automobile. If the sale is made in a home, the homeowner or apartment lessee usually gets a cut of the purchase for his hospitality. If the deal is made in a car it is usually an old one, since the police are authorized to seize and hold any automobile used in illegal transactions involving narcotic drugs.

Some writers suggest that a large organized criminal group is in charge of marijuana sales. This has not been proven. Several factors work against it. Cannabis, truly a weed, is too easy to grow, and the supply from Mexico is plentiful. There are, in addition, other sources available to those in the know which make the marijuana business essentially a small-operator affair. Moreover, the money is greater in other types of drug exchange. The result is that marijuana traffic cannot be controlled simply by attacking major crime syndicates.

ROLLING YOUR OWN

Once the buyer acquires his supply, he takes it home and hides it. Such individual deposits are referred to as "stashes." When it is needed for smoking, a portion is removed from the stash, manicured, and rolled into joints, unless the smoker prefers to put it in a pipe. Manicuring can be quite a process. One of the nation's news magazines (rapidly becoming known as an accurate source for the "how to" of drug abuse) suggests that the user force the cutting through a number-twelve mesh protective screen, such as that used in prison and detention homes, take out the stems and seeds, roll, ignite, and puff off to cloud nine.

Once rolled, however, it is not simply a question of puffing away. To smoke marijuana and acquire its effects requires a special technique. Cannabis cannot be mixed with cigarette tobacco for the purpose of turning on innocent youth. This is an old fable spawned by misinformation. The person who smokes cannabis knows very well what he is doing because the procedure requires his full attention and time if he wishes to become intoxicated. Although an increasing number of smokers are "going up" alone, cannabis smoking tends to be a social affair; users prefer to be with others during the trip.

Usually several smokers will meet in a room (teapad) or in a car. Sometimes they hole up in a closet for a better effect, since the fumes tend to concentrate in a small area. The holder of the marijuana then begins the ritual. He takes the reefer, which he has preferably rolled himself, and inspects it for flaws. It is, in most cases, a skimpy cigarette double wrapped, usually in wheat paper, and kept small on purpose since it burns more rapidly, is less expensive than thick joints, and can be consumed to its bitter end.

It is important that the twigs not perforate the paper, since this makes smoking more difficult and wastes the active ingredient. The ends have to be checked to make sure they are tucked in tightly so that the packed weed won't fall out while the cigarette is being passed around. These joints are far from being like their tailor-made commercial cigarette counterparts. Since they are irregular and uneven, it is common for one end of the reefer to draw more easily than the other. The smokers determine this before settling down to smoke.

Rosevear describes the use of the marijuana cigarette with compelling accuracy. After selecting the end to be lighted, he advises, the smoker wets the skinny weed down with spit. He may roll it around in a trough of spit puddled in his protruded lower lip; He may lick it sloppily with his tongue; or he may "let it all slide in." Rosevear continues: "Often the joint is a grey, soggy thing, repulsive looking, sad and unsanitary but the wetting moistens the joint and slows down the burning process."[24]

It is now time to light up. Even here the process is complicated. If the lighted end is not started correctly it won't burn evenly. This means that some of the cigarette could be wasted and the smoking time shortened. Additionally, smoke from poorly lighted cigarettes will often burn hot and be unpleasant to the taste. It is important, from an economic standpoint as well as a pleasure standpoint, that the smoker learn to light his fire properly. The best way is to hold the cigarette at eye level, center the flame, and turn the cigarette slowly, twisting it back and forth to assure even distribution of the flame.

Once the joint is lit it is kept in constant use. Each smoker drags deeply on it, holding the smoke in his lungs and flushing it down with short breaths (i.e., "cooling it") until he has filled his lungs to capacity. He then sits and waits for the "stuff to have a chance," which means to hold it as long and as deeply in the lungs as is possible in order to effect rapid and full alveolar transfer of the tetrahydrocannabinols to the bloodstream. "The object of marijuana smoking," advises Rosevear, "is to get the smoke into the lungs in the most efficient way, taste and flavor be damned. The throat is opened and the smoke drawn directly into it."

In a few short minutes the joint burns down to a butt. This butt is referred to as a "roach" and is a very valuable item in the world of marijuana since it is loaded with tetrahydrocannabinols that have concentrated there during the smoking. The roach, however, is very tiny and very hot to handle. To enjoy it one must hold it with a paper clip or tweezers, stick a pin through it, or, if one is very sophisticated, retain it with a jewel-bedecked roachholder. The latter is available in most psychedelic shops that sell all accessories for marijuana smoking.

Even with the holder the roach is too hot to hold to the lips. To overcome this it is held close to the mouth and the smoke is drawn in by a current of air caused by rapid inhalation through pursed lips. These concentrated fumes, like the others, are held deeply in the lungs as long as possible to acquire the full effect.

There are also many other ways of smoking pot. It can be smoked with special holders made from cardboard and foil, which permit an air-smoke mixture, or smoked in special or regular pipes with or without tobacco. The roach may be smoked as mentioned above or put into the end of a cigarette and taken as a "cocktail." If one prefers he may save roaches and make a full joint out of them when he accumulates enough. The method is the choice of the smoker.

And every smoker is seeking certain sensations. These vary, of course, but they also have certain features in common. To these we turn to see what the marijuana experience is like from the inside.

"That was strong grass! I've got visions of sugar plums dancing in my head."

the
pleasant
effects

4

Though nothing can bring back the hour
Of splendor in the grass, of glory in the flower
We will grieve not, rather find
Strength in what remains behind.
—WILLIAM WORDSWORTH

THE PLEASURABLE EFFECT of grass has been described in literature by various writers for the past two thousand years or more with an ecstasy that makes experienced users glow with delight and nonusers wonder if they might not have missed something worthwhile. This is the "Upsville" side of the marijuana trip, the only one stressed by pro-marijuana enthusiasts. Fortunately, it's the most common type of trip. If this were not so there would be little debate about weed because the "Downsville" side of the picture is far from pleasant. Understanding the positive side of the marijuana use is crucial if one hopes to relate to the marijuana controversy.

Youth realizes there are two sides to this question. Adults might as well admit it, too. The concept that a toke on a joint will condemn one to a life of crime, violence, and heroin addiction is now passé. Too many people have tried pot and their experience has belied the old doctrines. Today the decision as to whether one will use or not is a personal one, despite the law. It shouldn't be made with partial information.

This chapter, then, concerns the pleasant effects of pot. It is primarily directed to the over-thirty group who continuously wonder why kids "fool with *that* stuff." The idea that pot can be fun may be new to adults but for youth it is old hat. Except for a few historical passages in this chapter which might be new to them, young people are fully aware of the "up" trip on grass. Their "education" began five years ago when the use of the drug began to be glamorized by certain elements of the entertainment profession, popularized by certain segments of the newsmedia, and justified by comparable groups in the scientific, philosophical, and theological community.

This education brought a new philosophy to American youth: pleasure for pleasure's sake is not wrong.

But fun is not the only factor. Actually there is no single reason why a kid turns to pot for kicks, any more than there is a single reason why he turns on to grass as a psychopharmacological medium.

Pot use may serve as a way of attracting attention. Pot use may be a way to annoy parents who are too busy to notice junior unless he is openly violating some of their more cherished taboos. But most of all, pot is "in." The kids didn't decide this any more than they decide which record will hit the top ten. The establishment who stood to profit from drug traffic made the decision as soon as they dared sell the product. That is one of the ironies of the marijuana scene: kids have been sold the bill of goods that pot is "their" drug. The kids take the trip. The kids take the blame. But the adults take in the cash derived from what has now become big business: promoting pot, punishing pot users, and publicizing the crises that result.

The real crusade to Tripsville started with the good news, beginning around 1965, that pot "can't hurt you," that "everybody's turning on," and that you're not "with it" unless you blow grass.

Encouraged by adult "philosophers," some of whom are desperately trying to solve their own persistent adolescent hangups, more and more kids decided to "try and see." "It used to be that "better living through chemistry" was just another advertising slogan; now it is a sly joke to the young and a grievous worry to their parents," notes *Time* Magazine. "In their quest for sensory experience, an alarming number of kids are swallowing its message whole."[1]

One interested observer who has been encouraging liberal attitudes toward drugs for the past three decades is sociologist Alfred Lindesmith. Disturbed by the harshness of current pot laws, he concluded that the "system" has crumbled and should be changed. His advocation of legalized pot seemed at one time, strange to many. Today it has become almost prophetic. Now, with grim humor, Lindesmith notes, "If a kid goes to college these days and never develops an interest in marijuana he's got a problem and you should worry. He may be a loner or not accepted by his peers."[2]

Although this statement may be anathema to older persons, Lindesmith makes a significant point. Today's youth has been educated to believe that unless they have experimented with grass, they are "out of it." When Weil and Zinberg sought volunteers for their much publicized short-term study on the effects of pot, they found it difficult to find marijuana-naive persons among their student associates in the Boston area. When they did discover nonusers they found the students apologetic for not having tried the drug. It is difficult to believe this attitude did not influence the outcome of the study, particularly when one nonuser entered the program with the avowed intent to "prove'" in the experiments that marijuana really did not do anything, while another nonuser volunteer expressed an eagerness to get high because "everyone I know is always talking about it very positively."[3]

One significant aspect of this study was honestly reported by the investigators, but ignored by those who lauded the article as "proving" pot was safe (it didn't, nor was that its expressed intention): one accepted volunteer backed out the moment he found he would be experimenting with marijuana. He was an exchange student from India, and apparently had seen enough of the drug's effect in his own country.[4]

The chant that "pot is groovy" and "everybody is using" has been effective and so frequent that it has become a self-fulfilling prophecy. "I know, as do millions of Americans," a youth wrote *Playboy*, "that marijuana does not live up to its evil reputation. [My] experience was mild, pleasurable and beautiful; at no time did I forget who or where I was and at all times I retained perfect control over my body. And there was no hangover—no queasy stomach or splitting headache, no wooly tongue or burning eyes."[5] Another user agreed in *U.S. News & World Report:* "The problem is not with pot or those who smoke it, but with those who don't and refuse to allow others to pursue this pleasurable activity."[6]

Are these kids lying? Of course not. The experience they describe is exactly as they remember it or choose to remember it. Most probably they have never experienced or seen an adverse effect from the use of grass. Why is this? Because although conservatives have avoided a simple truth where this weed is concerned for many years, the fact remains, and is backed up by the experiences of millions of American users that the casual, nonabusive use of mild marijuana by reasonably stable persons in satisfactorily chosen settings is essentially an uneventful, inconsequential experience.

Before either side becomes too emotional over this statement, however, it would be well to read it again, for it is loaded with many qualifying conditions. Bluntly, the situation is this: if you're sure of the chemical content of your joint and your emotional attitude toward the effects of the trip is positive, if you can be certain your head is on properly and that your environment and fellow trippers are "cool," and if you can be certain that your personality is such that you are not likely to get dependent on the drug and that you know how to handle "flip-outs" should they occur. . . . , "right on, man." If not, it may pay to think twice.

One reason for all the confusion concerning the use of marijuana is that most American youths have never seen or smoked a really "good" joint. In many instances, much of the effect has been almost entirely psychological or, as HEW has noted, ". . .the totality of expectations brought about the set (attitude of the user) and setting (environment) of use. It is not uncommon," HEW continued, "for individuals consuming a psychoactively inert material to experience subjective effects which they erroneously attribute to an active drug."[7] HEW referred to this expectation reaction as the "Placebo Effect" since it has nothing to do with the pharmacological activity of the drug. At low doses, it noted, "it may be difficult to be certain to what extent an effect is brought about by the drug itself. . . ." Additionally, HEW said, this effect "may complicate results in a laboratory setting in which the placebo is so compounded as to resemble the active material in all respects except for the presence of the psychoactive constituents." The importance of this will be obvious later, but for the present it may be well to emphasize that sincere youths who insist that "their" experience with marijuana didn't hurt them may not have come into contact with marijuana at all, or at best they may have smoked a very low-quality weed.

Honest though the youths may be (which is more than can be said for certain "adult" advisors who see a chance for profit and approval if they noisily climb aboard the pro-marijuana carrousel), their interpretation may be inaccurate because of the effects of the drug itself. These effects involve the inherent characteristic of cannabinols to alter memory, values, and interpretations. There seems to be incorporated in weed use a reassurance that no matter what happens, pot per se is not to blame. Accordingly, grass enthusiasts tend to excuse the drug of any implication in the production of adverse effects.

It is interesting to note how frequently the "pot is cool" philosophy is associated with a phenomenon HEW has described as the "hang-loose ethic." In relating this to Congress, HEW stressed there was no indication pot *caused* these attitudes nor, for that matter, that the attitudes were *limited solely* to devotees of grass. It did stress, however, that these attitudes were frequently closely related to the use of marijuana.

The characteristics of the hang-loose ethic have been defined as: "dissatisfaction with own education and the system; opposition to the Vietnam war and the draft; approval of sexual freedom; feeling a communication gap between self and parents; anticipation of satisfaction from future leisure activities more than from work; participation in 'happenings' and mass protests; interest in underground newspapers; and belief in possible circumvention of laws (but not necessarily breaking them)."[8] To these, HEW might have added, "insistence that pot is innocent." In this latter attitude, marijuana users differ markedly from most other drug-taking groups.

Alcoholics generally "badmouth" booze. Heroin addicts always put down smack. Barbiturate addicts can't invent enough put downs about downers. Users usually relate to other drugs in a sort of armed truce in which they accept the good with the bad, hating every minute of the price they pay for their crutch. But pot. . . . Wow! The situation between pot and its fans is comparable to an ardent love affair, with devotees advocating their drug with an enthusiasm reminiscent of a Southern gentleman vigorously defending the honor of his lady.

This forgiving attitude is so recurrent it is documented frequently in medical literature. Chapple, in his study of 80 heroin and cocaine addicts, reviewing a previous phase of their drug taking, found that while these users talked disparagingly of their other drugs, "their attitude towards cannabis was very different . . . they were quite unprepared to say that they would give up smoking cannabis, even if their opiate addiction were cured; moreover, they talked of cannabis in terms of great enthusiasm, and in general they were agreed that there were no dangers attached to the taking of cannabis and that it 'wasn't a drug of addiction'."[9]

The attitude exists in practically every drug-taking situation. When Craig Gardner, a nineteen-year-old postal worker, dictated his last observations prior to committing suicide, the same pattern was repeated. "All I can say," was his comment, on the tape played at his funeral, "is, I had to find out myself—kind of a poor excuse, you know—but I really shouldn't have taken any dope at all—any acid—and I shouldn't really have started off with any grass. . . . marijuana either," he repeated, then catching himself, he qualified his statement with a line repeated so often by certain segments of the media and by users. "Of course, grass isn't bad—it's the acid that got to me."[10]

There is little question but that this recurrent, reassuring theme has made many youths unable to say no when pressured by peers into smoking grass. One smokes it or one is not "in." Parents should be sympathetic with this problem, in that it is a rare adult who can withstand the pressure to at least hold a drink in his hand at a cocktail party, because a nondrinking guest tends to make the drinkers nervous.

Wilson describes this peer pressure as it exists in England with language quite applicable to the United States.[11] Introduction to weed or hash in that country generally begins at a party where a supply will be available. Once the joints are passed around it is a rare kid who can stand out—like a potential nark—by refusing to toke up. Thus, after watching his more experienced buddies and noting that none of them drops dead, the novice takes a puff or two and toddles off to upsville. At this point anything may happen. Most likely he will suddenly experience, with the aid of his "guides," some time-sensory-memory changes. If he responds well to these he begins to enjoy himself. Should he go on a "bummer," he is in an ideal situation to manage it because users are usually more adept at handling adverse reactions (other than psychotic breaks) than are most non-drug-oriented medical personnel. This may explain why so few cases of marijuana intoxication are reported in hospitals. Most are handled on the "pad level" by experienced users. The cases that do reach the hospital more often than not may be poorly diagnosed by physicians who mistake panic reactions for organic psychoses. Succeeding treatment under these conditions is guaranteed to make the situation worse. Fortunately, continuing education for physicians in the drug abuse area is eliminating these experiences.

Wilson makes the statement that, "There is no such thing as a little bit of marijuana, the 'kick' is the ultimate, which is similar to being drunk."[12] There was a time when this author agreed with this point, but since then, and as my contacts with the current American drug scene increased, I can no longer accept it as being true. It may well be the case with the older, less facile users, as Tinklenberg has noted,[13] but it is most likely not the case with young people and with older, chronic users. With the young it is not uncommon to roll a joint, pass it around for an occasional, socially amalgamating drag to loosen restraints as a single martini might do, and create an atmosphere that is both relaxing and conducive to "rapping." The joint is used much as one might use alcohol: it serves the purpose of promoting a shared, relaxed group activity. In this setting users may not become "high."

"A person under marijuana intoxication appears vacant, generally breaks into an inane smile and responds to questioning slowly with a considerable time lag," Wilson notes.[14] This is a typical report from a trained scientist. To a user the situation is very different. The latter would probably think, "Hey, he's with it, man." To a knowing head, the smile is not vacant. It indicates relaxation and a change in time and sensory perceptions. The fact that a user does not reply at once to a comment or question is unimportant to his fellow "trippers." It gives them time to drift off on their own. Usually it is inconsequential whether or not a fellow smoker finishes a sentence, because, "hours" before, the one who posed the question answered it himself and moved on to another train of thought.

The gap between the nonuser and the user is tremendous. This problem tempts some investigators to be their own subjects. Sometimes this technique works, sometimes not. In the latter instance the investigator may find the drug offers one a release from tension as it distorts sensory and time relationships. If this happens he may not be able to make objective evaluations of his future subjective experiences. For instance, recently when an educator dropped by to discuss a problem with this author, the name of a researcher indirectly referred to elsewhere in this book came into the conversation. "Oh, you know Dr. X," the educator observed, "how interesting. You know," he continued, "the doctor used to be a welcomed guest in my home but lately he's become a pain in the social neck. You see," he explained, "the doctor began experimenting with pot a few years ago and found it quite to his liking. Now when he comes to my home all he does is sit in the living room, get stoned on grass, and make passes at my wife."

Significantly not once in the several years of government grant-supported investigation has "Dr. X" ever been able to find any "proof" of adverse effects from the use of pot. Furthermore, in recent months his primary activities have been in the direction of legalizing the drug for socio-recreational use.

A similar discrepancy in attitude, value judgments, and perception has been noted among college students volunteering for experiments with marijuana. If one expects a "good" trip, he will have one according to his own evaluation, regardless of anything else that may occur short of complete "freakout."

Stanford Medical School scientists experimenting with such volunteers noted in one instance that the youths seemed to be having a most unhappy session, with apprehension, fright, and depression being elements of their trip. Yet, when the experiment was finished they reported they had had a "wonderful time" and recalled experiences that were primarily pleasant.[15]

In contrast, other investigators have observed subjects who seemed during the trip to be euphoric and happy, only to discover, when the experiment was over, that the volunteers would no longer agree to further experiments because they felt their "trip" had been extremely unpleasant.[16]

The word of the user, then, may not be the most reliable

source of information concerning the effects of cannabis. This word, however, is still currently the best form of information available because the principal effects of pot are subjective. Techniques which are normally valid in investigating other drugs tend to be ineffectual where psychedelics are concerned. These drugs produce experiences which must be described by the user since, as is the case with pain, he is the only one who perceives it as he thinks it is.

The difficulty is that one must rely on the judgment of the user who may not be able to be as honest as he might wish to be because the experience he is undergoing tends to alter his ability to think and interpret. Researchers experienced in cannabis investigation are the first to admit this flaw. "The curious problem of the experimentalist," state Weil and Zinberg, "is that as he controls the laboratory environment more and more carefully so as to maximize his confidence in ascribing observed effects to known cases, his laboratory becomes less and less like the real world which is what he set out to study. Indeed, control can proceed to the point that the experimental results are scientifically impeccable but their relevance to anything in the real world is lost. Then if someone comes along and says, 'So what?'—as happens all too frequently in science—the experimentalist will be stuck for an answer."[17] Interestingly, the "so what" Weil anticipated arrived within a year of his observations in the research of Hollister: he asserts that virtually everything that usually occurs in a social situation can be replicated in controlled laboratory studies.

The complexity of the chemistry of marijuana is only now becoming obvious. Prior to 1964 investigators believed that the work of Adams and Todd in 1940[18] had revealed the chemistry of cannabis components, but it was only the beginning. HEW has described the continuing research that has been accomplished over the past three decades. "In the past few years," it says, "intensive investigations have clarified considerably the rather complex chemistry of marijuana. Most natural cannabinoids (a term used to denote all of the C_{21} compounds typical of and present in Cannabis sativa, their carboxylic acid analogues and their transformation products) in the plant have now been isolated and purified, their structures elucidated and analytical methods for their detection and quantification developed."[19]

"In the period from 1963 to 1968," HEW continues, "the true structure of the tetrahydrocannabinols was clarified . . . [and] at present, four major cannabinoids have been found in the plant. . . ." HEW notes that the major tetrahydrocannabinol believed responsible for the psychoactive properties of cannabis is Delta-9-THC (also called Delta-1-THC). Its isomer, the other major constituent of cannabis, is referred to as Delta-8-THC (also called Delta-1 (6)-THC). Other minor cannabinoids present in the plant include cannabigerol, cannabicyclol, cannabichromene and cannabidivarin.[20]

It is fascinating to note, then, with all this scientific background, that we know so little about this drug that HEW's report dated January 31, 1971, still states that "the health picture with respect to marijuana must at present be regarded as fragmentary and clearly incomplete. Many of the most important questions regarding the implications of long-term, chronic use will require significant periods of time to answer."[21]

Numerous factors noted above suggest most American youths have no idea what effects, if any, "good" weed can produce. Yet another unknown is a matter of special concern because it introduces one more potential for harm to the user. The problem is impurities. ". . . It must be recognized," HEW recently told Congress, "that other ingredients are sometimes found in the material that is smoked or ingested. Users are exposed to a wide variety of additives, diluents and contaminants, since marijuana is available only through illicit channels and systematic quality control is non-existent."[22]

"It is clear," HEW said discussing the American joint, "that an almost limitless number of compounds are available as possible contaminants ranging from deliberately added adulterants to inadvertent pollution by herbicidal action. At the present," HEW warned, "there are no means by which users can readily determine whether or not contaminants are present in marijuana."

The HEW report continued this discussion with an indication of the magnitude of the problem. When Marshman and Gibbins[23] collected 222 samples in 1969 to analyze actual content, and determined the ingredients in 197 of these, only 61.9 percent contained the drug that was alleged to be present. "In regard to the 36 samples alleged to be marijuana, with a high cannabinoid content, 'good grass' as it would be termed on the street," the researchers said, "some were marijuana cut with other substances and some contained no marijuana at all. Some of it appeared literally to be grass-lawn clippings; some of it looked like hay and smelled like hay. Our figure of 64 percent for samples that 'contained marijuana' includes all the samples that contained any marijuana at all. It is clear that a sizable portion of what is sold and smoked is not marijuana but other substances, sometimes of unknown origin."

The laboratory of the Bureau of Narcotics and Dangerous Drugs verifies Marshman's and Gibbins' findings. Of 191 seized specimens analyzed during the fourth quarter of 1970, 12 percent failed to contain the drug the purchaser thought he was buying. The same findings held true to varying extent for the other three quarters: 14 percent false claims for the first quarter, 16 percent for the second and 7 percent for the third.[24] With users being burned with such frequency, how can anyone accurately describe a "typical" trip?

It follows, then, that no one description of the marijuana trip will adequately relate an experience acceptable to all, or even to most, who have tried using pot. Just as there is no "typical" pot user, neither is there a "typical" pot trip. The trip will vary immensely depending on four factors which in turn may be altered from one episode to another. The factors are: 1) *the set*, i.e., the emotional attitude of the user toward the drug and the anticipated drug experience; 2) *the setting*, i.e., the environment in which the consumption of the drug occurs; 3) *the dose* of the drug itself which, except in laboratory environments where a specific substance is administered, cannot be either measured or predicted under current circumstances; and 4) *the personality of the user*, which basically is in constant change as new experiences and interpretations of these experiences are added to the "computer file" of his brain. This, of course, assumes that the grass in question is legitimate, and not a "burn" or a contaminated buy.

The marijuana trip, then, can be expected to be and generally is an unpredictable experience. Basically there are two types: "good" trips, which constitute the majority, and "bad" trips which, though a minority, can be both serious and disabling. The fact that most trips are good is an encouraging commentary on today's youth, assuming that various observers are correct in their decision that pot serves as a catalyst in the emotional experience which intensifies tendencies or ideas already present.

Kids may indeed take drugs, as Sidney Cohen observes, because they are bored, in pain, frustrated, or alienated. Such kids may find in pot a substance which will offer oblivion, surcease, quietude, togetherness, or euphoria.[25] This type of personality in essence determines its own bad trip, for most bad trips, other than toxic psychoses, may well be the amplification of a negative reason which stimulated the user to try the drug in the first place.

More likely youth tends to use the drug for reasons given *Time* by a Chicago college student who says, "You take it when friends get together or when you're going to see Yellow Submarine. It's not to solve problems, just to giggle."[26] Further, it tends to satisfy the adolescents' hunger for adventure, thrills, and risks. They view the activity as both desirable and safe, discounting that the smoking of a joint is any more drug abuse than taking a large dose of aspirin. Consequently, most marijuana trips in this country tend to be a socio-recreational activity, with users relaxing, giggling, enjoying each other and the mild time and sensory changes which frequently occur.

Such a trip may take one of several directions. There may be no reaction at all, with the potential user emerging from the experience wondering what all the noise is about. He may experience the giggly relaxation so often described, concluding from this brief exposure that the weed is innocuous and the potential for adverse reactions improbable. More often than not, the user follows Howard Becker's suggestions[27] and goes up with an experienced tripper who can tell him what to look for and how to enjoy the various subtle effects he might otherwise miss.

Regular users tend to seek a certain level of "high" and round off the experience at this point, since they wish to avoid adverse reactions. This "self titration" is generally successful if the weed has a low resin content. It is not as effectual if the resin content is high. It also tends to become impractical if the weed is eaten rather than smoked. The titration may be also effected by the phenomena of reverse tolerance, whose mechanism is described elsewhere.

If legalization does occur in the next few years the number of mild trips may give way to an increased number of bad ones. That this is inevitable seems indicated by the fact that even casual users prefer a "stronger" grass when they can get it, because of its increased effects and more rapid action. In the past the trend has been to minimize the effects of grass and express some concern about hashish. Now, the same mythology is being circulated about hash as about grass, i.e., it's "cool" and can't hurt you. The result is that hashish use is rapidly increasing among American youths who prefer a "better" trip.

The mild trip, though it defies categorization, is nevertheless frequently the same when set, setting, dose, and personality fit the appropriate requirements. If one emerges from this socio-recreational use, however, and progresses to stronger forms of grass, a number of things may occur. Our best descriptions of these experiences come from articulate observers who have taken the time to jot down their sensations for the education of others. One of the more graphic descriptions was written during the late nineteenth century by the poet Charles Baude-laire, who, with Théophile Gautier, was a founding member of the Club des Haschischins at the Hotel Pimodan in Paris.

Attorney John Kaplan objects to the citing of this descrip-tion, calling it the irrelevant, florid, poetical, drug-induced fan-tasies of a nineteenth-century French hashish-eater.[28] Stepping out of his role as an attorney and entering the discipline of medi-cine, he lodges three complaints as to why Baudelaire's com-ments are immaterial. First, he says, the drug was eaten, not smoked. Second, they "obviously" used huge doses; and finally, he says that the Haschischins used the drug to get stoned in a manner not typical of American use.

Kaplan's first point is invalidated by competent medical research. ". . . Previous studies of equivalent oral doses of syn-thetic THC," note investigators Melges, Tinklenberg, Hollister, and Gillespie of Stanford University, "suggest that the induced psychotomimetic effects are clinically similar to those associated with smoking potent marijuana. Thus, one need not be concerned about the relevance of studying the effects of ingested rather than smoked marijuana. The oral route of administration, at least at present, offers a far more precise way of regulating dosage."[29] Further, in contrast to Kaplan's assertions, American users not infrequently eat their grass. They do this, if for no other reason than that it minimizes their getting caught.

Kaplan's second point, (that Baudelaire took his drug in "what were obviously huge doses,") is a value judgment open to question. As for the third point, if Kaplan's experience has been limited to users whose only purpose was to giggle and not to get stoned, he has failed to establish acquaintance with a significant number of American pot users.

Baudelaire, in his descriptions, is discussing hashish, a drug five to six times stronger than "mild" American marijuana. But it is not much different from certain brands of Cannabis mexicana such as "coletus," where two tokes from a "bomber" can precipitate an experience quite similar to a low-keyed trip occurring on LSD. Essentially, his recital is relevant to all cannabis products, since they are all interrelated, varying only in their potency. Mild pot may indeed be "mild," but if one goes up the scale and takes a weed with a high resin content, he may precipitate many of the effects of the LSD experience.

"What does one experience? What does one see? Wonderful things, amazing sights? Is it very beautiful or very terrible or very dangerous?" These are the questions, says Baudelaire, the nonuser asks about the cannabis experience. They are childish questions, he muses, "such as might be felt by somebody who has never left his fireside, on meeting a man returning from distant and unknown lands."[30]

Baudelaire also dispels the illusion that the cannabis trip and sleep are similar. Man's sleep, he says, produces two kinds of dreams. There are those that relate to his ordinary life and those that are "hieroglyphic" dreams. These latter are absurd, unpredictable dreams with no relation to the characters and passions of the dream. The cannabis trip, however, he assures us, is utterly different from these dreams. It does not bring the user beyond the bounds of natural dreams, although the intoxication is in the nature of a vast dream. "It will always," he says, "retain the private tonality of the individual. The man wanted the dream, now the dream will govern the man," he notes, "[Man] wished to ape the angel, he has become an animal; and for a brief while the latter is very powerful—if power is the correct word for an excessive sensibility—because it is subject to no restraining or directing government."[31] Baudelaire makes it quite clear that everyone who wants to use the drug should realize that it will work no miracles; rather, it will only produce an exaggeration of the natural. The drug affects the brain, and it is the brain of the user which will determine the effects to be experienced:

A man will never escape from his destined physical and moral temperament; hashish will be a mirror of his impressions and private thoughts, a magnifying mirror, it is true, but only a mirror. . . . Here, then, is happiness. It is large enough to fill a small spoon. Happiness, with all its intoxications, follies and puerilities. You can swallow it without fear—one does not die of it. Your physical organs will be in no way affected. Later on, perhaps, a too frequent consultation of the oracle will diminish your strength of will; perhaps you will be less of a man than you are today. But the retribution is so distant and the disaster in store for you so difficult to define! What are you risking?[32]

With an awareness that makes him as contemporary in thought as Timothy Leary, Baudelaire warns that "every perfect debauch calls for perfect leisure." It is important, when one uses cannabis, that he protect himself from noxious influences because the drug not only exaggerates the user's personality, it also distorts the circumstances and surroundings present during the smoking session. It is as true today as it was in Baudelaire's time that one must not burden himself with appointments, he must have no domestic worries, he must be free of unhappy love affairs, if he hopes to have a good trip. "This is most important," Baudelaire warns, "for any grief or spiritual unrest, any memory of an obligation claiming your attention at a fixed time, would toll like a bell amidst your intoxication and poison your pleasure. The unrest would become an agony, the worry a torture."[33] If Baudelaire were alive today and speaking the language of the user, he might put it this way: "Any bringdown, any hangups, any hassles can cause a bummer when you're up on weed."

Baudelaire divides the cannabis trip into three different successive phases. They are: going up, experiencing physical and sensory effects, and, finally, hallucination. Beginners, he says, usually complain that nothing is really happening or that, if it is, it is too slow in taking effect. They wait with childish impatience and then, when the drug fails to function fast enough or in the way they think it should, they pretend, acting out what they think the drug should do even though it is not actually doing it. This sort of performance, he says, "gives great delight to old initiates who know just how hashish sets abouts its work." It is this same performance, i.e., the acting out of the thing one "thinks" should be happening rather than relying on the pharmacologically-induced experience, that HEW referred to as the "placebo effect." This phenomenon may make it quite difficult to separate the real from the fancied effects of the drug under investigational circumstances. Of further interest is the fact that while John Kaplan has put down Baudelaire's observations as "florid fantasies," they are in essence almost identical to the observations now being elicited in the laboratory by contemporary researchers. Further, as we shall soon see, these "irrelevant, poetical fantasies" are nearly the verbatim equivalent of both Rosevear's and Margolis' descriptions of the cannabis trip (and both of these lay authors are highly aware of the effects of cannabis).

When the drug begins to act, Baudelaire warns, it appears like the symptoms of a storm that hovers before it strikes. These symptoms develop and multiply as the incredible situation unfolds. The first symptom is a sort of irrelevant and irresistible hilarity. "Attacks of causeless mirth, of which you are almost ashamed, repeat themselves at frequent intervals, cutting across periods of stupor during which you try in vain to pull yourself together. The simplest words, the most trivial ideas, assume a new and strange guise; you are actually astonished at having hitherto found them so simple. Incongruous and unforeseeable resemblances and comparisons, interminable bouts of punning on words, rough sketches for farces, continually spout from your brain. . . . From time to time you laugh at yourself, at your own silliness and folly; and your companions, if you have such, laugh alike at your condition and at their own. But, since they laugh at you without malice, you laugh back at them without rancor."[34]

The mirth that occurs with cannabis intoxication, Baudelaire continues, "with its alternating spells of languor and convulsion, this distress in the midst of delight, generally lasts only for a fairly short time." Then the coherence of one's ideas becomes so vague, the conducting filament between fancies so thin, that the only ones who can understand the user are other users in the room with him. "And once again, on this question, too," Baudelaire muses, "there is no means of ascertaining the truth; perhaps they only think they understand you and the deception is mutual. This crazy whimsicality, these explosive bursts of laughter, seem like real madness, or at least like a madman's folly, to anyone who is not in the same state as yourself. Conversely, the self-control, good sense and orderly thoughts of a prudent observer who has abstained from intoxication—these delight and amuse you like a special sort of dementia. Your roles are inverted: his calmness drives you to ironic disdain." At this point the ridiculous occurs: "The madman begins to feel sorry for the sane man; and from this moment on the notion of his [the smoker's] own superiority begins to gleam on the horizon of his intellect. Soon it will grow, swell and burst upon him like a meteor."[35]

Once this childish phase is over there is a momentary lull in activity, then various physical sensations begin to occur. With Baudelaire, they were heralded by a sensation of chilliness in the extremities and a great weakness "in all the members." This experience, of course, is variable; each person feels or fails to feel specific sensations, depending on his particular trip. Baudelaire went through numerous physical tugs and pulls which are not usually described by cannabis users in this country, but after this period of individual experience his observations are consistent with those given by most contemporary users:

> . . . at this phase of the intoxication a new subtlety or acuity manifests itself in all the senses. This development is common to the senses of smell, sight, hearing and touch. The eyes behold the Infinite. The ear registers almost imperceptive sounds, even in the midst of the greatest din. This is when hallucinations set in. External objects acquire, gradually and one after another, strange new appearances; they become distorted or transformed. Next occur mistakes in the identities of objects, and transposals of ideas. Sounds clothe themselves in color, and colors contain music.[36]

Although this description is over a hundred years old it is, Kaplan to the contrary, still quite accurate for most "good" trips. It should therefore be clear, even to the uninitiated, that cannabis offers both the curious and the bored a gallery of sensory titillations that make the drug excursion both pleasant and fascinating. But this is not all, for in the last phase of prepsychotic intoxication one sees first illusions and then hallucinations that can be either most pleasant or very horrifying. "It sometimes happens," Baudelaire recounts, "that your personality disappears, and you develop objectivity—that preserve of the pantheistic poets—to such abnormal degree that the contemplation of outward objects makes you forget your own existence, and you soon melt into them. Your eye rests upon an harmoniously shaped tree bowing beneath the wind."

The next thing Baudelaire describes, although it might seem normal to a poet, is not the sort of thing many people experience even in a lifetime of drug use. Personification occurs, and as it does it seems quite real to the cannabis user. "You begin by endowing the tree with your own passions," writes Baudelaire, "your desire or melancholy; its groanings and swayings become your own and soon you *are* the tree." He offers yet another example: "let us suppose that you are sitting and smoking. Your gaze rests a moment too long on the bluish clouds emerging from your pipe. The notion of a slow, steady, eternal evaporation will take hold of your mind, and soon you will apply this notion to your own thoughts and your own thinking substance. By a singular transposition of ideas, or mental play upon words, you will feel that you yourself are evaporating, and that your pipe (in which you are huddled and pressed down like the tobacco) has the strange *power to smoke you.*" Under such conditions, Baudelaire concludes, "you seem to live several men's lives in the space of an hour. You resemble, do you not, a fantastic novel that is being lived instead of being written. . . ."[37]

It is interesting to note how closely contemporary writers agree in essence with the sensations experienced by Baudelaire. In recent months a new "pro-pot" book has appeared, written by Jack Margolis and Richard Clorfene, which (considering that its avowed purpose seems to be to encourage people to turn on), is both conversational and informative. Disagreeing with Kaplan on the advantages of eating weed as a means to get high, Margolis (who says he has never used marijuana) says that "Eating cooked grass is absolutely and unequivocally the best way to use grass." Not only is it easier, he insists, but it gets you more stoned and keeps you that way longer than smoking does.[38]

Additionally, he notes, if a knock comes at the door one can devour the evidence with pleasure. Smoking merely gets you high faster, and if one needs to get high that fast, he's probably using grass for the wrong reasons, and should forthwith give up weed and become an alcoholic.[39]

Comparing getting stoned to the learning experience of swimming, Margolis insists that anyone can do either if he can eliminate his fear of losing control, learn what and how one should feel, and then depart from reality—physically, psychologically, and spiritually. There's no such thing as happy grass or sad grass, he insists, just grass and the mood of the user.

The first sensations come on almost instantly if one smokes grass. If he eats it, brownies for example, it takes about an hour. Smoking marijuana allows one to slide into a stoned condition inch by inch. If one has eaten it, however, the onset is less predictable and may affect the user in the middle of a word. At this point, time and distance become confused and space alteration is totally unpredictable. One may not think this is so, but if he then tries to walk up a flight of stairs, he may find that the flight has become infinite in length. "It should be obvious that things which require good judgment of time and space (cooking an egg, tight-rope walking, driving a car) should be scrupulously avoided when stoned," advises Margolis.[40]

One now enters into a state Margolis terms "hungupedness." Insignificant things and tasks, such as picking lint off one's dog or staring at a spot on the wall, take on a tremendous importance. "You find yourself doing something inane for a long time and thoroughly enjoying it, even though every now and then you think you've been doing it forever."[41]

One thing about being stoned, Margolis notes, is that everything seems good, with nothing being bad except being busted— and he terms this a learning experience. The user becomes extremely passive, perhaps because of a "revised" law of inertia which states that whatever one is doing at the moment is so good that it simply has to last. "The rule," he says, "is that your body, if in motion, will tend to stay in motion unless acted upon by an outside force; and if it is at rest, it will tend to stay at rest, unless acted on by an outside force."[42]

Now, everything seems funny. ". . . [Y]our friend's teeth are a riot. A simple 'hello' brings on storms of laughter . . . going out in public in this mood can be a risky act because of the laughing problem, as you find yourself laughing at people who are not stoned and fail to see what is so amusing. Sometimes they hit you. . . ."[43]

Three years before Margolis sat down to write his observations on grass, Dr. Sheldon Cholst, a psychoanalyst, smoked a hashish cigarette and, while under its influence, jotted down his impressions. It was January 19, 1965—for Cholst, it was a memorable date. As is the case with many who try the drug a few times, enjoy the trip, and emerge from the experience with the same personality with which they began, Dr. Cholst came out of his drug trip with an impression that cannabis should be a legal form of recreation. "He who is evil is evil and will do so no matter what job or drug he takes," he says. "If only we could ban evil or the evil ones, we'd have no evil problems."[44]

ANALYZING THE MARIJUANA TRIP

Let us look first at some of the conclusions about the marijuana experience recorded by Dr. Cholst, a proponent of legalized cannabis. "I am writing now of the effect of hashish," he says. "I smoked it in a cigarette. Had some childish thoughts or memories—of me as a child knocking over a refrigerator and then hitting my mother for being mad at me and jumping into the fireplace and emerging unscathed and saying look what a delusion of grandeur I am. Unscathed—I can now do anything." Of this experience he observes:

> So, it makes you a child again—in mind or emotions or soul or unboring restless behavior. You move easily in thoughts and fantasies, one to another like a child. . . . Thus I was adult and child at the same moment. The fountain of youth has been found. The child lives in a world of wonders, he searches, finds, turns away and is afraid sometimes of being hurt or "put down" by adults. But now he is both—so he feels "high," tall like an adult and yet still a child.[45]

It would appear from these comments that one reaction the cannabis user may experience is a reversal of his thought processes and adult senses of responsibility to a childlike level. Is it not possible that precisely this regression is the factor that makes it so difficult for some to recognize the problem of cannabis abuse once they return from the delightful, synthetic escape to childhood? The user, according to Cholst,

> . . . has turned off adult reality—"what to do, where to go, what am I allowed to do" and has returned to the life of the free, primitive child who wanders in his happiness. . . . One's mind is free to wander, think, and all the restlessness is taken care of in the mind. . . . The limitations of mobility of the adult world (reality, laws, etc.) are gotten rid of. . . . Thus a man who is "stoned" is in a sense desirably paralyzed (partially or wholly) without the need for that motor activity which is indicative of the adult world.[46]

Once a person is under the influence of cannabis, Cholst observes, he no longer has a need to be concerned about the environmental dangers that previously disturbed him. ". . . [I]n the real world," he says, "the concern with danger, insecurity, fear of evil, have made him dress a certain way, listen to rules, frustrate himself, keep himself from being free—unable to do what he wants when he wants to do it."[47] Cannabis, Cholst says, is a "poisoner of frustrating reality," an "antidote for restlessness that is frustrated," an "instant joy and relaxation," a "chemical age-regression that allows us to be young and old at the same moment of time."[48]

The drug hashish, the "fountain of youth," "causes no harm," he concludes, "for what harm is there in being a child in the heart and in the mind . . .?" Cholst seems to have little patience with those who are not willing to try the hashish trip. "Those who do not have this capacity," he says, "those who are too square, too limited, too conformist, too brainwashed, not too bright, these people want the closed-in adult life. . . . These people who either constitutionally or environmentally cannot or do not want this release into childhood life—they will not 'turn on,' they will not feel 'high.' By and large," he argues, "those who wish to smoke already do, but there are some on the borderline who are too afraid they will like it too much and be drawn into the artistic or free life thus losing out on their Faustian bargain. They have sold their souls (their honesty, their desire for freedom, their insistence on truth, honor, dignity for all mankind) for the mess of pottage called financial success, prestige, and acceptance by society."[49]

Squares might not take this diatribe too lightly. They could, with reason, should they so choose, refer Cholst to Baudelaire's observation that it is at this point that the usual roles may be inverted and "the madman begins to feel sorry for the sane man," and that from this moment on the notion of the smoker's own superiority begins to gleam on the horizon of his intellect.[50] However, that would be unsportsmanlike.

Since Cholst's observations were made prior to the hippie movement, one cannot identify him with that group. But it is striking to find that the same philosophy is widely voiced by hippies who have taken the cannabis path. There is indeed a kind of conformity about it. This is particularly evident if one compares Cholst's philosophy with the "hang-loose" ethic described earlier in this chapter.

Cholst's praise for cannabis is so persuasive and his denunciation of the nonuser so pungent that nonusers may easily be cowed into silence. But the question that even Cholst's observations will not down is: how far can one go with cannabis before an irreversible disorientation and dissociation take over? For even reality, not to mention fantasy, can dull the spirit, as in the syndrome of the so-called "Polynesian paralysis." This form of indolence affects many Caucasians who stay too long in the South Pacific. Writing of this phenomenon on the island of Bora Bora, Coles Phinizy says:

Because they are both beautiful and bountiful, many of the small Polynesian islands that litter the South Pacific are dangerous places. At first sight of such beguiling shores, too many men fall in love and jump ship, foolishly believing that they have found a paradise where the mangoes are never wormy and worrying is against the law.

On any of a hundred Polynesian islands noted for their largess, a man—if he is not careful—can waste away in the midst of plenty. Although an island rat can get along on the fruit of a single palm, a man who tries to do so usually finds he cannot live by coconuts alone. . . . The man who goes to paradise to spend the rest of his days quite often finds after only a month that his senses are surfeited and starting to decay. The hibiscus and the dancing colors of the lagoon fade and are wasted on the eye. In time even the mango loses its taste and only the worm remains. Although none of the island songs mentions it, it is a fact that paradise has a sneaky way of turning a complex man into a discontented vegetable.[51]

If overexposure to an excess of natural beauty can do this, when the mind is presumably operating normally, it can certainly be argued that overstimulation of one's sensory faculties by psychotropic drugs can do at least the same, if not worse. The effect with drugs, however, is likely to be quicker and more lasting.

How far can one go in his search for total freedom from responsibility and for a childlike response? This depends to a great extent upon the individual and the society that must tolerate and care for him if he decides to drop out. While some individuals may take the cannabis trip and apparently emerge with a continued dedication to the realities of life, there may be far more who cannot make this transition; such persons may become social nonentities or liabilities, and cannabis may have been the agent that helped turn a productive person into a useless social burden.

VARIETIES OF RESPONSE

When one decides to take a trip with cannabis he can expect to feel the first sensations within minutes after smoking his cigarette. "A range of studies have been conducted of the drug's acute effects," HEW has noted. "As is true of other drugs, generally the effects are closely related to the amount that is consumed. There is general agreement that at the usual levels of social usage the typical subjective effects are: alteration of time and space perception, sense of euphoria, relaxation, well being and disinhibition, dulling of attention, fragmentation of thought, impaired immediate memory, an altered sense of identity, exaggerated laughter and increased suggestibility. Other less common effects are dizziness, a feeling of lightness, nausea, and hunger. As doses higher than the typical social dose are consumed more pronounced thought distortions may occur including a disrupted sense of one's own body, a sense of personal unreality—of being unreal, visual distortions, sometimes hallucinations and paranoid thinking. The more marked distortions of reality or psychotic-like symptoms become increasingly common if the dosage used becomes extremely high. Most users smoke to the point of 'high' which they find pleasurable and at which they are able to control the effect. It is, however, difficult to predict individual reactions. Rarely, individuals may become quite anxious or panicky on even low doses. When eaten, effects are less predictable and more difficult for the user to control."[52]

The new HEW report thus agrees with previous observations that one cannot anticipate a specific pattern of behavior when cannabis is used. This is due to the fact that the drug seems to have both excitatory and depressant activity. Its effects will differ from time to time and place to place and from person to person. Thus the singularly distinguishing feature of cannabis use is its unpredictability of effect for each person.

This unpredictability must be emphasized even though some writers imply that each trip on cannabis is identically the same and thus predictable in effect. If each trip were always the same, the use of cannabis would soon become prosaic. Even in the face of the variety of cannabis effects, many persons find it necessary, once the cannabis experience becomes too definable, to go on to something else more stimulating in order to gratify their psychological needs.

It is odd but true that some people are so constituted that they cannot derive significant effects from mild cannabis intoxication. Baudelaire noticed this long ago among hashish users. If it is true with hashish it is even truer with the use of less potent cannabis. When the effects fail to occur, the frustrated user has the choice of trying to fool himself and his friends, quitting, or trying something stronger.

In any event, the more common reaction to smoking cannabis is the rapid onset of a feeling of "inner joy" that is totally out of proportion to apparent motivation. The user soon finds himself dreaming, relaxing, lolling in the delicious state of effortless nothingness produced by the drug. It is inaccurate, however, to assume that this is always the case, for some people become quite agitated during the early stages of the cannabis trip. This reaction is not seen in the majority of users.

The delightful state produced by cannabis is referred to as being "high." If the intoxication becomes intense the feeling is described as being "stoned." If the user is alone he may "trip off" and be quiet and drowsy. In company he may be talkative and hilarious. Ideas begin to flit through his mind almost uncontrollably, flashing like bolts of lightning, often illuminating, but seldom striking home. The flow of thoughts for some is so overwhelming that, try as they may, they cannot communicate their ideas. This usually strikes the user as hilariously funny, and he begins to titter the high-pitched, giggly laughter so common to cannabis users.

Some beginners need an unusually large amount of cannabis to attain the state of being high. Acknowledging this, Rosevear[53] (who also admits that the only typical and predictable action of a marijuana smoker is the smoking of marijuana) assures his readers that, if the correct procedure is followed, the desired mental effects will present themselves. "Ideas about a variety of subjects continue to flow in a disrupted sequence," he says. "They are usually connected with the smoker's activities prior to smoking. Some events obscurely hidden in the past will be clearly brought to mind, yet transactions and activities only a few seconds old are likely to be forgotten. . . . It is not uncommon for a smoker to stop talking in the middle of a sentence and ask his companions what he was talking about, and very often no one in the group can remember."[54]

As the intoxication progresses and the senses become acutely aware, touch and perception become considerably altered and time and space seem distorted and unimportant. "Man," an adolescent user once said, "when I'm up on weed I'm really living. I float up and up and up until I'm miles above the earth. Then, Baby, I begin to come apart. My fingers leave my hands, my hands leave my wrists, my arms and legs leave my body, and I just flooooat all over the universe."[55] A user may become quite uncoordinated as time goes on, although he himself may fail to recognize it. His complex intellectual capacities are impaired, particularly his speed and accuracy. Walking up the stairs or climbing into a car, for instance, can become interminable journeys complicated by stumbling, slow, uneasy movements. Obviously then, situations that require little or no physical effort are best suited to the cannabis trip; television, listening to music, or just sitting around are the preferred activities. Playing games that require decision or skill is usually a poor occupation for cannabis users, since both movement and decision are hampered.

The basic personality of the individual is apparently not appreciably altered by using cannabis. His behavioral reactions may change, however, because of reduced inhibitions and a changed interpretation of events. This is often touted as an advantage, but it may be a very real disadvantage if one's basic personality is antisocial and hostile to begin with, as is the case of many who are drawn to the continued use of this drug.

The use of cannabis promotes a feeling of self-confidence that is usually, if not always, unwarranted. The user acquires a feeling of exultation and omnipotence, but such a sensation can quickly dissipate as a result of some negative factor and be replaced by feelings of anxiety and paranoia. Such feelings and the trip they occur on are referred to as a "bring down" and a "bummer."

Bummers are but one of several kinds of adverse reactions which may occur if the trip gets out of control. As we shall see, adverse reactions occur in novices, and they are not unknown in "seasoned" trippers as well. The up trip on marijuana can be a delightful experience but the down trip can be horrifying. How far out one can flip and how far down he can crash will be the subject of the next chapter.

"It's Goliath all right . . . probably stoned again!"

physical effects

"... something is happening
and you don't know what it is
Do you, Mr. Jones?"
—BOB DYLAN, BALLAD OF A THIN MAN

*P*EOPLE WHO USE MARIJUANA as a socio-relax-
ant drug take it with the intention that the psychic effects will
be predominant. The physical effects are considered the price
one has to pay for the emotional and mental trip, and are generally ignored, much as one does the increased heart beat, per-
spiration, shortness of breath, and similar body responses which
accompany the enjoyment of athletics.

Because the body's response to pot varies, as does the
mind's, with the individual and the amount of the dosage, each
user has his own concept of what "really happens" when he
"tokes up on a joint." In this regard, even Rosevear admits,
"One must realize that any recorded effects are subject to the
poetic license and accuracy of the narrator (and to his memory)
as well as to the intensity of intoxication."[1] This unpredict-

ability has led to a wide variety of opinions from a number of sources. As is usually true with marijuana, a comparison of these sources causes the reader to wonder if the "experts" are talking about the same drug.

Polarization of opinion has become a highly emotional issue. As we shall note in Chapter Eleven, the discussion of cannabis has almost become a way of life with certain groups. Usually their goal is predetermined. Whether pro or con, each carefully selects from the literature, quoting copiously from those papers which tend to support its point of view and ignoring those that disagree with the ultimate goal. For these groups it is the goal that seems important, not truth per se. Long ago these antagonists determined that pot was good or that pot was bad; that the job before them is to prove their point, rather than to explore the effects of the drug.

Often the question being discussed is not concerned with pot as a drug, but pot as a symbol and catalyst for social values. Erich Goode,[2] approaching this issue with an almost evangelic zeal, notes that one critical problem centers around different value systems and the life styles of various groups. He indicates that the gaps among these groups will never be resolved because of vast differences in the perception of reality that exist between two generations.

This may be idealistic and wishful thinking on the part of men dedicated to defending the use of cannabis. New surveys suggest that the younger generation is also split in its thinking, with many youngsters refusing to accept the highly liberal, anti-establishment thinking promulgated by the avant-garde.[3] If we consider that in a few years a disproportionately large number, perhaps the majority, of American citizens will be under the age of 35, this split in thinking assumes tremendous importance. If the split continues, it means the "battle" which may determine the behavior and value systems of tomorrow will not erupt between younger and older citizens; the eruption will occur between opposing groups in the same age bracket, i.e., under age 35.

Goode asks, "What one society or group or individual takes for granted as obviously harmful, others view as obviously beneficial or even necessary. Before we can rationally discuss marijuana or debate the question of whether pot has a 'desirable' or a 'noxious' effect," he remarks, "we would first have to establish the fact of the desirability or noxiousness to whom."[4]

Goode correctly states that anti-marijuana forces will argue against the use of the drug and employ, when doing so, the same reasons against the drug that pro-marijuana forces use to laud the use of it and to promote its legality. "In other words," he says, "we have here not a disagreement in what the effects are but whether they are a 'good' or a 'bad' thing."[5] The disagreement goes farther than that, however. It includes arguments about what information should reach the youth who now has to decide whether or not he will try marijuana.

Another area of contention focuses on the acceptance of "proof." A problem also exists where the interpretation of proof is necessary. The approach to this contention will vary from discipline to discipline. An attorney's proof is different from that of a physician. A doctor may see, as did millions of people, one assassin shoot another assassin; he will then most likely assume that the second assassin is guilty. The attorney may not. The attorney may assume there is insufficient proof and spend months quibbling over minor points of law. He may harass witnesses whose testimony fails to support his point of view. He may debate emotionally over factors which are totally irrelevant to the case in the hope that he can sway a jury into accepting his arguments.

One more critical difference between the approaches to a problem made by law and medicine is that when a lawyer seeks to verify a point, he reaches his zenith if he can obtain a favorable verdict from the court. If he is really pressed, he may seek a majority opinion from, say, the Supreme Court. Here, if he induces five of the nine judges to hold his opinion, he wins, regardless of whether or not these opinions correspond to reality.

The scientist, by contrast, has to verify his case first by prediction and then by gathering data in a systematic fashion to support his hypothesis. No court, per se, can rule on the scientist. His discipline demands that several "courts" render an opinion on his work. He must not only reasonably establish his point via recognized procedures; he must, as well, have his hypothesis tested and proved if he is to establish his case among his peers. Further, science demands that in addition to the original researcher, other investigators using similar techniques must gather comparable data and achieve similar results.

Attorneys sometimes fail to comprehend this. Kaplan,[6] for instance, has recently written a book in which he carefully dissects previous medical findings and observations, apparently in an effort to cast doubt on any opposition to his conclusion that the current marijuana laws should be repealed and the drug legalized. He seemingly does this on the basis that, in his opinion, current evidence does not sufficiently satisfy the requirements of a court of law for the adequate arrival at a verdict. If solving the pot dilemma were a legal problem only, we would most likely have had an answer long ago. Demanding a scientific evaluation on the other hand not only brings into play different rules and different dimensions, it prolongs the time needed for a conclusion.

Each discipline has its own system of investigation and its own set of responses to investigative findings. Within the field of medicine it is usually the laboratory researcher who makes the initial observations regarding the safety of a given drug. The researcher, however, most often works in a nonclinical atmosphere; thus it is not uncommon that his conclusions will differ from those made by clinicians. The doctor in private practice, especially if he works outside of a university research setting, immerses himself in the care of his patients. Rarely will he depart from this setting to complain to the editor of a medical journal that certain drugs are causing bad reactions. If he does it is usually through the medium of a "letter to the editor," a single case report or a similar observation. Such communications are often written in haste, do not include sophisticated methods of evaluation, and are lacking in many of the criteria required by professors who ultimately often finalize medical opinion.

Although these casual comments fail to meet the criteria of more critical investigators, they are, nonetheless, important. This is particularly true if enough physicians in private practice take the time to record their conclusions, for it usually happens that they represent an even larger segment of fellow clinicians who have arrived at the same conclusions but have failed to take time to report them.

For most drugs, observations of adverse reactions are sufficient to warn the medical community that it should take precautionary measures to prevent further problems. If the drug is so critical it cannot be replaced—chloramphenicol, for instance, (a valuable antibiotic recently accused of occasionally causing blood disorders)—its use is continued cautiously and it is administered only when indicated. If the drug can be replaced by another and if the profession can bypass the pressures of the particular drug manufacturer who stands to lose if the product is discontinued, it is discarded.

The only critical exception to this thinking (other than to-bacco) where socially important drugs are concerned is mari-juana. With this drug, numerous disciplines (including some physicians' groups) have indicated they are willing to make an exception; they have taken the stand that the drug must be proven unequivocally *harmful* before we stop using it rather than proven reasonably *safe* before unlimited and socially ap-proved use is granted.

"Several studies on marijuana use in other countries—notably India—have indicated addiction, physical degradation and psy-chiatric disorders as consequences of long term marijuana use," notes the founder of the Haight-Ashbury Clinic, Dr. David Smith.[7] "These studies," he continues, "however, were of hashish . . . which is more potent than the marijuana preparations com-monly used in the United States. Furthermore," he adds, "social and cultural factors are important determinants in the effects of marijuana use; hence cross cultural comparisons are risky."

Smith is correct in these observations provided there are no qualifying factors. Unfortunately, such factors exist in abun-dance. The general trend among most marijuana users in the United States is to use the best grass possible. Some of these substances, in this author's experience, far exceed hashish in their ability to produce what have, in the past or at least, been considered adverse reactions. (This phrase is qualified because some users of potent cannabis seek psychotic-like episodes. If this is their goal they will not interpret the experience as ad-verse. Second, some of this group will argue that psychosis as it is generally defined is desirable. If this is their goal it is difficult for them to understand why others do not relate to this experi-ence which, incidently, they argue is actually reality. The same group has been known to debate quite sincerely and for long periods of time that we have no proof we are here, that we are real, or that the state usually accepted as reality is a valid ex-perience.)

Although Smith's comment concerning the dangers of making cross cultural comparisons is generally appropriate, America is an exception to the rule in that the United States has a unique sociological feature—it is a combination of diverse nationalities. This combination of peoples from many nations has always been one of America's great strengths. But in recent years, the "melting pot" has become a "boiling pot"—a series of seething, restless communities. To assume that any *unpredictable* thought-altering substance is going to be beneficial to this situation is the height of folly.

Noting that the best studies in this country indicate that marijuana as commonly used here is not addictive, nor does it promote crime, moral deterioration, or psychological instability, Smith also adds that "It can produce toxic reactions both acute and chronic."[8] Some of these adverse reactions are physical.

One of the problems facing today's student who is groping for some conclusion regarding his own relationship to marijuana is that much of the information he needs to read is buried in medical literature. Frequently, if he does find it, he can't understand the terminology.

Wilson, for instance, in discussing the use of kif in Morocco, states that it "stimulates oneirocritic imagery, amplifies emotional overtones and facilitates the kind of collective osmosis characteristic of smoking parties. These parties," he advises, "are usually accompanied by interminable, blissful and friendly word-spinning, but not infrequently a mood of resigned akinesia will give place to impulsive release in action."[9]

Wilson can't be criticized for talking to his fellow physicians in the language of their discipline; however, neither youths nor the press for that matter can be expected to become ecstatic over this bit of scientific information. If Wilson were 18 instead of a mature adult he might have said this: "When Moroccan kids turn on to their brand of pot they tune in to a dreamy, happy trip that helps them rap and relate to one another. Most of the time they just lie around relaxed with their bods sort of out of it as far as doing much is concerned but now and then somebody suggests they split and get it on. If this happens the party may get out of hand."

For the past five years we have been assured by many segments of the communications media that there is no valid evidence that pot is bad. "Insufficient research has been done to come to any conclusion concerning the detrimental effects of cannabis," we're told. It's not true! More research has been done on cannabis than on the majority of drugs currently on the market. The problem is that some if not most of this research has been performed under circumstances which are not approved by modern researchers. Interestingly, scientists attempting to apply usual techniques to marijuana research often find that such approaches are inapplicable in investigating pot.[10] This has caused many to conclude—as have observers in the past—that something about cannabis drugs does not ring true. As continuing experiments fail to exonerate it as a safe socio-relaxant, more and more concerned investigators are advising caution in pot use, until we have acceptable proof, pro or con.

When youth and the not-so-young sit down to "rap" about grass, the tendency is to look for physical evidence to help decide whether or not marijuana is safe to use. Many argue that if a drug doesn't affect the body in such a way as to be clinically measured it must be okay to use it. This emphasis on the physical, with a deemphasis on the mental effects of a mind-altering substance, can be misleading. Many physical cripples in society contribute significantly to both themselves and to others despite their handicap. This is seldom true of mental "cripples." As an example, an eighteen-year-old patient lies in a Los Angeles hospital with a relatively healthy body, possessing a mind that may never function again. He blew it by mixing his hit of heroin with pickle juice. Ironically, many of the physicians at this hospital are crippled in body by polio; yet, because of their keen minds, they are useful, valuable citizens.

The effects of cannabis on the mind are difficult to measure. Most of these tend to be subtle and affect those areas of the brain which, through their power of logical thinking, philosophical ability, and reasoning, differentiate man from the lower animals. These psychological effects will be discussed later. For the present this discussion will center on physical effects as we currently know them.

Until recently it was believed that there were few if any lasting effects in the body resulting from smoking grass. Now, this is being questioned. On the other hand, since large numbers of young Americans have used pot with seemingly minimal effects, it is obvious that a definite distinction has to be made between the casual nonabusive users and those who choose to make the extensive use of the drug a part of their life style.

Becker's detailed account of the steps necessary to become a successful marijuana smoker emphasizes the difference between those who use the drug for pleasure and those who use it for escape.[11] As physical changes are discussed in this chapter *this distinction must be kept in mind.* Unfortunately those who choose to assume that *any* use is abuse will find this disconcerting.

It is true that one may "play around" with a joint and if it is mild enough derive essentially no ill effect from doing so. This is especially true if pot is used as part of a group activity, much like a martini, to provide something to do while tolerating or enjoying other humans at the party. If a user wants to achieve the cannabis effect, however, he must go through a sequence of changes in attitude towards and experience with the drug if he hopes to finally appreciate its more exotic effects.

Step one requires that the joint be properly smoked. One feature of this is the rapid, deep inhalation of the smoke and the holding of this smoke in the expanded lung long enough to afford transfer of the chemicals from the terminal air sacs of the lung into the blood stream.

The second step is the need to absorb enough cannabis products to achieve the production of psychopharmacological effects. This, in itself, is not enough, however. One has to recognize that the effects are there and learn to appreciate them. Only then can new effects be achieved which, as they appear, must be appreciated too. If one lacks enthusiasm for these effects the show is over.

Appreciating marijuana is a learning experience and is generally the product of education of novices by more experienced users, although one may, with minimal difficulty, teach himself. The problem is that in the early stages effects may occur which are both unpleasant and frightening. The psychological aspects of this will be discussed in the next chapter. The physical ones, related here, may be bad enough to turn the user off after one trip. Whether he returns to the use of pot again will depend not so much on his own curiosity, which by then may well have been satisfied, as by the activities of his peer group. If his friends use it, he will be encouraged to join them. If he fails to comply he may find it necessary to change his circle of friends, depending on the willingness to accept a continuing nonuser in their ranks. Being drunk in the presence of a nondrinker is bad enough, but being high in the company of a nonuser can lead to bad trips because of the possibility of ensuing paranoia. Thus it is the decision of the majority of a given pot-using group as to who remains in the group and who is invited by derision, disapproval, or outright instructions to go elsewhere.

Remembering, then, that there is a world of difference between the casual, nonabusive user of "pot" and the chronic abuser, particularly in persons susceptible to its dependency-producing effects, let us see what happens on the usual trip.

For most casual users there seem to be few lasting ill effects, physical or mental, from the occasional use of pot. Conservatives have long cited the increase in pulse rate, the congestion of the whites of the eyes, the dryness of the mouth and throat, the dizziness, nausea, and occasional vomiting that occurs with casual use of pot as a deterrant to use. Those who enjoy pot as a euphoriant or social relaxant accept these negative features of the marijuana with aplomb. Citing such body reactions as a deterrant to smoking or eating cannabis is useless.

The usual trip on cannabis occurs within a few minutes after the weed is smoked. If one ingests the drug, it may take an hour or more for it to take effect. Experienced users who smoke grass develop the capacity to titrate their intake so that they have relative control of their "high." This control, however, is not always constant and, as will be discussed later, a long-term user may suddenly have a bad trip for no apparent reason.

The total marijuana trip may take from three to five hours after which time the effects usually wear off. Generally this is true of the effects of mild weed, but it may not be true of especially "good" grass whose effects may remain as long as twelve hours. Reports have reached this author, however, of the presence of "hangovers" which last from hours to days. Admittedly, bad hangovers from the use of pot seem to be rare. They do occur, however, and in some instances the effects may be due to the type of grass the user smoked. The cannabidiol content of midwestern cannabis, for instance, seems to exceed the tetrahydrocannabinol level and thus may give a less satisfactory trip.[12] To date there has been no satisfactory explanation for the presence of hangovers which may last from twenty-four to forty-eight hours. In such instances the user experiences a prolonged lethargy, headache, mild anxiety, slight paranoia, varying degrees of irritability, and an inability to concentrate. With the supply of cannabis being erratic and the presence of contaminants variable, it cannot be stated at this time whether or not such adverse effects are totally due to marijuana per se.

The presence of nausea and vomiting is of interest to this author because it seems these symptoms may be more mechanical in origin rather than due to central stimulation. Many smokers, especially the uninitiated, tend to gulp large quantities of air in their attempts to deeply inhale and hold the smoke in their lungs. This smoke is highly irritating and may cause direct stimulation of the stomach lining that in turn causes nausea. This irritation, combined with a stomach full of air may lead to vomiting. Generally gastric distress does not commonly occur. If it does it is usually eliminated with practice. This author is aware of some smokers, however, who have never managed to eliminate nausea or vomiting. For some, these reactions occur each time they "go up." In these users a conditioned reflex probably exists which may never disappear.

Gaskill states that cannabis may affect the functioning of the alimentary canal: digestive disturbances, nausea, and vomiting accompany the drug's use.[13] This, however, is common to virtually all the psychotomimetics and is not unique to marijuana. Allentuck's studies confirmed Gaskill's, adding that diarrhea occurred in several of his subjects during the 48-hour period following smoking.[14] Adams additionally suggests that cannabis has an atropine-like action, although pharmacological evidence of this is not entirely satisfactory at present. If this is true, however, it may explain why so many users have dry mouths, for atropine specifically decreases the production of saliva.[15]

Respiratory rate, blood pressure, and deep tendon reflexes seem unchanged by the drug, although the total experience may affect these physical responses.[16] The presence of pupillary dilitation is no longer thought to occur.[17] Pupillary size as a measure of cannabis use has always been a poor criterion. Pot users, especially during a bust, are usually so "hyper" that their pupils almost completely dilate because of the sudden adrenal response to being placed under stress. In addition, smoking often takes place in a quiet, dark place where the environment usually encourages dilated pupils.

Bloodshot eyes, on the other hand, are an almost consistent finding among cannabis users. This feature has been highly profitable for certain eye drop manufacturers. Aware parents, therefore, can now add the presence of eyedrops among their youngsters' possessions along with odor-cutting incense, the spittoon, and a renewed interest in colorful comics to their list of "things to watch for" if they suspect marijuana use. "Tea-shades" (sunglasses) also are still worn to protect the light-sensitive eyes of some users, although the fad has caught on to the point of being ridiculous.

Another problem related to eyesight is not so well known. It was reported by Mohan and Sood[18] some years ago and indicates that cannabis may temporarily paralyze ocular muscles. The case in point is that of an eighteen-year-old boy who began to feel giddy and sleepy shortly after ingesting food that contained Cannabis indica. The giddiness persisted for several days. Soon he began to experience difficulty in turning his eyes to the left. The problem increased in severity until his eye muscle movements disappeared and his eyes became fixed toward the right. They remained this way for a week during which time he had to turn his head far to the left in order to see ahead. Then, slowly, the muscles began to function properly, but it was six weeks before the situation was satisfactorily resolved.

Smoking cannabis produces some specific effects on the respiratory system. As the session progresses and the smoke is inhaled, the irritant effect causes the mouth to become dry. The throat becomes so scratchy that coughing and clearing of the nasopharynx is commonplace. Phonation is difficult and the voice may assume a highpitched, strained tone. This irritation may continue long after smoking, particularly if the user smokes again at frequent intervals. The effects of this irritating smoke are particularly noticeable in persons suffering from asthma and comparable diseases of the respiratory tract.

David Smith, qualifying his comment by noting the amounts necessary would have to be large, says, "Since marijuana in the United States is ordinarily smoked we can suspect as a chronic effect increased susceptibility to respiratory disease, as with tobacco smoking, although this effect has not yet been documented with marijuana."[19]

One fascinating rationalization observed among chronic smokers is that pot "clears out the lungs." They "prove" this by noting the copious secretions which pour out of their respiratory tract as a result of repeated insults to the tender linings of their lungs. Such secretions would be pathological if they occurred in young healthy adults but this point seems to escape the smokers. Hawking, clearing, coughing and spitting, they bring up continued mouthfuls of irritating secretions formed by their otherwise probably healthy lungs as the respiratory passages try to protect themselves from the effects of the irritant smoke.

On the positive side there is one happy economic result. The spittoon industry has suddenly staged a comeback for a product that for a time seemed doomed to remain in antique shops.

The possibility of respiratory disease and resulting crippling effects seems so real to this author that it is difficult to understand why some choose to debate this point. Chronic users insist on immediate lethal proof of the drug's ability to produce adverse effects before they will even consider that disease might result from smoking pot.

In recent months medical literature has revealed at least two cases of byssinosis,[20, 21] a lung disease caused by chronic inhalation of hemp fiber products. It is true this is of interest only to those who handle the raw plant for a period of years. Some interesting speculations, however, can be offered connecting lung disease and the continued use of pot. But first a word about tobacco and pulmonary crippling.

With no deference to tobacco merchants, it has only been recently, within the past three decades perhaps, that tobacco has been shown to be a destroyer of lung tissue, a producer of respiratory ailments and quite possibly a highly potent carcinogen. Why not before? Although it has been shown that tobacco can produce respiratory change in the absence of smog, one may postulate that prior to our age of air pollution the atmosphere lacked a significant number of lung irritants, which, when placed in combination with those in tobacco smoke, caused the production of disabling lung diseases. Smog and industrial air pollution may be with us whether we like it or not, but tobacco and other toxic inhalants need not be.

Tobacco smoke is usually deeply inhaled only by some; the technique for smoking cannabis, on the other hand, requires deep inhalation, holding the smoke in, and, if one is a connoisseur of the art, forcing it through the alveoli into the bloodstream via a modified Valsalva maneuver (i.e., inhaling deeply, holding the breath then forcibly trying to exhale without permitting air to escape through the mouth or nose).

One can advise a cigarette smoker not to inhale, but not the marijuana smoker. To fail to inhale deeply and to hold the smoke voids the trip. On the other hand, it is fortunate that most tobacco smokers do not use the same technique for to do so would probably make a significant number of them quite ill. When Weil[22] was training his nine "naive" subjects for his marijuana evaluation study, he initiated a practice session during which the subject had to smoke two hand-rolled tobacco cigarettes by taking long puffs, inhaling deeply and holding each for 20 seconds. Five of these subjects had described themselves as heavy cigarette smokers prior to the experiment, yet, when they smoked tobacco in the same manner as marijuana, they developed acute nicotine reactions after two tobacco cigarettes.

Techniques such as these which force highly irritating cannabis smoke combined with other air pollutants into the lungs are without question a greater threat to pulmonary anatomy and physiology than tobacco has ever been. Much can be said about the cancer-producing effects of irritating, hot, inhalants, but cancer, frankly, is the least of one's worries where respiratory physiology is concerned. One need only treat severe asthmatics (cannabis has been mistakenly used as a therapeutic agent for this disease in the past), marked pulmonary fibrosis, or severe emphysema to confirm this.

Cannabis also produces marked effects on the blood vascular system. Ames,[23] in 1958, demonstrated that the drug could produce a tachycardia (increased heart rate) in man, a fact that was explained twelve years later by Isbell who showed that this effect was due to the presence of $\triangle^1$-THC.[24] Gaskill, in 1945, reported a type of fainting observed in some cannabis users which he related to vaso-vagal syncope.[25] In this situation the patient lost consciousness, his pulse became slow and irregular, his arms and legs became cold and clammy, his blood pressure fell, and he generally appeared to be in shock. This effect seemed to pass in fifteen minutes or so but the user was left with an intense headache. Later Ames,[26] in 1958, showed this headache could occur quite independently of the severe fainting Gaskill described.

Tinklenberg[27] notes that the cardiovascular effects produced by cannabis use are of particular importance to older (over age 30?) people, in that the increased heart rate can induce coronary insufficiency (an inadequate blood flow to the heart) with measurable electrocardiographic changes. With this in mind he poses this moral: don't try to bridge the generation gap by turning on your old man unless he's a jogger.

Ames showed that oral administration of a cannabis extract can cause marked diuresis (urine production) an hour or so after intake.[28] This diuresis is accompanied by a selective loss of sodium and bicarbonate. In healthy persons this may not be significant, but in persons with incipient, unrecognized disease it may precipitate problems.

One should never eat *raw* grass. The outcome can be disastrous. It can cause gastrointestinal, electrolytic, and (indirectly) cardiovascular upsets. Even pot advocate Jack Margolis warns, "Don't eat raw grass if you want to get stoned. Eat raw grass if you want to get sick." [29]

Cannabis, then, is apparently not as innocuous as some once felt, although others tend to persist in the feeling that it is safe. The problem with feeling "too safe" is that as more and more researchers investigate this drug under modern laboratory conditions, they obtain mounting evidence that the observations recorded by physicians of the past were not too far off. Miras, for instance, has reported marked changes in the electrical activity of the brain in chronic hashish smokers [30] and Kew, in 1969, [31] reported examining a twenty-one-year-old chronic cannabis smoker and finding he had cirrhosis of the liver. The boy had no other history of liver disease and had taken no drugs that would explain the problem. Intrigued by this, Kew solicited the help of a dozen English marijuana smokers in their late teens or early twenties with similar histories. All came from good homes and none had nutritional problems. Eight of these twelve had mild liver dysfunction. Three of the young men who had abnormal biochemistry results also submitted to a percutaneous liver biopsy. The specimen showed "in all the hepatic cells, the presence of striking parenchymatous degeneration with swelling and vacuolation of the cytoplasm." One of the men's liver biopsies showed a marked obliterating destruction of the arteries in the organ; another patient who, in addition submitted to a kidney biopsy, showed the presence of bile-casts in the tubular lumen. In simple English, the findings indicated the youths had sick livers at an age in life when their livers should have been healthy. Furthermore, there was no satisfactory explanation except for the common denominator of cannabis smoking. With due respect to this report, these findings do not *prove* that liver damage may occur from using pot. The point this study raises, as is true of so many interesting studies, is that cannabis may have a deleterious effect on the body. Thus, further research is indeed indicated and until it is accomplished, caution must be urged where any decision to legalize pot for general distribution is concerned.

One of the most frequent arguments offered by those who currently wish to legalize marijuana is that we do not have sufficient information to prove the drug is dangerous.

The idea that we might as well go ahead and use a substance and see if we get hurt before we make it illegal has been almost completely limited to marijuana. Much of this philosophy has been promoted by those who enjoy and/or need this drug as an emotional support. This group, additionally, has been aided by a growing number of prominent and semiprominent individuals who, possibly for the sake of debate or ego gratification, seem to be willing to take a public pro-marijuana position before adequate information is available.

The argument that we are not sure that pot is dangerous is specious and immature. It may be true science cannot satisfactorily prove to those who wish to smoke pot that it is dangerous, but it is also true that we can offer no assurance that it is safe. The real issue, then, is that we do not know what would happen in our labile culture if marijuana were suddenly legalized. In all probability, if we were discussing any other drug about which we had even less evidence of negative effects than we do concerning cannabis, society would insist on holding off on legalization until "more returns are in." Yet with pot, and with pot alone, a significant number of Americans, some of them highly intelligent, seem willing to throw caution to the wind.

This lack of caution and willingness to experiment with a drug that users reassure each other is totally safe has resulted in some bizarre activity. In the late 1960's a number of people, apparently determined to get high in the quickest way possible, attempted to "mainline" their pot. Some of these cases were reported in medical literature, the first by Henderson,[32] who treated a twenty-two-year-old Englishman. A year later King and Cowan[33] (as did Gary and Keylon[34] in 1970) had the opportunity to care for two youths who tried a similar stunt.

The general effects of the experience (all patients survived) are summarized by King, who notes, "The immediate toxic effects include nausea, vomiting, diarrhea, dryness of the mouth, and a burning thirst. Ataxia [muscular incoordination], diffuse muscle tremors and rigidity, cold extremities, and intense precordial [heart] discomfort associated with shortness of breath followed by several days of severe abdominal colicky pains may occur. These symptoms may persist for several days. Additionally the liver and spleen tend to become engorged with blood and are usually found enlarged. Intravascular coagulation of blood may occur shortly after injection which may result in pulmonary infarction (death of a segment of lung tissue). Additionally, blood infection may occur as a result of the injection of contaminated debris."

Mainlining grass is a dangerous way to get kicks. One may wonder why an otherwise intelligent youngster would do such a thing. On the other hand, why not? American youth has been told so often that "pot can't hurt you" that some apparently take this myth and go all the way . . . down.

Jaffe, in the current Goodman and Gilman, states there "are no lasting ill effects from the acute use of marijuana and no fatalities have ever been reported."[35] It is true that acute effects of marijuana intoxication pass rapidly just as it is true that adverse effects may linger for a considerable time depending on the habits of the user. These effects will be discussed in greater detail in the next chapter. Where death is concerned, however, the literature contradicts the notion that no one has died from smoking pot. Fortunately, the number of reported cases is small.

Deakin, in 1880, reported a death occurring from taking Indian hemp.[36] Walton, quoting Ewens, reported two cases in 1938.[37] In 1969 Heyndrick published the details of another death due to fatal intoxication occurring in a cannabis smoker.[38] As a matter of practical interest the lethal dose in humans is more than 100 times the pharmacologically effective dose and ranges from 100 to 5000 mgs./kg. of body weight. HEW notes the lethal dose in animals is between 20-40 mg./kg. intravenously and 800 to 1400 mg./kg. orally, depending on sex and species.[39] Animals receiving these high doses die in respiratory arrest with autopsy findings revealing pulmonary edema with hemorrhage.

In recent months additional interest has been evidenced by researchers concerning the possibility of damage to the fetus when it is conceived by parents who smoke pot. As far as chromosomal damage is concerned it has not, to this author's knowledge been adequately demonstrated. In fact when Martin[40] and Neu[41] attempted to produce such damage in laboratory animals, they were unable to do so.

Pot, on the other hand, has been proven to be definitely teratogenic (baby deforming) in animals. Persaud, in 1967[42] and again in 1968,[43] was able to produce marked fetal deformity in experimental laboratory animals. Geber's work[44] in 1969 produced similar findings and as doses were increased throughout pregnancy a significant incidence of fetal malformations of the brain, spinal cord, foreleg, and liver occurred.

The fact is that at present we do not know whether or not cannabis affects an unborn baby, and the whimsical response on the part of some that the only thing research indicates is that "if you're a pregnant animal, lay off the grass" is not altogether consoling. In human pregnancy it may also be well to "play it safe," since less has been proven about pot in this area than about any other popular intoxicant. As Isbell notes,[45] it's a good principle for mothers-to-be and nursing mothers in general to take as few drugs as possible. In the latter instance it's practical because tetrahydrocannabinol is fat soluble and may well appear in the mother's milk. Some may argue this would only give junior a groovy trip and might make him less prone to wail at night. But they aren't sure. It may not be that simple.

For a long time there was very little information available concerning the metabolism of cannabis in the body. In 1965, however, Miras was able to trace C^{14} labeled tetrahydrocannabinol after it had been injected into the abdominal cavity of experimental animals. The presence of the drug was noted in body fluids within thirty minutes after administration. Most of the C^{14} activity was found in the liver, but appreciable quantities were also discovered in the kidney, brain, and lung. Interestingly, large quantities were also found in the testes.[46]

The body seems to hang on to cannabis products once they are introduced. Miras was unable to recover more than 6.65 percent of the total dose. Significantly, this dose was administered by injection rather than smoking. Smoking, apparently, could be expected to have a far more demonstrable effect, for Joachimoglu and Miras have been able to show that tetrahydrocannabinol is better absorbed from cannabis when smoked than when it is injected.[47] Isbell later (1967) demonstrated that in man $\triangle^1$ THC is more potent when smoked than when it is taken orally.[48] This may be due to a more rapid absorption of the drug from the lung. Further the drug when smoked may be less detoxified than when taken orally, since it doesn't have to pass through the liver via the portal veins when it is inhaled. Miras' finding that the lungs of experimental animals contained high concentrations of the drug may suggest that the excretion of cannabis may occur through the lungs as well as through the kidneys.

More recently four scientists at the National Institute of Mental Health injected 0.5 mgs. of radioactively tagged THC (this is about a tenth of the amount usually absorbed by smoking

one marijuana cigarette) into the blood stream of three non-
smoking college-age volunteers. For the next ten days the researchers measured the residuals of THC and its metabolites in
the blood, the urine and the feces of the volunteers.[49]

Fifty-six hours after the injection the scientists found that
half the original THC still remained in the bodies of the volunteers. By the seventh day 90 percent had been excreted. As did
Miras in his animal experiments, these men noted that THC may
temporarily accumulate in fat or in other tissues, such as the
lung, which have an affinity for drugs. Agreeing with Miras,
they note that if this is a consistent finding it is clinically significant since most grass is smoked rather than eaten or injected.
From a research standpoint it is important to note, however,
that it has not as yet been determined whether or not residual
THC or its metabolites remaining in the body after smoking
have a deleterious or influential effect on the body or mind. If it
turns out that these chemicals remain individually or collec-
tively psychoactive, then one may validly question whether or
not the user who smokes several times a week is ever free of the
influence of cannabis.

A number of researchers have now noted, as has been known
on the street for some time, that frequent or chronic smokers
seem to need much less grass than a novice to get a high. It may
well be that the reason for this is the residual accumulation of
cannabis products in the body. The mystery of reverse tolerance,
therefore, may finally have been scientifically explained.

The argument is often offered sometimes in jest, which is the
most deadly putdown of all, that just because experiments in
animals show certain findings there is no reason to assume that
the same results will occur in humans. Frankly, this is good
logic assuming that one also understands that the reverse is also
true. Since animals in the laboratory are more expendable than
humans it is wise to view with caution any indication that a drug
has dangerous potentials. If the thalidomide tragedy taught us
nothing else it should have taught us that.

Laboratory experiments have shown other interesting things
about cannabis. In general, the animals came out second best.
Researchers have noted, for instance, that the administration of
cannabis produces a decrease in spontaneous behavior associated with an altered responsivity to stimuli that, interestingly,
was "difficult to describe."[50] In this instance body temperature

was lowered as the dose intake was increased and changes occurred in brain chemistry.

Miras also noted that body temperature of experimental animals dropped significantly as compared to controls and that a higher maternal death rate occurred in the newborns of treated animals in this series two or three days after delivery. In this study, in contrast to others, however, teratogenesis (deformed babies) did not occur. Miras also noted that intake of cannabis resin significantly reduced the uptake of iodine-131 by the thyroid. He further noted that the reproductive activity dropped significantly as compared to controls.[51]

In test animals, cannabis tends to behave somewhat like barbiturates. It prolongs hexobarbital sleeping time, reduces convulsant activity, raises the threshold for electroencephalographic and behavior arousal stimuli, and depresses certain nerve reflexes. Additionally, cannabis may prolong the stimulant action of amphetamine.[52]

Cannabis also works synergistically with certain other drugs. This fact has been grasped by a number of wine producers who responded by pushing their product among young users. "Try a new high," they urge in billboard advertising, while through the other side of their mouths they "tsk tsk" about the drug abuse problem.

Cannabis has also been studied in cats. The results have produced some observations on the ability of the drug to depress the reticular formation of the brain,[53] impair impulse conduction along major nerves,[54] drop the blood pressure, and depress respiration[55] through what may be a central (brain) depressant action, and impair motor (muscular) activity and variably depress conduction in both the brain stem and spinal cord.[56]

Dogs fared less well. Bose's experiments[57] with graded doses of cannabis extract showed behavioral changes, mainly excitation, for the first ten minutes after the drug took effect, followed by increased activity, restlessness, then depression and ataxia (muscular incoordination).

The positive advantages of using cannabis can be defined simply in one word for most people: pleasure. If another goal is sought it is probably the state Wilson calls "supernormality." Whether or not this result justifies the incumbent risks is something each person must determine for himself.

While it is true that the effects of cannabis, as far as we have positively determined for the moment, are primarily aimed at the mind, it is not at all so that the body escapes with minimal effect. It may be that many persons will never experience the problems thus far discussed. But it is not true that these problems may not occur.

". . . [P]harmacological evidence . . . ," Wilson states, "indicates that in the individual, cannabis can produce unpleasant or pathological effects of a temporary or chronic nature on the excretory, alimentary, respiratory, and cardiovascular systems; similar effects appear in the majority of individuals in the automatic and central nervous systems. Pharmacological evidence suggests that there is considerable intra-individual variation in the severity of effects which occur both in man and animals. In the minority of individuals very severe chronic effects may be produced. The reasons for these idiosyncratic reactions are not known and it is not possible at present to determine beforehand which individuals will develop such idiosyncrasies. Such evidence as is available indicates that individuals who are under stress, who have mental instability, or who suffer from neurosis or incipient psychosis, are more likely to develop severe and chronic illness as as result of taking cannabis."[58]

CANNABIS AND MEDICINE

Throughout the centuries cannabis has been tried for almost every conceivable ailment. In some instances it did no harm; in others it was quite detrimental. In American medicine the fluid extract of cannabis has been used on occasion because some doctors felt it had a sedative or local analgesic effect. Today, it is no longer considered to be a valid therapeutic drug. The American Medical Association's Committee on Alcoholism and Drug Dependence supported this judgment with the recent statement: "Cannabis (marijuana) has no known use in medical practice in most countries of the world, including the United States."[59]

With all due respect to the AMA statement, which reflects an opinion of current policy, it might be well to note that it is not absolutely proper to conclude that cannabis has no valid use. In fact it may be used with certain salutary results in some instances. The problem is that the negative effects may outweigh the positive ones. Furthermore, there is a critical problem involved in standardizing the dosage. Science, in addition, needs to determine (and it has come a long way toward doing this) which elements of the plant are salubrious in effect and which, if any, are specifically detrimental. There is also a question if it is proper to utilize cannabis with its potential ensuing complications when other less complicated drugs can be substituted with equal effect.

This problem of drug substitution has long plagued the discipline of pharmacology. It arose for instance with the case of heroin, which is a valuable analgesic and euphoriant, but which is undesirable because of its tendency to involve the user emotionally and physically. If there were no substitutes for heroin, it might well be in current use. But there are, and since they present less problems, heroin has been excluded in their favor.

There is, on the other hand, no substitute for cannabis. It is a unique plant that possesses numerous pharmacologic properties. It was used frequently as a medicinal in the Eastern world, but as was true with other drugs, this use was not attended by research. In the early twentieth century, physicians once again became interested in cannabis as a medicinal, but this fascination was cut short by the hysteria of the thirties and its anti-marijuana campaigns. As a result, the use of the drug once again fell into disrepute.

From a research standpoint, investigation is less hampered now than in the past, but it is still difficult for many researchers to conduct the type of work they feel necessary because of current legal restrictions. Some of their proposals are fascinating, but they involve the use of human volunteers. Until recently, except for a few isolated instances where institutionalized inmates were given the chance to volunteer for experiments, research on an average cross-section of people was almost unknown. Weil's work in 1968 reversed this trend and his first conclusion, i.e., that "it is feasible and safe to study the effects of marijuana on human volunteers who smoke it in the laboratory,"[60] heralded a new vista for investigating this drug.

From a therapeutic standpoint cannabis may be of value in numerous situations once the necessary requisites for its use are fulfilled. One in particular fascinates this author since it has had and is having increasing application despite the current laws.

This involves the use of the drug at time of delivery by young pregnant women living in communes, who disdain using modern facilities, preferring instead to give birth at home. The point here is that these girls used cannabis prior to delivery, with seemingly salutary results for the mother. What effect, if any, is present on the child is yet to be determined. Cannabis, however, does offer some remarkable features for this experience, all of which have been reported in medical literature in the past.

Another application, also frequently mentioned in medical literature, is the use of cannabis in the treatment of alcoholism. It has been noted in various cannabis-oriented cultures that the use of alcohol declines steadily once pot use becomes established. Youth in these areas are quick to note, usually with caustic criticism, the inconsistencies persistent between the enforcement of alcohol law infractions by minors compared to violations of the cannabis laws. This argument will be discussed later in the book. Over and above other comments on the subject of drinking, however, a surprising number of individuals now seem to be "solving" their alcoholism by substituting pot for booze. Some who do seem to be able to better adjust to the pressures of everyday living using weed as a relaxant than they did when they resorted to alcohol. This observation will be greeted by knowing smiles of approval by marijuanaphiles and violently opposed by ultra-conservatives, particularly those who enjoy alcohol. Which side, if either, will ultimately prove to be correct has yet to be settled.

"Flying and hashish don't mix, Abdullah."

Drawing by Oldden; © 1969 *The New Yorker Magazine*, Inc.

bummers

If all a drug does is kill you, it isn't so bad. It's the quality of life it provides you if you live that should be of most concern.

—ANONYMOUS

*C*ONSIDERING THE PLEASURE one can obtain from relaxing with a joint, it is tragic that the activity should have undesirable complications. Yet, for some, these complications exist and to ignore them can be costly. Even more costly is the rationalization that, "It can happen to the other guy, but I'm different." Doctors of medicine are notorious in their ability to make this rationalization. The result, sadly, is that physicians have the highest rate of involvement with legalized drugs of abuse of any discipline. Fortunately a tight control is kept on the physician's performance, and he is rapidly stopped by the profession if such involvement occurs. Fortunately, too, physicians have a high recovery rate when properly handled. But the problem continues. Some doctors rationalize that they are too smart to get hooked, but if they need relief all they have to do is reach out, and the drug is there.

The situation isn't much different for American youth. Highly educated, affluent, having easy access to almost any drug they might wish to try, young people employ the same mental mechanisms to excuse their toying with drugs. "It can't happen to me," they state. Maybe not, but "it" surely is happening to somebody.

Margolis and Clorfene are surprisingly candid about the bad effects of weed, considering that they wrote their book to show that pot "is not harmful in any way, psychologically or physiologically, does not lead to the use of hard narcotics, and should be made legal subject to the same or similar regulations which now apply to the use, distribution and sale of alcohol and tobacco."[1]

"Only occasionally does it cause unpleasant experiences," they note, ". . . in fact we will give it more emphasis than it really deserves which may tend to scare off some people."[2] The problem is that grass changes reality. As long as this change is pleasant the trip is good. If it is unpleasant or lasts too long a "bad" trip occurs. If it is only moderately unpleasant or annoying it's called a bummer instead of a bad trip.

The nature of the change depends on the attitude of the user and his knowledge of how to manage the trip. "It was offered to me and I tried it," a girl told Becker.[3] "I'll tell you one thing, I never did enjoy it at all. I mean that it was just nothing that I could enjoy. Oh, yes, I got definite feelings from it but I didn't enjoy them. I mean I got plenty of reactions but they were mostly reactions of fear."

This girl obviously never got off the ground. Neither did the subject in the La Guardia report who smoked one cigarette, became restless, agitated, dizzy, fearful of his surroundings, and afraid of death. In addition, he had three short periods of unconsciousness.[4]

Various things can happen when one "goes up" on weed. If one passes the euphoric state and continues going up (or down), his judgment and memory tend to become impaired. He soon becomes easily irritated and may, if sufficiently intoxicated, become confused, disoriented, afraid, and filled with an apprehension he may die. Behavior is impulsive and mood reactions are variable. Not infrequently the user experiences phantasmagoria (i.e., the sensation that figures are dwindling into the distance or rushing toward him at tremendous speed, increasing in size as they approach). As one user put it, "It's like looking through the zoom lens on a camera."

With increasing doses hallucinations may appear. If they are pleasant the user will usually trip on them and remain high. If they are unpleasant he may experience deathly fear. If the proper personality indulges in an adequate amount of drug at the proper time, he may enter a true psychotic state. Hallucinations that occur during this state are most unpredictable and sometimes have a depressing tone. An eastern university professor, for example, tried to approach the drug scientifically by inhaling a large amount of a potent form of it. In his mind he developed a pair of blue wings, leapt into an inkwell, flew around, and was trapped inside it for some two hundred years before his power to reason returned sufficiently to permit him to escape.[5]

A cannabis trip usually lasts from three to six hours following cessation of intake of the drug. By twelve hours all symptoms but a slight lethargy and hunger are gone. These are the most usual durations, but cannabis illusions may linger for some time. One of the most common is the user's insistence that he has communed with God, gotten in tune with the universe, or in some similar manner explored the mystic and occult. No matter how much evidence is accumulated to disprove these reactions, the person who experienced them is so thoroughly convinced that it is virtually impossible to shake him from his belief. On some occasions, however, men have been sufficiently objective in their research so that they have been able to prove to themselves and others that most, if not all, of the drug-produced psychic "miracles" are in essence adverse drug or psychotropic reactions. Of the numerous examples of this sort the following were brought to the author's attention by psychiatrist Charles Wahl, and they may stand for the results of objective research into the cannabis experience.[6]

The first is told about veteran physician Oliver Wendell Holmes and involves his experiences under nitrous oxide anesthesia. It was administered for a tooth extraction and the experience that Holmes had under the drug was so powerful that when he emerged he believed he had been given a miraculous revelation of tremendously important social dimensions. Since he could not recapture the vision he persuaded his dentist to reinduce him with the gas so he could know it again. As he was going under he called for a pencil. His face was transfixed by the power of his vision. Before he lost consciousness he wrote his message, and when he came to he called for the paper to see what he had written. The paper read: "Lord, what a stench!"

In another instance a woman had similar convictions while having a dream. She also grabbed paper and pencil and wrote down her discovery before lapsing back into sleep. In the morning she seized the paper to read her revelation. It was: "Hogamus, higamus, men are polygamous. Higamus, hogamus, women monogamous."

Wahl was able to make the same sort of experiment as Doctor Holmes and the woman, but in this case on three cannabis users who were convinced, as are other users, that the insights achieved under the influence of the drug transcend anything accessible by other means. The psychiatrist tape-recorded their conversation when they were on a trip. Later, when they played back the tape, one youth was so disappointed and appalled by the verbal drivel coming from the recorder that he sat down and wept.

"The psychiatrist," Wahl notes, "is forced to the answers that Euclid gave to Ptolemy I, who was interested in learning geometry but who wanted to do it the easy way. Euclid said to him, 'There is no royal road to geometry'." Drugs, this psychiatrist says, cannot create human ego-strength or personality. They may temporarily warm the user, but when he emerges from his drug-induced dream he is colder and more empty than he ever was before he went up on his poison.

Youths who are reasonably stable (that is, those who are not susceptible to psychological dependence on the drug, who are knowledgeable enough to handle bummers and even bad trips when they occur, and who can contend with transient psychotic reactions without ego destruction) may have little to worry about where the use of pot is concerned. First of all, they will probably never see or experience a bad trip; second, they probably could handle the situation if one arose, providing they didn't completely flip out.

Others are not so lucky. "The darker side of pop drugs is the fact that some users have serious emotional problems," states psychologist Phyllis Kempner. "Many of the kids who are most deeply into mind-changing chemicals have been troubled long before taking drugs. They have taken drugs to help them cope with these difficulties."[7] This is unfortunate, for during the vulnerable years of adolescence drugs can be a medium of escape that prevents one from learning how to grow up.

Adolescence and early youth are particularly critical periods. If one evades pressures occurring then and fails to learn how to cope with adversity he may never make it to adulthood either emotionally or mentally. "Excessive indulgence in cannabis is apt to produce in healthy individuals and more so in susceptible individuals mental confusion which may lead to delusions with restlessness and disordered movements. Intellectual impairment as well as disorientation may show itself in various ways," Chopra advises.[8]

If one becomes overly involved with mind altering drugs it may well cause him to change his total life style. "Wishful thinking becomes prominent," Farnsworth notes.[9] "Preoccupation with isolated aspects of sensory experiences may replace all other sensations. Most characteristic of all is the abandonment of long-term patterns of striving."

As an example, a senior medical student with an excellent academic record, already admitted to a medical school, consulted Dr. Farnsworth. The student felt that his energy was being diverted from his studies because of the problem he was having with pot. He had been using the drug extensively during his senior year and had found that whenever he faced a crisis it was easier to "take pot" than it was to study. "Under its influence he was convinced that studying for examinations was not as important as other things. He wanted help, stating explicitly that he considered the use of marijuana harmful because it encouraged him as well as his friends who used it to 'evade reality and pursue illusory goals'."[10]

Farnsworth has had enough experience with this problem, as have a growing number of school physicians, that he has openly discouraged the use of pot on the Harvard campus. Despite this, the problem continues. As it progresses, an increasing number of students find themselves in need of help. The interesting thing is that often, as they ask for assistance, they continue to be defensive of the use of marijuana. One student who consulted Farnsworth, for instance, denied that his extensive

use of marijuana was adversely affecting his academic performance, "but said that while under its influence he lost both
the desire and ability to study. At the end of the semester his
grades dropped precipitously. He refused psychiatric help, saying that although he knew he had an emotional problem, drugs
had nothing to do with his academic difficulties. Whether he is
right cannot be proven at present," Farnsworth observes, "nor is
it relevant, since he is in trouble and does need some kind of
help." [11]

Farnsworth states that in neither instance cited above did
marijuana "cause" the original conflict. But it is significant that
it contributed nothing positive to the situation and probably
added to the problems each person faced. "Indeed," Farnsworth
notes, "it may have delayed or prevented effective approaches
to the solution of their conflicts." [12]

"You can understand your immediate problems better," a
user told Chapple. [13] But Berg has a different opinion. [14] "Contrary to claims of indescribable delights by some drug takers,"
he asserts, "most people abuse (not casually use) drugs to relieve
anxiety. They're not pursuing pleasure, they just hurt less on
drugs."

When Becker observed that one must learn to smoke pot and
to enjoy the sensations he perceives, he also stated it was
important to recognize that the continued user "develops a disposition or motivation to use marijuana which was not and could
not have been present when he began use. . . ." [15] In other words,
notes Blum, "learning to enjoy or to derive satisfaction from
marijuana is an active process in which the individual invests
much psychic energy and time. Once he has done this, and once
he becomes part of a group that reinforces this activity, he is
apt constantly to seek justification for his behavior even if it
means altering or distorting information which may be contradictory to his newly acquired beliefs. The heavy user will tend
to rationalize, deny facts, and reveal a narrow, almost rigid manner of thinking concerning the drug subject. In general he will
convince himself that marijuana is a healthy and effective drug.
Perhaps for some individuals this drug does serve a positive
purpose; perhaps for others it is an illusion." [16]

This duality where marijuana is used is confusing and clouds
the issue of use vs. abuse. Smith notes, for instance, that "mari-

juana use may in fact have a beneficial effect on certain adolescents facing identity problems,"[17] and quotes a case of a fifteen-year-old who, feeling unwanted at home, established a new identity for himself as a cool "head" among friends in the drug subculture. Having found a group that would accept him and in which he felt important, he was able to do better in other activities including school.

The present author has seen similar situations except that in some instances the youths find their identity in becoming the chief dealers in their communities, solving both identity and financial problems through this medium. It is a value judgment as to whether this is good or bad.

Wilson notes that among chronic users, marriages tend to be even less stable than in the straight community and cites the case of a successful businessman who used pot nightly as a means of relaxation. His use, however, literally caused a separation of communication in his family. "On the other hand," Wilson states, "marijuana may be keeping many predelinquents in a passive, harmless state; for these people (assuming they had to use some drug) it might therefore be preferable to amphetamine usage."[18]

The confusion is not clarified by psychiatrists, who, as a group, fail to agree on the effects of the drug and/or whether its use should be sanctioned. The survey by Dr. Paul Lowinger of Wayne State University School of Medicine in Michigan, for instance, found that 12 percent of interviewed psychiatrists considered the use of marijuana a definite sign of psychopathology, 72 percent said it might indicate psychopathology, and 16 percent were undecided. Of the 163 psychiatrists who responded to the survey, 120 had no personal experience with pot, while 43 had tried it at some time with 15 of these, mostly under age 40, using it regularly.[19] If the latter statistics are carried to their bitter conclusion, one may conclude that according to the value judgment of the majority of the group, 9 percent of its own membership showed definite signs of psychopathology.

Farnsworth, however, having worked with Harvard students for many years, has a firmer opinion about marijuana. Citing his own observations as well as those of others in similar positions, he is concerned about those youths who become dependent on the drug. Once involved, the user tends to become preoccupied with it, he says, and as time progresses, his value judgments change. He becomes satisfied with whatever there is, and seems in a sense to have been robbed of his ability to make appropriate choices.

Furthermore, he notes, "the more sensitive and perceptive judgment you have to exercise, the more you are likely to be harmed. If you don't matter," he tells his students, "it doesn't matter very much whether you use marijuana or not because it won't be noticed. But if you are a person of great promise and ability and have to use it under conditions that require a clear sense of judgment, that particular series of qualities are the ones that are most likely to be harmed."[20]

"Drugs can be a way of evading the painful process of growing up," notes Dr. Eugene Falstein. "They offer a wonderful opportunity for rebelling against parental authority and a way to avoid capitulating to 'squaredom'."[21] Physician James Mathis agrees, noting, "Survival in the future may require a degree of maturity and stability greater than ever before. This maturity requires the process of adolescence with its mastery of anxiety-provoking situations, its search for a role in life, the amalgamation of sexual identity, and all of the attendant pains and discomforts . . . at no other period of life is a brain-disorganizing drug more contraindicated," he warns. "It does not appear logical to encourage an escape from this process of maturation."[22]

Pot smoking creates adverse problems, a correspondent to *Science* complained, and habitual use of marijuana can and does seriously alter the behavior and personality of immature young people. Four things may happen, he observed, and they can all lead to disaster. They are: sudden unreasonable alienation of the child from his parents, the breaking up of old friendships with the acquisition of a new and different sort of buddy; a sharp drop in school grades; finally, an abandonment of commitments and plans for the future.[23]

It has become fashionable for many adults to brag that they are with the "in" crowd: they not only smoke pot, but insist that "it never hurts" them. Others are like the children described by a youth to *Time* magazine who "would come and tell you when they were stoned just to impress you."[24] Adults with this attitude may inadvertently cause harm to their younger friends.

The adult who advises a youth to turn on to pot because he, the adult, uses it and it seems safe for him, is the worst source of information and the poorest possible person to educate younger people. It is quite one thing for a person to use drugs if he is mature, has his goals in mind or nearly achieved, is successful and motivated, and knows from having used and reacted to numerous other drugs in our chemically-oriented society that he can use a drug casually and enjoy it. It is quite another thing for a youth, who has as yet all of his identity crises before him, and practically no living experience behind him, to assume that if he takes a mind-altering drug it will affect him the same way it has affected the adult.

Cannabis can do undesirable things to one's head and to one's behavior. Although simple tasks may remain unimpaired with moderate highs, complex discrimination can be hampered. Giving a dose of 0.03 cc. of THC per pound of body weight to 18 subjects at the University of Utah, Dr. Lincoln Clark found there was a marked inconsistency in performance.[25] The subjects could no longer estimate time adequately, usually overestimating the length of their experience. Too, they showed poor comprehension on reading tests when results were compared with their normal reading ability.

"I learned not to walk into a store stoned," a user told *Time*. "A pot-high woman friend had to go shopping for a few hot dogs, rolls and a six-pack of Coke. She came back an hour later $60 poorer, with six bags of groceries: things like brandied peaches, cans of baby shrimp, caviar, and lots of pickles."[26]

The ability to comprehend is altered, too. "Conversation tends to become diffused," the same adult told *Time*. When people throw out feelings and images, you don't just nod and say politely that you understand—you are right there with the fellow who is talking, looking at the same thing." He noted that once someone in the group suggested that the music they were listening to reminded him of the monumental effort a snail makes when he pulls itself across a lawn "Instantly," the man said, "everyone was grooving on this image of those huge blownup snails painstakingly but nobly pulling themselves across the wet grass."[27]

This can be fun, but it can also ruin relationships. Many persons become paranoid to some degree under the influence of grass, and it is not uncommon for one to think he "sees the real person" when he looks at a buddy. Sometimes a feeling of hostility arises and fails to disappear after the trip is over. Justified or not, a wall may develop between the two former friends. Sometimes it never disappears.

ADDICTION VS DEPENDENCE

"Any discussion at the present time about the nonaddictive, or possibly addictive, properties of cannabis is incorrect, ill-informed and scientifically and internationally out of date," Wilson notes.[28] That should settle the question. It doesn't. In general it must be admitted that in this country, and with the type of cannabis currently being used by most people, addiction per se with its tolerance and withdrawal phenomena, is non-existent as far as we have been able to ascertain. Enough evidence has been introduced, however, to cause one to question whether or not true addiction might occur with heavy use of grass by susceptible individuals.

In 1964 the World Health Organization's expert committee defined the characteristics of cannabis-type dependence as follows:[29]

1. A desire (or a need) for repeated administration of the drug because of its subjective effects, including the feeling of enhanced capabilities.
2. Little or no tendency to increase dosage, since little or no tolerance is developed.
3. The development of a psychic dependence on the effects of the drug that is related to subjective and individual appreciation of these effects.
4. The absence of physical dependence so that withdrawal symptoms characteristic of an abstinence syndrome fail to occur when the drug is discontinued.

The question of tolerance and physical withdrawal is by no means solved. Recently, McMillan and his associates have shown that tolerance to THC can be initiated in animals and that it is much the same as tolerance to morphine.[30] Additional experiments have suggested that humans may become more sensitive, rather than less, to some effects of marijuana with repeated use. This does not mean that tolerance in humans to THC has been clearly established, but it does establish the possibility.

As a matter of fact, not all authorities agree with the statement that cannabis does not cause physical dependence or withdrawal. It is true that, with the milder forms of cannabis most often currently used in this country, physical dependence has not been reported. This is not true of Cannabis indica. In 1949, J.

D. Fraser, the deputy medical superintendent at Whittingham Hospital, Lancashire, England, reported nine cases of acute withdrawal and physical dependence upon Cannabis indica (actually to the THC in the plant).[31]

Summarizing his findings, Fraser concluded that some Cannabis indica addicts apparently cannot live without their drug if it is suddenly withdrawn. If they are thus deprived of it they develop a dangerous mental illness. While noting the total incidence of this type of reaction was probably small in the British Army, Fraser also felt that many cases occurred which did not come to the attention of medical officers. "Clearly it would be safer," he finished, "if known *Cannabis indica* addicts were not employed on foreign service."

"With the emphasis on physical dependence," notes British researcher P. A. L. Chapple, "the intoxicating effect of the substances has often been overlooked. Suppose that it be granted that there exists, as yet, no proven physical dependence on the drugs of the cannabis group, what if the individual becomes dependent on the euphoriant effect? Without this effect life is empty, meaningless. That everything in life is only worthwhile when seen through the rose tinted spectacles of this particular experience."

"Add to this," he argues, "that he or she is prepared to go to any lengths to acquire this experience. And further, that this self-indulgence is expensive, illegal and naturally makes him erratic in his work, which has little importance to him anyway. One might ask, if this person is not addicted what is his psychiatric state?"[32]

"Quite large numbers of people seem able to take cannabis without showing much tolerance or physical dependence," he admits. However, he observes that "Large numbers become dependent on the intoxicating (euphoriant) effects to such an extent that they aver they would not be willing to live without it. They would go to any lengths to get it—this in my group means that if it were not available and they were in some crisis situation they would take or resort to heroin." Along this line it is interesting to note the same situation occurred recently in America when Operation Intercept was in effect. Then, as occurred in Chapple's experience, the cry was, "You're driving us to take harder drugs by depriving us of marijuana." It was also the cry of the ancient Indian writers who warned that taking away this nonaddicting drug from its adherent would "cause widespread suffering and annoyance and to large bands of worshipped ascetics deep-seated anger."[33]

"Difficulties arise," Chapple continues, "because most addicts aver that they are able to give up cannabis at any stage. This is also believed by most addicts about any drug (or alcoholic beverage) that they might be taking except narcotics. Moreover, the circumstances in which the drug is taken seem of the greatest importance."[34]

Assuming most people casually use pot with minimal or no adverse effect, how bad can the situation become? Louria compares the true chronic user to the chronic alcoholic. The drug becomes the center of his life and he withdraws from society in a drug cocoon. "A current estimate," Louria says, "is that 2-5 percent of those who use marijuana on more than several occasions will become potheads."[35] Former NIMH Director Stanley Yolles is less hopeful. He estimates that while 65 percent of people quit after experimenting one to ten times, 25 percent become social users and 10 percent become habitual users.[36] If it is true that in some schools such as Stanford University, 70 percent or more of students at the law school use pot[37] (and this seems more a pothead's dream than a reality), the situation could be critical. In this case these young men will help write tomorrow's laws. More importantly, along with their peers in other disciplines, they will determine the status of tomorrow's world. If their involvement with drugs is for relaxation and recreation, that is one thing. If, however, they use drugs to evade reality, and statistically a percentage of them will, their influence may be destructive.

Fortunately we have evidence that there is a considerable difference between the chronic or would-be chronic user and the curious, experimenting youth. Whether the potential "head" can determine this is debatable, but psychiatrists recently noted that the heavy user often has impaired social adjustments (in contrast to Professor Lindesmith's observation[38] that if a kid wasn't interested in pot, he might be a loner and something might be wrong with him).

"Interpersonal relationships with their own mothers and women in general were frequently described as poor and there was a trend toward a less satisfactory sexual adjustment in this group," researchers noted. Similar findings have also been discovered in chronic LSD users and researchers note that heavy marijuana users frequently also use more potent mind altering drugs as well.[39]

"One wonders," they speculated, "whether lack of an effective mother-child relationship with its unmet dependency needs has given birth to an inability to get close to people and a subsequent 'wish for fusion' (with persons or nature) through the drug experience." Although these chronic users usually had high levels of intellectual attainment, their work adjustment was generally poor, with many performing functions that were well below their mental capability. Additionally, they had an air of self-neglect and exhibited a general lassitude and indifference, a carelessness in personal hygiene and lack of productive activity.

Heavy users were also hostile, lending support to some speculation that marijuana may actually serve as "an effective medication for the relief of feelings of anger, resentment and aggression." If this is so, the group noted, then it is perhaps true that psychedelic agents are being used for tranquilization on the street level, much as other drugs are used by the "Establishment" for similar purposes.

THE QUESTION OF APPEARANCE

"I can recognize a chronic marijuana user from afar by the way he walks, talks and acts," Professor C. J. Miras of the University of Athens once remarked in an interview in Los Angeles.[40] Miras, of course, could not possibly recognize *all* chronic users of cannabis, since there is a marked difference in individual variation in susceptibility to the effects of the drug. However, as Miras has noted to this author, it was not his intent to make a blanket unqualified statement. His "off the cuff" remark was intended to convey that in his experience, where it related to cannabis users with whom he had contact, certain adverse characteristics tended to recur. Since Miras made his controversial statement, others, some who might have criticized him in 1967, have corroborated his observations. Because they have, however, is no sign the community as a whole accepts the findings.

Miras defined a chronic user as one who smoked two joints a day for a period of two years or longer. At this point in these users' experience, he said, "you begin to see the personality changes that typify the long time user—the slowed speech, the lethargy, the lowered inhibitions and the loss of morality. . . . They will accept as perfectly plausible things which five years ago they did not even like to hear discussed. They will become suddenly violent without any apparent provocation," he said. "They will even kill."[41]

Miras' observations were made on chronic hashish smokers in Greece and were based on some twenty years of study. For this reason some can argue effectively that ethnic and drug potency differences could make a difference between the observations of Miras and those that might be seen in this country. Interestingly there hasn't been much difference when those men who dared to speak their convictions on the subject of adverse reactions related to the abuse or long-term use of cannabis finally made their observations known.

Five years ago, the chief psychiatrist at the University of California's Cowell Hospital was quite certain that pot was harmless. In an interview with *Oakland Tribune* reporter Larry Spears in May 1970, however, he expressed a change of opinion.[42]

"I can detect the effect of marijuana on people's thinking for 24 to 48 hours after they've used it," he told Spears. "If I listen to someone in therapy for some period of time, I learn his way of thinking, his quality of thinking. I hear qualitative differences that other people don't; that's how I make my living. What I'm listening for is the limitations on their thinking—all of us have limitations. And if a guy comes in after using pot, the limitations on thinking that are characteristic of him become much more so."

The immediate effect of marijuana "is to exaggerate whatever is pathological in people's thinking," Dr. D. Harvey Powelson said. "This is not invariable. I'm sure that I can't tell if some have used it, but I can tell about others as long as a week after. There appears to be no effect on certain kinds of schoolwork," he said, "unless you take very large doses; fairly complex abstract thinking is not interfered with much. But judgment about doing well or worse is interfered with much sooner than is ability. If you swim, you may be able to swim as well as usual, but you may think you're swimming a lot better than you really are."

When this happens, he notes, commonplace things seem to become profound insights. A few bars of jazz, a routine observation, may be considered to be supremely creative. "No one argues any more that it leads to great insights," he said of the users in his area. Instead, they merely say, "I'm high."

"High" per se, however, is not only difficult to measure, it is almost impossible to define. "Marijuana users know what it is to be 'high'," *San Francisco Chronicle* writer David Perlman notes, "and nonusers think they know. But there has been little scientific evidence to define a 'high' and almost none to explain just which centers of the human brain are affected by marijuana or what mental processes are damped or stimulated."[43]

Some will criticize Powelson's observations. In fact, the Editor of the *University Clip Sheet*, which reprinted the newspaper article, made it very clear Powelson's comments were an educated guess and that some of his colleagues disagreed with him. Powelson's response was that anyone who has been around the drug people any length of time recognizes that heavy users "move in a funny kind of way." Just as a dog that has had distemper in the past moves in a certain way or the alcoholic, now dried out, still ambles in a marooned weave, he explained, the pothead has his own characteristic walk even when he's down.[44]

"I would describe it as disconnected from their center," he muses, "as if strings were moving their hands and feet instead of something in the center . . . it's come about because there's been a physiological change in the central integrative mechanism that governs the way people walk."

Powelson also notes the problem of persisting paranoia which tends to be present in people who chronically use all types of mind influencing drugs, including pot and alcohol. Taking a different approach from that of Margolis and Rosevear who feel the paranoia is due to police harassment, and would stop if tomorrow the weed were readily available, Powelson states, "there are people who see the whole world in terms of 'me' and 'them'. As soon as they see something happen they say, 'somebody did it'." They tend to blame everything on the cops because the cops are looking for them. Powelson feels this is a weak excuse. "That duality is paranoid thinking," he notes, "and is exaggerated over a period of time by the use of drugs. I would be willing to say," he remarks, "that if you made marijuana legal tomorrow and these people no longer had to worry about police, that they would become paranoid about something else."

Interestingly, Powelson feels that the use of pot is beginning to diminish in the Berkeley area, something avid users might be the first to deny.[45] This is true, he says, even though police have not diminished their efforts at enforcing the law. "I think," he says, "they [the users] are learning from the experience of seeing the effects on other people." Of equal interest is the fact that Dr. Andrew Weil, who was once at the National Institute of Mental Health, and who says he has never seen evidence of lasting brain damage from the heavy use of marijuana, holds another opinion. "The only direct evidence I have," he said, "indicates that there is nothing to support Dr. Powelson's contentions."[46]

Disagreeing with Weil, however, is another man of national stature who has come to conclusions similar to those of Powelson. He is Louis J. West, Professor of Psychiatry at the University of California in Los Angeles. "Regular use of marijuana for three to five years can probably result in personality changes similar to those observed in some persons taking LSD for shorter periods," he remarked in 1968.[47] He based his opinion on interviews conducted with several hundred marijuana users in the Haight-Ashbury area of San Francisco from the fall of 1966 to the spring of 1968. He noted that continuous use of pot can result in apathy, loss of effectiveness, and a diminished capacity or willingness to carry out complex, long term plans. The ability to tolerate frustration, he said, and to concentrate for long periods, to follow routines or successfully master new material is also decreased. Verbal facility is also often impaired, he noted, both in writing and in speaking. For many middle-class students, a slow, progressive change from conforming, achievement-oriented behavior to a state of relaxed and careless drifting has followed the use of significant amounts of marijuana.

Interestingly enough, Establishment-oriented observers are not alone in coming to the conclusion that the use of pot has its bad side. Comments are also beginning to come through from the drug counterculture itself. In April of 1971, an "ex-dope dealer" in Berkeley, California, concluded he had seen enough and promptly and voluntarily went out of the dealing business. He chose to express his views in, of all platforms, the *Berkeley Barb*, a controversial San Francisco underground paper not editorially inclined to badmouth pot.

Questioning whether or not the *Barb* would have the "guts" to print his letter (it did), he complained that "Many people really believe that the only danger in smoking grass is the danger of getting caught."[48] "I've been using cannabis for about six years," he acknowledged. "I've been dealing it for almost as long. I could continue to make lots of money doing it, but I cannot in good conscience go on feeding the habits of my customers."

The writer has little going for him as a scientific investigator. He has performed no double blind studies, he has acquired no governments grants . . . nothing, . . . unless living in the culture, smoking and dealing in grass, and seeing how one's close friends react to it for half a dozen years has meaning.

"It wouldn't be so bad if pot-lovers turned on once a week or so," he continued, "but the vast majority of users get stoned every day, and it becomes a habit—a passive habit, no better than our parents watching TV and drinking booze or downing tranquilizers."

"I want," he said, "to discuss some of the bad effects this has had on my clients and myself: Heads suffer from poor memory. I've seen this many times and I can only hope that my own memory will be back to normal some day." He continues to complain by enumerating other problems: lassitude, lethargy, low vitality—including lower sexual appetite. "Actually," he says, "these are the effects of a cannabis hangover. For the perpetual user, they become permanent attributes, and sometimes lead to a dependence on stimulants. This lowered vitality, or slowed metabolism, may be a sign of poor utilization of vitamins or changes in the thyroid gland."

Our ex-dealer is obviously treading on thin ice in trying to practice medicine without a license. He could be open to extreme criticism—if he gave a damn. The point is, he could probably care less about Establishment attitudes. Speaking strictly on a gut level to buddies he hopes to warn of a bad trip, he makes observations which scientists are now cautiously reporting in increasing numbers, qualifying their findings, of course, with the observation that we need "more research."

"Heads tend to have abnormally coated tongues and bad breath," the ex-dealer complains. "Because they usually stick together, it's a rarely-noticed effect. Have you ever smelled the water of a water pipe? That's what their breath smells like." Smoking, he continues, can damage the mucous membranes of the mouth, nasal passages, throat and lungs. He suggests users become more susceptible to infection and catch colds that last for months. Further, he complains, heads never can smell or taste as well as nonheads. "While I was in India scoring hash," he notes, "I learned that Indian dealers never smoke. They know it ruins their sense of smell and taste by which they judge the product."

"Because of their poor sense of smell, heads often don't realize how stuffy and stale a room is," he continues. "They will sit in a smelly room with no air circulation on a beautiful sunny day, getting stoned and growing more and more pale." The ex-dealer continues his argument against the "pot is cool" philosophy by complaining about the effects on the smoker's eyes. "The blood-shot eyes of a head aren't pretty," he grumbles. "Even worse is the jaundice that often sets in after months of heavy use. I hate to think of what's happening to the liver and brain."

"I wouldn't be at all surprised if it's eventually found that cannabis can cause hemolytic anemia," he postulates, getting out of his discipline again, ". . . because the effects of cannabis abuse are so similar to this disease: weakness, pallor, jaundice, and sore liver. Several people have told me of pain in the liver after heavy smoking." Incredible! This cat's beginning to sound like a conservative researcher!

He complains of other things. Not being able to fight infection, for example. "One couple," he says, "told me they could not get rid of the clap [using tetracycline] until they stopped smoking grass. I once had a staph infection on my knee which tetracycline wouldn't knock out until I quit smoking." The disgruntled dude also seems to think pot smoking causes one to grow old faster. ". . . [H]ave you ever noticed the dark circles under the eyes of the heavy smoker? . . Maybe," he shrugs, "some day these harmful effects will be generally recognized, as lung cancer is recognized to be a consequence of cigarette smoking."

Maybe, but not for a while. Let me ask you, buddy, do you know that according to the cigarette companies there's no "proof" that tobacco smoking causes lung cancer? Let me ask you something else. How do you know all the things you've been seeing over the past six years wouldn't have happened anyway? How could you be so unscientific as to indict pot when it could have been nutrition, genetics, poor environment, other drugs . . . anything but pot . . . that caused these things?

Better go back to the pad, buddy, and smoke and deal for another six years. Then, providing you can eliminate all these possibilities, maybe somebody will give some credence to your observations.

It so happens that well-to-do but unstable young people are the most likely to be hurt by the use of pot, warns pediatrician Doris H. Milman.[49] Such youngsters are likely to develop acute psychoses, have their lives completely disrupted, and become multiple drug addicts.

Dr. Milman was stimulated to publish her observations after studying 11 students—10 adolescents, and one young adult—who had developed chronic or acute schizophrenia after drug use. All of the students were from middle- and upper-class economic and educational environment and all were above average intelligence. "All of these young people had quick tempers, little tolerance for frustration or postponement, and little tolerance for anxiety. They demanded instant gratification and instant relief and found that drugs offered both of these."

Obviously the drug was not the "cause" of the problem. Further, Milman's study, as is true of West's observations, did not contain controls, and thus must be considered observations which need further critical evaluation. Too, as is so frequently noted, the problem described seemed to be a part of the individual's personality. But two questions are not answered. Would the psychotic episodes ever have occurred had they not been triggered by the use of mind altering drugs? If they had occurred, would they have been as critical?

Marijuana was used by all of these students, LSD was the second drug most often used, and amphetamines third. All began with pot; then those who needed something different progressed to stronger substances.

Even if an adolescent fails to become psychotic from drug use, Dr. Milman said, drugs blunt the pain of psychological conflicts that arise during that age period and postpone problem-solving. The result is that such a young person emerges as an immature, drug-dependent, poorly-integrated adult. The risk of marijuana use is compounded in this type of youngster, she noted, because they tend to experiment in their search for relief from psychic discomforts.

In the two years that have passed since Dr. West's comments on his observations in the Haight-Ashbury district, there has been little mollification of his viewpoint. If anything, he has become more concerned. Citing on his own an objection similar to that voiced by Weil concerning Powelson's observations (observations incidentally, which could not be measured adequately in the sterile confines of a laboratory with current techniques available), West admits that objective scientific data is lacking to back up his clinical impressions. This, perhaps, is not as great a problem as it might at first seem, since most of the effects produced by marijuana are subjective as well, and must be defined on the basis of what the patient reports to his investigator.

"I would feel remiss," he stated, "if I didn't voice these suspicions. At the same time I am afraid to because I don't want them used as a basis for more punitive legislation. The law," West told *Los Angeles Times* reporter Harry Nelson, "should protect the kids, but the present ones only complete the downhill trend begun by the smugglers."[50]

Since it is no longer newsworthy or popular to be against pot, the remarks made by West show both integrity and courage. Basing his impressions about personality changes on his own observation of long-term users—observed for longer than three years—Dr. West said he had formed a clinical impression that marijuana does change personality in some chronic users.

Changes noted included apathy, diminished ability to concentrate, impaired skill at communicating with others, a fragmentation of the flow of thought, and a loss of insight. "What I have seen," he said, "is not schizophrenia, not rebellion against the Establishment, but what I believe to be biological changes in brain function because of the use of marijuana." It is interesting to note that similar observations were made by Miras as long ago as 1953.[51]

Chapple had also noted that pot seems to demonstrate an unusual ability to vary its effects in person to person and from time to time. He found, too, that abstinence from the drug for a while seems to enhance its later effects when it is used again. Thus, when Chapple performed his study of 80 hospitalized cannabis takers, he indicated, as did Miras, West, and Powelson, that he could tell when a patient had been chronically using marijuana.[52] Interestingly, these impressions were formed long before laboratory findings confirmed that cannabis chemicals were retained in the human system for varying periods of time.

"It was often possible to know that patients were taking cannabis while in hospital," he said, "because they became lazy; they would giggle fatuously and this was not infrequently the prelude to leaving hospital altogether and relapsing to heroin again." All of Chapple's patients had had episodic use of cannabis and had later progressed to the use of stronger drugs. This experience brings up another touchy question. *Does the use of pot lead to the use of stronger drugs?*

THE STEPPINGSTONE THEORY

The "steppingstone" theory which indicates that pot *causes* one to turn to the use of more dangerous drugs, because of something inherent in the chemical structure of cannabis, is as dead as the Dodo bird.

"Escalation between cannabis and opiates certainly does occur," Wilson states; "those in whom this takes place probably are those mentally unstable individuals who have a predisposition to use drugs and would tend to find satisfaction and an acceptable form of release from their cares and stresses as a consequence of taking a variety of centrally acting drugs."[53]

The concept of direct escalation to heroin from marijuana has been promoted primarily by enforcement officers who, as is true with the association of pot, crime, and violence, have found the two in combination so often they concluded that one led to the other. The proof or denial of this point, however, is a scientific one, and while scientists have often castigated the police for their "stupidity," it has only been recently that they have deigned to offer police their cooperation in clarifying this issue.

Some of the philosophy of "pot-to-heroin" has been promoted by the drug user's willingness to agree to almost anything if "big daddy will turn the key," i.e., if the police will let him out of jail. As a result troops of addicts over the years have co-operatively testified that now that they are leaving jail, they are (*a*) cured and (*b*) they would never have gotten into this mess if it hadn't been for dirty old pot. Such individuals might well have been expected to enter the drug world and escalate in their habits regardless of the drug they used. Pot seemed to be the culprit because it happens to be one of the easiest drugs, one of the most pleasant, and frequently the most reassuring because casual users seldom see serious adverse effects. Thus pot is often, if not usually, the initial drug chosen for experimentation. If experimentation progresses to misuse, it is then not at all uncommon for abusers of pot to abuse other drugs as well since multiple drug involvement seems to be one of the pathognomonic features of the contemporary drug abuser.

"There is no question that certain individuals abuse progressively stronger drugs," David Smith notes. "It is apparent, however, that these individuals are seeking a chemical solution for their own personality problems. They use one drug, be it alcohol or marijuana, to excess, without long-term resolution of their inner conflicts; they then move to a more potent agent, again using it compulsively until severe physical consequences ensue or they decide that they cannot handle drugs."[54]

It would seem, however, that a person who wished to "blot" reality through the use of a soporific, sedative narcotic such as heroin would find the "mind-opening" effects of pot highly distasteful. Yet, as Chapple showed,[55] pot was the one drug that the users in his series would not agree was harmful, nor would they agree to let it alone once they emerged from the hospital confines. How come?

The answer lies once again in the uniqueness of cannabis and its ability to almost be all things to all people. Pot, cautiously used, tends first to stimulate the central nervous system and then later to depress it.[56] Only when the individual gets an unexpectedly "good" grade of grass, or fails to "titrate," or is unsuccessful in his titration does he begin the high trip usually available only to those who seek it. Consequently, the heroin user takes cannabis much as the casual user—for euphoria and sedation.

"LSD and cannabis have comparable psychopharmacological effects," Wilson notes, quoting Isbell's work.[57] Students do change from cannabis to LSD, as Dally found,[58] and as is discussed in another section of this book. They state that the effects of the drugs are similar, although they note that the effects of cannabis cannot be controlled by chlorpromazine as can those of LSD.

Although the steppingstone theory is not valid per se, it is a fact, however, that certain aspects of marijuana use do encourage (but do not force or lead the user to try) the use of more dangerous drugs. Surveying 75,000 university students, Doris

Milman found the following situation: "Marijuana was the first illicit drug used and the most widely used illicit drug being employed by more than 80 percent of drug users; also two thirds of drug users employed more than one drug. These facts, taken together," she notes, "lead inescapably to the conclusion that marijuana is the first step in the direction of drug abuse."[59]

Taking quite a different stance from that held previously by law enforcement, the Director of the Federal Bureau of Narcotics and Dangerous Drugs refutes the concept that "a joint today means a junkie tomorrow." Asked by *U.S. News & World Report* if smoking pot on a regular basis often leads to the use of "hard" drugs, Mr. John Ingersoll replied, "No," as far as pharmacological terms are concerned.[60]

The vast majority of people who try pot use it one to ten times and quit, he said. The correlation between frequent use of marijuana and the use of other drugs is due to the fact that the chronic user is exposed to a drug subculture. "In this environment," Ingersoll said, "he is thrown with people who use other drugs. And it is a matter of record that the explosion in marijuana use has been accompanied by a sharp upturn in heroin use."

"If you associate with a group whose orientation is drug-seeking and you accept this style of life, you are likely to look for bigger and bigger kicks. Two thirds of the people with whom we had contact as admitted drug users in 1969," Ingersoll said, "were using more than one drug."

A frequently heard concept concerning progress from pot to "smack" is that one has to buy pot illegally, and therefore has to associate with the underworld, which turns him on to harder drugs. This may occur, and if so, is an argument in favor of legalization. The idea that pot doesn't lead to heroin is "a bunch of crap," a young user told *San Francisco Chronicle* reporter Jim Brewer.[61] "It's all illegal. You have to go to the same dealer to get it. If he can't sell you grass, that same cat is ready with the hard stuff." Perhaps. Yet one is reminded of the paranoia Dr. Powelson described[62] and the excuse that "somebody else," not the user, is to blame. The dealer may indeed offer a drug more potent than pot, but it is the user that must decide if he wants to go that route. Interestingly the large majority of pot users find it desirable and convenient to say "No."

BUMMERS: A SOURCE OF CONCERN

Some time ago a sententious poet wrote a brief verse for the *New Yorker* in which he echoed Margaret Fuller's celebrated nineteenth-century comment, "I accept the Universe." The line has some relevance for those who feel they must escape the world through the use of drugs. Then, in a marked library copy, a whimsical reader, who knew his Victorian history, added a remark to the poet's observation, which was the reply Thomas Carlyle made to Margaret Fuller: "You had damned well better!"

Not everyone agrees with Carlyle, however. Thus the search for the "safe" euphoriant and/or drug of escape continues. As more and more personalities turn on and the drugs obtained are increased in potency, more and more bad trips and bummers will occur. What causes these unwanted reactions? Currently it seems there are two basic reasons. The first has to do with the attitude (set), environment and associates (setting) and the reasons which encouraged the subject to try the drug. The second is the pharmacological effects of the drug itself. Quite probably one is seldom separated from the other.

Margolis notes that Gestalt psychologists believe that people view the world in terms of patterns.[63] If the patterns of the moment are good, then an exacerbation of these patterns by a mind-altering substance will usually produce good trips. If the patterns are bad, bummers or "flip outs" may occur. In this sense it can be said that most bad trips are the result of using poor reasons for going up.

The second factor is that the drug itself is intensely variable. Dosage is the biggest problem, in that too high an intake will inevitably produce bad results. Individual variation and idiosyncrasy also adds to the confusion. No one person reacts to the same drug the same way at all times no matter whether the drug is aspirin or cannabis. Thus it is not always possible to predict exactly one's reaction to any drug to the full degree. There is always variation. With some drugs, such as cannabis, this variation may be intense and highly unpredictable.

From his layman's standpoint Margolis' comments about bummers are quite revealing. "The worst possible manifestations of depression are hysterical crying, overwhelming self-pity or suicidal wishes," he notes.[64] He further states that bad experiences (i.e., a sour love affair, an unhappy marriage, a pointless career, insecurity or an inability to communicate well) may lay the groundwork for a bad trip. "If you've had these experiences," he warns, "then you might have them to a deeper degree when stoned; and if you haven't had them before you well might when stoned. The reason is that although you've thought of these things before and have been able to accept them or shrug them off, the influence of the grass gives them a distorted sense of importance and terribleness."[65]

"We might be scaring you needlessly, but our occasional desire to achieve integrity demands that we be honest," Margolis notes, but he counterargues that the trip is rarely sour and besides, as his friend Ernie's grandfather has noted, this is no reason not to use grass. "Just because horses occasionally [defecate] on the street is no reason to stop using horses," Grandpa noted. At this point Margolis makes an interesting psychological slip. "Unfortunately," he says, "Ernie's grandfather was later trampled to death."[66]

Bummers, Margolis defines, are mild forms of unpleasantness which occur because someone has suddenly inserted a negative stimulus into the scene. One is sensually stimulated while stoned, he notes, and therefore keenly involved in some activity or thought. If someone interrupts this reverie the intrusion may be exaggerated or distorted. If someone "tastelessly decides that it would be puckish to hit you in the nose with a spitball," Margolis notes, "you could interpret the act as one of severe hostility and go into a bummer."[67]

In the world of pot, however, rationalization often solves an immediate crisis. In the case cited above, Margolis notes, the person hit would probably "stare at the spitballer with such a look of contempt and pity that he too would soon be into a bummer. Then you would feel guilty for throwing him into a bummer and be into still another bummer. Then he hands you a slice of orange jelly candy and everything is fine again."[68] It would be wonderful if bummers and bad trips were always that simply handled. Unfortunately, it doesn't work that way.

Another problem occurring with bummers is a state of paranoia manifested by the suspicion that others are plotting against you or that you might become injured physically or psychologically. Tinklenberg notes that in his research a number of paranoid reactions have occurred among his volunteer subjects. Appropriately, the delusional theme usually centered around scientists doing "bad things" to them.[69] Actually, Margolis argues, this sort of reaction is not really paranoia, which properly defined, is a state of fixed and highly systematized delusions. More aptly, one suffers from a paranoid state which is similar to paranoia, but which is expressed by anxiety due to an irrational and unfounded fear that one is being persecuted.

Margolis notes the paranoid state is quite common, and justified in most instances, since one is violating the law and thus is apt to be busted.[70] His point is well taken, for, as we shall see shortly in discussing panic states, particularly in older people, this fear may well be the basis of a bad trip.

Margolis states the paranoid sensation occurs because things are distorted and thus misinterpreted. "If the paranoid state becomes too uncomfortable," he advises, "simply mention it to the others. Ask them politely to stop laughing at you. They will instantly deny that they are laughing at you, and then begin to feel paranoid themselves because they think you're picking on them."[71] Complicated, isn't it?

PANIC REACTIONS

One of the most commonly seen acute reactions to pot is panic. Usually this is due to the user's interpreting the physical or psychological effects of the drug to be signs of impending death or insanity. Most often, states Weil, these are self-limiting although they may become so severe as to be incapacitating and may simulate acute psychosis, especially if the patient finds himself in a hospital ward.[72]

Usually such people are tearful, anxious, depressed, withdrawn, or agitated, Weil notes, but they are not disoriented, hallucinative, or psychotic. Weil warns against diagnostic panic states as acute psychotic episodes and in particular against treating them as such since this "only prolongs the panic by inadvertently confirming the patient's fears of a mental breakdown."

If Erich Goode's description of the high effects of pot are valid, and considering his continued investigation into the problems and assets of marijuana use over the years it is reasonable to assume his interpretations are proper, it is not surprising that the uninitiated or unguided tripper frequently panics. This is especially true if he is older, has a different system of values than the younger group, and has developed sets of fear, anxiety, and apprehension which he associates with a potentially "dangerous" or illegal activity.

Some of the results of using pot, especially in its "higher" trips, have been outlined by Goode.[73] Included are an increasing irrelevance of realism; the loss of interest in plot of films and novels; a glorification of the irrational and the seemingly non-sensical; an increased faith in the logic of the viscera rather than in that of the intellect; a heightened sense of the absurd; an abandonment of traditional and "linear" reasoning sequences, and the substitution of "mosaic" and fragmentary lines of attack; *bursts* of insight rather than *chains* of thought; connectives relying on internal relevance, rather than a commonly understood and widely accepted succession of events and thoughts; love of the paradoxical, the perverse, the contradictory, the incongruous; an "implosive" inward thrust, rather than an "explosive" outward thrust; instantaneous totality rather than specialization; the dynamic rather than the static; the unique rather than the general and the universal.

Sociologist Goode notes aptly the importance of recognizing the difference in value judgments which emerges from different disciplines, different subcultures, and different goal-oriented people. Those with conventional, traditional, and "classic" tastes in art will view the results just described in a rather dim light. A person who opposes marijuana and who empirically feels that its use is harmful, he notes, "is very likely to dislike contemporary art forms and vice versa." These two forms of appreciation, he says, are not necessarily causally related but emerge instead out of the same matrix.[74]

Smith, who has reported three cases of marijuana-induced psychosis offers the valid advice that " 'uptight' Americans committed to the current dominant value system should not experiment with illegal drugs even though they might be quite capable of handling accepted intoxicants such as alcohol." He also suggests that if the legality of the drugs were reversed the experiences of the user would be reversed.[75]

With due respect to Dr. Smith, this author disagrees with the simplicity of effect implied in this statement concerning legality. Anyone who has been drunk on alcohol and up on grass knows the effects are quite different. One may get drunk on booze and not become overly panicked by the effect of being narcotized, but one may not view the sensory and time altering effects obtained by using grass with the same aplomb. Smith's cases involved three members of the Establishment (two doctors and one reporter) who had espoused current value systems and were immersed in the current Establishment per se. They were in their mid-thirties and used grass for the first time in "far out" environments. In essence they almost courted a bad reaction. But it is debatable, in this author's opinion, that had they used legal alcohol vs. "legal" pot under the same circumstances, their "flip out," if any, would have been similar. Pot is far more disruptive of ego strength, a point we shall note in experiments to be discussed further on.

FLASHBACK PHENOMENA

One feature, only recently described with any frequency, that is capable of precipitating a panic reaction is the flashback phenomenon. Early in 1968, this author began receiving numerous comments from young (high school) users that they were experiencing flashbacks. In essence the flashback is a state in which the individual repeats a previous experience he had while under the effects of a drug without having recently taken that particular drug.

The experience seems to have Pavlovian elements, i.e., one sees, hears, tastes, feels or smells a stimulus while tripping, and later, when the same stimulus appears (especially if circumstances are similar) the "trip" recurs without taking the drug. If the trip is pleasant the user does not object. In fact, he may enjoy it. Keeler reported in 1968 the presence of four such instances in drug-free individuals.[76] These were purely marijuana flashbacks in that none of the subjects ever used other hallucinogenic substances. Two of the recurrences were unpleasant and resented by the patient. Thus they could be defined as adverse reactions. The other two experiences were appreciated and pleasant and viewed by the users as desirable rather than adverse.

Keeler suggests that the persistence of the biochemical effects of cannabis may explain the spontaneous recurrence of a trip. This may well be, particularly since recent experiments suggest that cannabis products accumulate in the body.[77] Other reputable investigators dispute this concept, however. Tinklenberg notes that evidence is lacking that the cannabis products which accumulate in the body have psychoactivity. The mystery of "reverse tolerance" refers, he feels, to a phenomenon which might better be explained entirely on a psychogenic basis and thus can best be explained by the learning theory.[78] This author (ERB) feels, however, that the flashback probably does not occur without a sensory or chemical trigger, although this has yet to be proved.

"I was driving along a road when I suddenly noticed a red airplane warning light flashing in the distance," a sixteen-year-old youth told this author. "Suddenly, man . . . wow, I was on the same trip I had been on three weeks ago." (There had been a flashing red light in the apartment the night the youth had had his last marijuana experience.) "Trouble was," he said, "I was driving pretty fast at the time and I noticed I was just sitting there with my foot on the accelerator and my hands in my lap enjoying the light. It was all I could do," the boy said, "to pull over and let the thing pass."

Keeler notes that his experiences with marijuana users suggest "that spontaneous recurrence of drug effect may be relatively common and that this event may often be accompanied by a degree of anxiety sufficient to constitute a psychiatric emergency."[79] This is undoubtedly true although it seems that the stimulus tends to wear thin after a while and loses its trigger effect unless it is accompanied by or replaced by a stronger stimulus.

Music may be one critical stimulus, especially drug-oriented music which is so frequently played at pot parties. Officers who pull youths over, under the impression they look as if they are "up," yet find no drugs, may well have been correct in their original assumption. When the police arrive at the driver's door the music (stimulus) is turned down or off and the kids have crashed because the possibility of a bust brings them down. This effect on driving has yet to be studied if, indeed, it can ever be adequately examined under present laboratory conditions.

Flashbacks are also important in that they seem to be a reasonably frequent complication associated with the use of LSD. Such flashbacks were quite common in the Haight-Ashbury population, causing Smith to note that, "There is no question that marijuana can serve as a trigger for an LSD 'flashback' just as any psychoactive drug, including alcohol can, but this," he notes, "is not a primary reaction."[80]

This phenomenon is not new to this author. A number of years ago a friend unknowingly took a dose of LSD at a party. For five years he "tripped" and "flashed" without realizing the problem. In due time his "friends" told him about their "joke." In the meantime he had attempted suicide on several occasions and had lost his job as manager of one of the country's top rock groups.

Today, this man cannot smoke marijuana without flashing his acid trip and the flash is bad. But then, as Smith noted may occur, he can't drink alcohol either. Both bring on severe bad trips which are momentarily incapacitating.

Favazza and Domino corroborate this point in their report of an eighteen-year-old college student who smoked pot regularly. Then, and only once, he used LSD.[81] Three months later he smoked grass again, only to precipitate a wild flashback of his previous LSD session. The flashback was intense, lasted two hours, then receded. Even so, the youth was hallucinative the following morning, imagining he had animal claws in his back and feeling as if there were a cloud in his head and constant wind in his face.

For the next three weeks he was too frightened to sleep. When he put his head down he saw puffed up faces and large clocks pointing their hands at him. At this point he urgently sought psychiatric help and was given reassurance and drug therapy to calm him. Three weeks later he was reasonably stable again. Reviewing this situation the authors concluded that marijuana can trigger the recurrence of a bad LSD trip. Any person who has experienced a frightening reaction to acid, they advise, might well be careful not to use any further hallucinogenic drugs, including marijuana.

It should be noted in the proper parlance of the day that there is no "proof" these things occur. Such case reports are based on subjective comments of the users who "might have been prejudiced" and "who might have hallucinated anyway."

If flashbacks could be prevented through the medium of avoiding further exposure to drugs, the problem would be reasonably easy to solve. Nothing "cures" a drug dependent person from returning to the use of his drug more than having the hell scared out of him by recurrent bad trips. Flashbacks, however, are not totally dependent on the reuse of drugs. They may be triggered, as noted above in the cases of the flashing red light and of hearing music previously enjoyed while tripping, by a repetition of stimuli.

The author has another friend who used to be a firm advocate of LSD, pot, peyote, DMT . . . you name it. It was, he insisted, "God's medicine" because it brought him to the gates of heaven and permitted him to visit with the Virgin, the Saints, and other celestial inhabitants. This was great for two years when suddenly the geographic location was altered and he found himself in purgatory. To date he has not managed to extricate himself from this situation and every time he flashes (he long ago gave up drugs, including pot which precipitated wild, bad trips), he finds himself back in the hot environs his theologians taught him existed in the hereafter.

The problem is that numerous visual stimuli also flash him. The author has a rather loud, multicolored psychedelic couch in his rumpus room. One glimpse of this is worth about three hours in purgatory for this man, who now is as fervent an evangelist against drugs as he once was in favor of them. He quite frankly admits that if it were not for the bad trips, he would probably still be smoking and dropping.

Flashbacks have not as yet been even superficially explored, due to the fact, among other things, that it is highly impractical to attempt to do so under current laboratory conditions. Johann Rush, who has studied this phenomenon extensively, particularly as it related to the Manson trial where the defendants allegedly used drugs, feels there are three distinct types: historical, incorporation, and prophetic.[82]

The historical flashback is the one most commonly described. It is the recapitulation of a previous experience, real or imagined, that occurs when triggered by the proper stimulus. It should be noted that flashbacks should not be confused with "flashes" or "flashing" which are different. These latter two experiences are immediate and constitute a currently experienced unit of thought or activity. The terminology is not new, having been long ago dreamed up by the Establishment which spoke of having a "flash of thought" with the same intent of meaning

as the hip youth who states, "Hey, man, I really flashed on that."
In the youth's case it is a bit more complicated in that the episode usually involves an experience as well as a thought.

The incorporation flashback is thought to involve the assimilation of a current experience, thought, book, value, or idea into
the life of the one experiencing the trip. One may argue this is
more of a flash than a flashback except that when it happens it
seems to the viewer the event has previously occurred and is
returning to his thoughts, even though it is a part of an immediate and continuing experience. While flashing one may, then,
read a novel that relates, as an example, the story of a deity who
has returned to earth. The subject may not only believe this experience is a part of his life but, if he is mentally aggressive
enough, may foster this impression in the minds of susceptible
followers. Usually this type of reaction is an acid experience
although this author has reason to believe that cannabis of high
resin content may achieve the same effect.

Margolis, in his advice as to how to treat a person on a bad
grass trip, notes, "You also remember that under the effects of
grass a person is highly suggestible. He will have a tendency to
believe what you tell him. So the first thing to do is remind him
that he smoked a lot of grass and that grass distorts reality—so
whatever he's thinking is not as bad or as important as he thinks
it is.[83] If this advice holds true for managing bad trips it may
not be far fetched to assume it could be used to foster negative
impressions as well. Those who have never obtained really
"strong" grass or who have never seen or experienced a significant adverse reaction to pot may smile and deny this is a possibility. There is a reason for this: those who smile have only felt
part of the elephant.

The prophetic flashback involves the belief that one has received information and advice from the future. Remembering
Goode's description of what may occur when one has a high trip
with cannabis[84] and recognizing that psychiatry has for years
accepted the phenomenon of déjà vu, the concept of a prophetic
flashback may not seem irrational on second thought. (Déjà vu,
French, meaning "already seen," is a phenomenon in which
the subject incorrectly believes what he sees is the repetition of
a previous event.) In the non-drug-oriented subculture, comparable experiences may be considered "revelations" and those
who receive them "prophets." The phenomenon is common

among faith healers, who presumably are drug free in their habits, and is considered a divine event. The same interpretation is proffered as an explanation of the subculture which uses drugs as a sacrament for religious exploration.

One additional interesting aspect of the flashback phenomenon is that a number of youths have now reported to this author that they experience these reactions sporadically when they are stopped by police for routine traffic investigations even though they may have been drug free for some time.

There is to date no valid explanation for this. One may postulate, however, that since the drug experience basically offers an escape from the pressures of current reality, it may be that the mind may utilize this learned mechanism to escape when it faces tribulation in a non-drug environment.

Youths reporting this phenomenon come from the milieu where multidrug consumption is common and thus it is difficult to determine whether cannabis can accomplish this alone or whether it is a concommittant effect of several drugs or the "flashing" of a stronger psychotropic such as LSD by cannabis. If this becomes increasingly reported it will undoubtedly become a topic for future investigation.

"Well, well, if it isn't Mrs. Willington's son Weston,
all grown up and smoking and drinking and
hallucinating and all."

Reprinted from *Medical World News*, January 19, 1968, by permission of
Henry R. Martin.

bad
trips

Fools and wise men are equally harmless. Dangerous
are those who are half foolish and half wise and see
only half of everything.

—ANONYMOUS

*"T*HE USE OF MARIJUANA never leads to phys-
ical dependency. No tolerance is developed and no abstinence
syndrome or withdrawal illness occurs with marijuana," San
Francisco drug expert Joel Fort recently told the court of the
State of Michigan. "Marijuana has no direct relationship with
mental health problems," he continued. "I know of no people
being admitted to mental health hospitals in this country solely
because of problems associated with marijuana use.... marijuana does not cause crime nor does it cause sexual 'excesses.'
Marijuana does not induce psychoses or psychotic breaks. Marijuana does not cause progression to any other drug."[1]

This author would be delighted to stop right here and agree
with Joel Fort, if the good doctor were correct. It would mean we
had found a reasonably safe euphoriant that could be both spon-

sored and legalized by society. Unfortunately, Fort's observations do not coincide with those already made or now being
made by other clinicians and clinical investigators.

Fort is no more out of step or inaccurate in his observations
than is the student who insists, "Nothing this beautiful could be
bad." The problem is that once again marijuana is not being
viewed in its total perspective. Fort's disagreement with this
author (ERB) may be best explained by his own summary of
his background.

"Most of what I have learned about marijuana has come from
my work as a public health specialist, with particular specialization in the drug use and abuse fields and in my work as a sociologist. The limited part of my work that deals with the practice of
psychiatry has taught, and could teach, very little about marijuana because a psychiatrist, or indeed the physician in general,
rarely sees a marijuana user."[2]

If this quotation were written several years ago, one could
understand the discrepancy between Fort's observations in San
Francisco in the heart of the drug subculture and those made
by this author, whose primary research has been divided between San Francisco and Los Angeles. The quotation, however,
was a part of sworn testimony in the State of Michigan on
April 6, 1970.

If one compares Dr. Fort's background with that of this
writer, the situation becomes more confusing, for both of us have
spent considerable time working with users at essentially the
same levels: the street, the "pad," and the emergency room clinic.
One can only conclude that the two of us see a different type of
user and, for that matter, a different type of general physician
and psychiatrist. In contrast to Fort's observation that doctors
rarely see a marijuana user, this author has had more speaking
requests than he could fill in the past five years from both gen-
eralists and psychiatrists who have not only encountered adverse
reactions to cannabis in their patients but who, in some instances,
have been unprepared to cope with them.

It is true, however, that most marijuana reactions are not
seen by physicians. As Talbott noted, even in Vietnam the physicians see only those cases demanding professional intervention
because possession of cannabis is illegal and users fear legal retribution. Further, most bummers and even some bad trips are
handled by buddies both here and in " 'Nam" the same way

friends manage a companion stoned on alcohol.[3] That few cases have been seen by physicians is not nearly as significant, therefore, as the fact that more and more are being brought to the attention of clinicians. The importance of this is compounded because only a minority of doctors take the time to publish their experiences.

Bummers, while annoying, are seldom cause for great concern. Bad trips, however, may seriously handicap their victims. Kaplan, quoting briefly from comments made by this author (to the California State Senate Public Health and Safety Committee in 1967, in which reference was made to adverse reactions under high toxicity), states that aggressive reactions occurring as a part of a psychotic break are "so rare that it has not been described in any recent scientific paper." Mr. Kaplan was not only quoting inaccurately; he was, as we shall see in this chapter, extremely premature in his conclusions.[4]

One frequently hears the comment that "nothing" valid has been done by researchers where cannabis effects are concerned, and/or that the investigations performed are irrelevant because the techniques failed to measure up to the critics' standards; it should, therefore, prove informative to examine in some detail a few completed research projects.

Weil and Zinberg's interesting paper, for instance, received nationwide headlines because there were quotes which could be extracted to "prove" marijuana was essentially harmless. A careful perusal of the authors' work reveals that they did not intend to "prove or disprove popularly held convictions about marijuana as an intoxicant." They were, instead, concerned with collecting "some long overdue pharmacological data."[5]

Some media vigorously picked up the authors' initial results, e.g., "that no adverse marijuana reactions occurred in any of our subjects."[6] It would have been unfortunate if adverse reactions had occurred, considering that one of the critical points the authors were able to show was that the drug could be used safely on human volunteers in the laboratory. If they had failed to demonstrate this, their experiment might have set marijuana research back several years.

A second factor concerning the absence of adverse reactions is that the test was well controlled and performed on young volunteers carefully selected for their mental and physical health. These "prime" subjects were then exposed to marijuana smoking for four brief periods spaced a week apart. Furthermore, "set" was positive in that some of the volunteers expressed the desire to validate the impression that marijuana was harmless. With this "stacked deck," the "hurrah" by pro-marijuana groups over the lack of adverse reactions appeared inane. And in their glee over the apparent lack of serious adverse reactions, they overlooked the value of the experiment: namely, the recording of the drug's pharmacological reactions.

Despite the experiments and despite the law, each person will ultimately decide whether or not he will try pot. Those who choose to do so after studying the facts are on their own, and one can only wish them good luck and a pleasant trip. Those who choose to do so because they have relied on half truths, however, may suffer consequences they might have avoided if they had had adequate information.

TEMPORAL DISINTEGRATION AND DEPERSONALIZATION

In early 1970, four Stanford University researchers, Melges, Tinklenberg, Hollister, and Gillespie began a project aimed at studying the effects of marijuana on human volunteers as these effects related to the subjects' ability to think and function. Specifically this group was interested in three primary activities: the effects on immediate memory, the production of depersonalization, and the precipitation of temporal disintegration.[7,8,9]

Memory effects involved the ability of the person to recall and to think after exposure to cannabis. Depersonalization is a phenomenon in which the person views himself as unreal or strange. The state is best explained by such statements as, "My body seems detached as if it and myself are separate," or, "I feel like a stranger to myself." Occasionally these feelings persist after the trip, and often they are accompanied by delusions. "I was standing by the dresser," a jazz musician commented after a rather hairy trip, "when I noticed my body lying over there on the bed. I buried my body in the woods. Then I got on the train and came back to town. Since then I have been a soul."[10]

Temporal disintegration is a kind of mental incoordination. In this state the subject has difficulty retaining, coordinating, and serially indexing special memories. In the Stanford experiment emphasis was placed on studying the disruption of memories of the past as they related to future goals. The investigators also studied the influence of distortion of the person's ability to perceive things that were happening in the present as well as his anticipation and expectation of occurrences in the future as they related to important goals he wished to pursue.

When temporal disintegration occurs it leaves the individual with feelings of confusion about the past, present, and future. Since each person relies on his ability to relate to his past and present and to correlate these memories or current awareness with his hopes and goals for his future, the researchers postulated that should one's temporal experience become fragmented and disorganized by a chemical substance (i.e., cannabis), the change would also introduce feelings of depersonalization and memory confusion.

To explore this postulate, eight healthy male graduate students in their twenties were hired and advised they would be tested on "feelings and attitudes" which occurred during the drug experience. All students had used marijuana before, but none had used it or taken any other psychedelic drugs for a month before the experiment. All men were examined for adequate physical and mental health prior to their acceptance.[11]

The researchers extracted tetrahydrocannabinol from marijuana supplied by the Bureau of Narcotics and Dangerous Drugs (belying a constant cry that the Bureau "prevents" research, although giving due respect to some who complain, it is selective in granting an official "go ahead"). Using thin layer and gas liquid chromatography, they demonstrated their extracts contained, primarily, $(-)$ - $\triangle^1$-THC, with smaller amounts of cannabidiol and cannabinol also being present. They calibrated samples into three dosage levels: 20 mg. (the usual amount taken in an average smoking party), 40 mg., and 60 mg. They also devised a placebo which tasted like the cannabinol-containing samples. Since previous studies have shown that equivalent oral doses of synthetic THC induced essentially the same psychotomimetic effects one achieves from smoking, they were not concerned about possible criticism that the oral route was less relevant than that provided by inhalation. In addition they noted that the oral route of administration for the present offers a far more precise way of regulating dosage.[12]

Using double blind controls the researchers gave the eight subjects three oral doses of either 20, 40, and 60 mg. each, or a placebo dose, during four different test sessions. Neither subject or examiner knew which sample had been administered. The sessions occurred one week apart under similar conditions. The subjects refrained from eating for an hour prior to ingesting the dose and waited another 45 minutes before eating again, to insure adequate absorption. Once the test began, the men were examined at intervals of 1½, 3½, and 5½ hours. These examinations occurred at the same time of day on each occasion, and each subject was tested in the same environment by the same psychiatrist for approximately a half hour at each time interval. To be certain they had maximum cooperation the subject was asked to repeat the instructions of each task every time it was administered. If he seemed to drift under the influence of the drug he was asked to walk about until he felt ready to perform. Between testings the subject could either talk with the psychiatrist, sleep, read, or listen to music. The music consisted of pre-taped folk songs which were used throughout the month of experimentation.

"It is important to point out," the researchers noted, "that we did not correlate one 'state' such as a given magnitude of temporal disintegration on a particular test session with another 'state' such as the degree of depersonalization reported at that time. Rather, we correlated *changes* that occurred contemporaneously from one test session to the next and thereby removed the stochastic (the ability to proceed by guesswork) dependency between serial measures in the same subject."[13]

The subjects were tested with complicated mathematical problems. They were, for instance, given a variable number from test to test beginning with numbers 106 through 114 and asked to subtract 7, then add 1, 2, or 3 and repeat such alternate subtraction and addition until they reached the exact goal (between 46 and 54) that was specified for each trial. This is not the thing one might do every day, perhaps, but the tests used the same mental mechanisms one must employ to arrive at goals and pursue directed and organized thinking in daily life.

The researchers found that high oral doses of THC induced temporal disintegration in normal subjects, that the phenomenon stemmed partly from impaired immediate memory, and that it was associated with disorganized speech and thinking. They also found that the poorest performances occurred at the 1½ hour period after ingestion and that higher doses prolonged the temporal disintegration.

Sustained attention and long-term memory operations did not appear to be affected by THC, nor did increasing doses cause significant increases in mistakes during long-term memory operations. Short-term memory, however, was impaired and the impairment was unaltered by the dosage; i.e., the small dose had the same effect as the larger ones. As dosage was increased it did affect, however, the increase in errors made in the serial or "working" functions of immediate memory. In the mathematical goals set for the students the errors included loss of place, failure to alternate between subtraction and addition, and blocking. One subject noted, "I'd pick out a number now and then go ahead . . . Coming back, I'd forget which number I just did or what I was supposed to do next." This experience reminds one of Margolis' remark: "It should be obvious that things which require good judgment of time and space should be scrupulously avoided when stoned."[14]

With increasing doses of THC, there were progressively more errors in reaching the goal. Students kept going past the goal until later when they checked themselves; although they remembered the goal accurately, they had not brought it into awareness at the right time.

The researchers suggest that temporal disintegration may account for the disorganized speech patterns which occur under marijuana intoxication. "I can't follow what I'm saying. . . ." one student complained, "can't stay on the same subject . . . I can't remember what I just said or what I want to say . . . because there are just so many thoughts that are broken in time, one chunk there and one chunk here."[15]

The Stanford group found, as did Clark and Nakashima[16] that "impairments in immediate memory from marijuana intoxication do not follow a smooth time-function but, rather, are episodic, brief in duration and not always under volitional control. These episodes often interrupted the speech patterns of our subjects and seemed to be associated with the intrusion of extraneous perceptions and thoughts."

". . . I just felt very confident and able to remember the numbers . . ." one student observed . . . "then when it came time to give them back, I'd see and hear, mostly see, I think, all kinds of numbers. And I wouldn't know which ones were the right ones." Another subject commented: "I can understand which I'm thinking, but I can't understand which I'm saying . . . because there are so many thoughts in between what I'm saying . . ."[17] Observations such as these help explain why a growing number of educators are going on record as saying that, from the experience of their students, a more than casual use of marijuana is not consistent with a successful academic career. It also explains the increased number of visits to clinicians by users who have become "hung up" on pot and realize that if they don't kick its use, they may fail to reach important goals.[18,19,20]

"Everything's pretty mixed up. . . ." one volunteer subject told the Stanford group despite researchers' effort to minimize, through reassurance and encouragement, the influence of impaired attention on performance. "I lose track of what's been happening. And it sometimes even seems like a long time has passed, but I know it hasn't because I'm generally still in the middle of a word or sentence." These effects abated, fortunately, in three to five hours for most subjects, although some described residual impairment for as long as 24 hours.[21]

As might be expected, each of the Stanford volunteers showed a unique pattern of changes in his emotional response as his trip progressed. Since neither the subject nor the investigator knew which dose of drug (or the placebo) the subject had taken, it is interesting to note not only this wide variation of effect, but also this: as drug-induced temporal disintegration and depersonalization occurred each subject tended to view the effects they experienced differently.

Four of the men noted more positive feelings: two reacted with predominantly negative effects and two had mixed positive and negative emotional responses. These patterns, the group noted, "appeared to stem from different personality dispositions about losing control and individuality. Also, at higher doses, the fear that the loss of control and identity might not end gave rise to panic reactions in three subjects. The THC-induced sense of timelessness impaired their realization that the drug effects would eventually wear off. One subject, under the influence of 60 mg. of THC (only three times the usual 'party dose') characterized his panic as "helplessly drifting forever," unable to direct his thoughts and actions, "locked in infinity . . . a never-ending slosh, with my mind bouncing like a yo-yo."[22]

There is, of course, a significant difference in approach to this type of experience. The occurrence can intrigue some, particularly if they have been up enough to reassure themselves they have a reasonable chance of coming down; it can terrify others.

No one person can make the decision to use a mind altering drug for another; to encourage the wrong person to use such a drug, pot or LSD, may court disaster. One student remarked that if he could put LSD into LBJ he might help the problems of the nation. He could not perceive (considering this complicated man's mind and conscience) that it might, instead, have produced the world's most disastrous "trip," had it occurred during Johnson's tenure in office. The same criticism can be made of rock singer Grace Slick, of the Jefferson Airplane group, who once tried to "turn on" President Nixon.[23] Taking a whopping 600 microgram dose along to a White House party, she hoped, apparently, to dump it into the President's drink; however, she chose Abbie Hoffman as her escort, and sharp-eyed White House guards decided not to admit them.

"Boy were they right," Grace said. "I really would have done it. I figured the worst thing a little acid could do to Tricia [who had invited fellow alumni, including Miss Slick, of Manhattan's Finch College to the White House party] was turn her into merely a delightful person instead of a grinning robot. But we were aiming for the Old Dad, hoping he might come to the party and have a cup of tea. Far out." Far out, indeed. So far out that a cup of "tea" might well have crippled the nation.

The Stanford group also noted that five of their eight subjects reported transient episodes of suspiciousness when they felt they were no longer in control of their thinking processes and their reactions. This made them feel controlled by others, a common reaction users experience in the "pad" on high or poorly managed marijuana trips.

Summarizing their findings, the Stanford group explains that the fragmentation of temporal experience co-varies with strange and unfamiliar attitudes about one's self. Perhaps, they reason, this is due to the person's feeling less familiar with himself during marijuana intoxication because he loses the perspective of continuity of the self through time. The trip can be good if the personality structure is right and if the user recognizes the experience is short lived. This "good" effect may be due, they think, to the fact that an altered sense of time and sense of self causes the person to be less concerned about what will happen to him. The same reaction has been communicated to this author by returning service men who frankly stated that pot helped them control fear when going *in* to combat.

"Normal consciousness is like a movie," the Stanford group notes, "in which each frame of a film merges with the next to give the impression of a continuum with smooth transitions of content." When the subject is mildly high the frames of the film remain separated. As long as each frame is clear the user "grooves" on its content which "is often an inner vision or fantasy." Each single frame is considered as it passes and noted before the user looks at the next one. The experience is supported by the fact that the user recognizes some stability since an organized progression of thought is present.[24]

When the user is really stoned, however, he grabs one segment, ignoring the others. He loses his sense of time and space and begins to flash on the one image; as he does, completely different thought contents begin to flash in and out. "These flashes," the researchers note, "are inner fantasies from past, present and future, admixed with outside perceptions, all telescoped into one frame." Without an associative sense, the experience seems timeless and may be either delightful or terrifying, depending on the personality of the user and on his associates and the surroundings.

When one has normal consciousness, the group explains, he acts on sensory input as a censor. If he is in control he can detect matches and mismatches between the expected and the actual. As he compares the *now* and the *then*, he can predict, plan, and make adjustments to reach his goals or, if warranted, modify his goals. To do this he has to keep track of time and distinguish between past, present and future. If he forgets what came before or after experience, however, he will have difficulty placing that event in his sense of time. If perceptions become confused with memories, or with expectations inferred from memories, it will be difficult if not impossible to distinguish between what is happening, what may happen and what one hopes will happen. The situation then becomes grossly disorganized as does the person involved.

This author has noted for some time the tremendous variations (some good, some bad) in the same individual as he trips under different circumstances or on different occasions. The casual user may see few if any of the adverse side effects and thus may deny they occur. But this author, observing reactions from the use of potent cannabis alone by users who have never taken LSD, has noted effects that very closely resemble the acid experience. One of these adverse reactions is the fragmentation or splitting of one's ego.

"I suddenly became three people," one uncomfortable user told this author. "I wasn't really frightened because I knew the thing would pass, yet there was a nagging fear that I might be wrong. I turned, impossible though it may seem, into three separate personalities. One simply observed the scene as one might look at a television set. The other two tended to work together, one as a monitor, the other as the traveller or 'experiencer' taking the trip.

"Thoughts moved so fast it was as though someone was holding a deck of cards, letting them slide from one hand to the other. As each card dropped it held a thought that for the moment was extremely clear; but the moment that card passed, the thought was forgotten and a new thought intervened, equally clear, yet instantly forgotten as another thought arrived.

"Periodically I would become paranoid, filled with the fear I was going insane, that I might be busted, that my friends might turn on me or that I might be physically harmed. When that happened the part of me that was a 'monitor' would say, 'It's cool, man. Everything's all right . . . it will pass . . . just relax and take it all in and enjoy it.' And as the 'traveller part' of me heard this it would go back to watching the kaleidoscopic changes on the cards, tripping on thoughts I would probably not recall consciously again, sometimes enjoying, sometimes resenting the experience.

"In the meantime the 'observer' would occasionally blot out the activities of the other two sections of myself. They did not disappear but instead were sort of tuned out as one might turn down a television set so he can make a phone call and yet watch the picture. The observer remained aware and had good recall of the total experience (although he could remember none of the cards or the thoughts on the card which the traveller viewed in rapid succession) and occasionally entered into a rather marbled conversation with fellow users. These discussions could be recalled later with meaning and reasonable content."

In time the flow of uncontrollable thoughts passed and the monitor and traveller parts of this subject's ego faded. He remained "sort of floating" for four or five hours and was moderately incoordinate for this time, although if forced, he could "maintain" reasonably for short periods of time. Some effects of the trip lasted for 36–48 hours. They consisted of excess irritability, some anxiety and paranoia, headache, listlessness, and a lack of ambition which slowly faded after two days. The grass in this case was "coletus," a type of cannabis consisting primarily of high resin-containing pollen which comes from central Mexico. The setting was a comfortable "pad," and all of the users were familiar with smoking pot.

The experience brings up several contentions concerning the use of marijuana, especially since recent research has noted that the body retains cannabis chemicals in the system for several days following intake. It has been suggested[25] that this retention opens the mind to programming. It has also been suggested that if one repeatedly uses cannabis and if it is indeed stored in the body, there is a question if the chronic user (or even one who uses every other or every third or fourth day) is, ever actually "down." If these observations are sound, the use of marijuana may have serious personally and socially damaging effects.

THE AMOTIVATIONAL SYNDROME

"One final alleged chronic effect of marijuana use," comments Stanford Professor of Law John Kaplan, "is what is called the amotivational syndrome. The argument here," he states, "is not that the long-term marijuana user becomes mentally ill or suffers brain damage, but that for some not yet understood reason he simply loses interest in everything worthwhile and drops out of society."[26]

"It is hard to evaluate this type of argument," Kaplan admits. "Certainly, there does seem to be an alarming number of young people dropping out of our society and this has come most to public attention during the sudden increase in marijuana use in the past few years." Kaplan argues, however, that a "chicken and egg" problem exists here. Was the person headed for dropout prior to the drug use, or did the drug cause the dropout? He further argues that if "drug use is to blame for the amotivational syndrome, the likelihood is that the effective drug is not marijuana but LSD."

"Finally, and most important," he argues, "we should not be prepared to accept any hypothesis of causation until some mechanism can be postulated that is consistent with the facts we know."[27] This argument resembles the old story of the small town that was situated in a valley beneath a hairpin curve in a mountain road overlooking the town. Accidents mounted, cars came crashing down into the village, and the town folk split into two factions determined to "do something" about the problem. One group wanted to put a fence at the turn in order to stop cars before they crashed over the cliff. The other group argued that there was no proof that the fence would do any good and championed the establishment of an ambulance station at the foot of the cliff to care for any survivors. While cars continued to crash over the cliff, the debate dragged on.

"So far as the amotivational syndrome is concerned the only attempt to do this (i.e., postulate some mechanism that is consistent with the facts) relies not on any scientific work," Kaplan says with tongue in cheek, "but upon the authority of *Sports Illustrated* Magazine. Dr. Edward Bloomquist, in his book *Marijuana,* relying on this authority compares marijuana use to life on the island of Bora Bora."[28]

Kaplan's book was published in late 1970. To give him the benefit of the doubt, he might have needed a year to research the possibility of the existence of an amotivational syndrome prior to making this statement. It should be reasonable to assume that by early 1969, if he had made any attempt to do so, he could have found the postulation necessary to convince himself that amotivation is more than a soft breeze on Bora Bora. Apparently he failed to achieve this.

In Napa, California, in mid 1968, during a tape-recorded debate involving this author and Mr. Kaplan, the latter happened to notice the following letter (written to the *Los Angeles Times* on March 20, 1968) by a mother whose son had dropped out. The letter was written in opposition to statements made by a candidate for district attorney for the City of Los Angeles who hoped to obtain votes by advocating the legalization of pot. Noting this letter, Kaplan announced to the audience his relief that I wouldn't have time to read it. The letter read as follows:

"As a mother of an eighteen-year-old boy charged with possession of marijuana, I most emphatically say that I do not need scientific proof to see what damage it can do. I watched my son travel the typical road to ruin . . . from a student who enjoyed music, drama, and sports to a useless filthy college dropout with no other aim in life than to live in a carefree dream of distortion."

"He went all the way," she noted: "loss of appetite, long deep sleeps after the drug wore off, short attention span, poor memory, inability to read, talk, or even communicate for more than a few minutes. His continued defiance is a definite hindrance to his return to normal, as he had come to enjoy it so much."[29]

One could attack this mother's comment. Users, for instance, are always supposed to be hungry after smoking pot. One might also argue that the boy was already disturbed. The problem with this is that until he started getting *hung up* on pot (not casually smoking), he was apparently motivated. One can argue (and some do) that he would have dropped out anyway. But one can also argue that he might not have, or that he could have put off dropping out until a time in life when the consequences would have had less serious effects. One might also argue that a soldier killed by a bullet in Vietnam would have died anyway sometime. True. But fifty years of life is worth a debate.

Commenting on his interpretation of the Bora Bora simile, Kaplan notes that the "effort to link the amotivational syndrome with marijuana sometimes reaches even more absurd lengths." He then relates the notation of a researcher who caused amotivation in a cat by feeding it marijuana, and the inevitable rebuttal by another scientist who stated that the cat was inactivated because it was "overdosed." The latter point, which Mr. Kaplan says is "very strong," was corroborated by the fact that the cat died a few days after the experiment.[30] But how does one know, as Kaplan suggests, that the cat died of a drug overdose? Following the professor's reasoning, it might be that the cat would have died despite the experiment.

"In terms of social consequences," says Dr. David Smith, the Haight-Ashbury Clinic's noted director, "there does appear to be the marijuana equivalent of the alcoholic commonly referred to as a pothead. The potheads I have observed" he notes, "become stoned almost daily with marijuana and become anxious if grass is not available."[31]

Writing in mid 1968, Dr. Smith observed, "This habituation or psychological dependence is disruptive in that [potheads] tend to ignore personal and social responsibilities such as personal hygiene, health work, etc. It is interesting that an unusually high incidence of 'potheads' reported using alcohol to excess at one time, but rarely use 'booze' unless 'grass' is not available. Certain younger individuals," he says, "who regularly use marijuana also develop what I have called the *amotivational syndrome* [a term devised by Dr. Smith some two years prior to the publication of Kaplan's book to describe this phenomenon] in that they lose the desire to work or compete. Such cases come to the attention of a physician only if the patient becomes anxious over the loss of a drive he deems highly desirable or if pressures are exerted by important personal associations."

Smith reports two interesting cases involving this syndrome.[32] The first involved a twenty-four-year-old, moderately successful businessman, married, with a child, a suburban home and other achievements, who smoked "grass" intermittently for four years, then decided to turn on daily and drop out (there is no notation as to which occurred first). He moved to the Haight-Ashbury as a "free man" where he cohabitated with a girl and lived what he described as a "very happy and anxiety-free" existence. Then came the bomb.

Over a six-month period he noted he could not enjoy sex to the extent that he and the girl felt necessary. By the time he consulted the clinic, he had failed to have sexual relations with his girl for a period of three full weeks. "He was persuaded to discontinue 'grass' on a trial basis," Smith reports. After he did so, "his sex drive gradually returned and he felt 'normal' the month after cessation of 'grass.' "

Smith also cites the case of a twenty-two-year-old medical student who after a successful first year in college started smoking grass with friends, became "sick of the phony struggle for grades," and promptly dropped out of the competition. After much debate the boy decided to move back home, stop smoking grass, and go back to school. A year later he seemed reasonably happy with his future career in medicine.

"Certain individuals use marijuana to escape reality and themselves," Smith accedes, "just as certain individuals abuse alcohol in the same manner. It would appear that the ratio of marijuana users to abusers," he notes, "is approximately the same as alcohol abusers to users," and implies that personality rather than pharmacological factors are the prime consideration.[33]

The latest HEW report to Congress in 1971 tends to agree

with this. "The fact that there are many worldwide reports of heavy, chronic cannabis use resulting in loss of conventional motivation and in social indifference is of particular interest in that there are now some reports of somewhat similar findings among American heavy users of marijuana. Unfortunately," HEW states, "American use patterns are frequently contaminated by the use of other drug substances, making interpretation difficult. It is not certain to what degree this 'amotivational syndrome' is the result of marijuana use per se or of a tendency for those who lack conventional motivation to find drugs unusually attractive. If one confines his use of the term to a description of the present American scene one must conclude that present evidence does not permit the establishment of a causal relationship between marijuana use and the amotivational syndrome. There is, however, increasing evidence that frequent, heavy marijuana use is correlated with a loss of interest in conventional goals and a development of a kind of lethargy," HEW warns. "Research in humans is being conducted in an attempt to determine to what extent this observed correlation is due to alteration in brain functioning."[34]

These observations give one pause for thought. To date there are nine million alcoholics, most of them intelligent, capable people when they are not drinking. Would they have dropped out if they had not become alcoholics? Maybe. Would they, without alcohol, have adjusted to what most people accept as reality? Who knows? Would the camel's back have broken without the final straw? As pro-marijuana pundits frequently note, that which is real, desirable, necessary, or worthwhile depends on one's personal point of view.

"As yet there is insufficient information to allow any statements to be made about the long term effects of cannabis on intellectual development and ability," researcher C. W. M. Wilson notes. "The evidence obtained from students, however, does indicate that when they use it frequently and regularly, it impairs their ability to work and interferes with their normal social contacts. The psychopharmacological effects of the drug are such that users tend to frequent each other's company particularly, and often exclusively," he states. "It can hardly be doubted that this will interfere with students' education, recreation, and development in a modern university, especially since the duration of action of the drug would prevent students from coming to their classes, or would cause them to come in a partly drugged condition."[35]

Wilson fortifies his opinion by noting studies indicating that the long-term, sedative effects of pot may be of importance in this connection. Citing the La Guardia report (the clinical, not the sociological section) and the work of Marcovitz and Myers in the military,[36] he notes that the investigators found marijuana users to have extremely poor and irregular work records. Little desire to work as well as records of unemployment and part-time work were common in the subjects studied; selective association with other marijuana users reinforced both their habits and attitudes.

PSYCHOTIC REACTIONS

One of the continuing debates centering around the use of marijuana involves its potential to produce (or its failure to produce) psychotic or psychotomimetic reactions. "Several studies on marijuana use in other countries—notably India—have indicated addiction, physical degradation and psychiatric disorders as consequences of long term marijuana use," notes Dr. David Smith.[37] "These studies, however," he warns, "were of users of hashish . . . which is more potent than the marijuana preparations commonly used in the United States."

This raises again the inevitable question: will American pot users be content with low grade grass? Perhaps many will. But it is equally clear from the constantly increasing amount of hashish and stronger varieties of cannabis that are being confiscated by police (and which represents at best only 5 to 10 percent of the actual amount entering the country), that a growing number of users seek "good grass." It has been this author's experience that those who keep searching for more potent material are, frequently, those whose personalities are least capable of coping with the effects produced.

"Most people," Weil notes, "who become high on marijuana find the effects pleasant. A surprisingly high percentage of those who find the effects unpleasant turn out to be ambulatory patients with schizophrenia. In fact, patients with a low threshold for psychosis often shun marijuana after an initial encounter."[38] Interesting! But how can one be certain he is not prepsychotic?

"I have observed two patients with schizophrenia, as manifested by disorders in association, inappropriate affect, and disorganized behavior, improve dramatically after they stopped taking marijuana," notes psychiatrist Martin Keeler. "I have observed three patients with severe anxiety and two with depression that started during a marijuana reaction but persisted for some time afterwards. I have observed two other patients with severe anxiety secondary to the spontaneous recurrence of perceptual and kinesthetic (denoting one's ability to perceive his muscular movements) sensations first experienced during the marijuana reaction. The number of instances reported is small," Keeler notes, "but they occurred in a small population composed largely of nonusers. If many people use the drug to any great extent, many psychotic and psychoneurotic states will be precipitated or aggravated."[39]

". . . [I]t appears to me," Weil notes, "that in borderline personalities, the effects of marijuana on secondary perception may constitute a stress that pushes patients in the direction of derealization, an experience generally perceived as frightening. . . . The occurrence of these atypical reactions to marijuana in persons with low thresholds for psychosis suggests that the drug might also be capable of precipitating true psychotic breaks in these patients."[40]

It is not the purpose of this book to imply that psychosis is frequent or that it usually, if ever, follows the casual use of low-resin marijuana when reasonably stable people use it under nonstressful circumstances. There is, however, a flagrant dishonesty being practiced by certain experts who deny that there is any relationship between the use of cannabis and adverse psychological reactions.

This practice is obvious even to those who, like *Time* magazine, seem to have changed their attitude towards pot from one of conservatism to one of cautious acceptance. ". . . [I]t is clearly irresponsible to say as some extreme defenders do, that pot is no more harmful than cherry pie," an editor notes, while at the same time implying that he feels more research is indicated.[41]

Too often a diagnosis of psychosis is made when in truth the reaction is one of uncontrolled panic triggered in a person who cannot relax and "flow" with the psychic activity produced by the drug. But psychotic episodes do occur, particularly in persons with prepsychotic tendencies. Smith notes these reactions are characteristic of the personality structure of the user and that the drug intoxication merely triggers the psychosis.[42] This may be so, but it does not vindicate use of the drug nor deny that it plays a role in incapacitating the victim.

Significantly, the number of reports of psychotic reactions, most of them recent and written in this hemisphere, seem to be increasing in medical literature. The increase of such reports tends to parallel the persistent rise in marijuana use seen among North Americans. In a 1967 Gallup survey, only 5 percent of Americans on campus had tried pot.[43] The number rose to 22 percent in the spring of 1969, and by December 1970 had reached 42 percent. As the use factor has risen, the incidence of adverse reactions has also increased. Surprisingly, some fail to recognize this association is present while others, suspecting it, seem reticent to admit that it can happen.

The problem of whether or not cannabis can induce a true state of either temporary or permanent psychosis has been studied by numerous researchers. Isbell stated unequivocally that low doses of $\triangle$-^{1}THC were capable of causing psychotic episodes,[44] while Allentuck and Bowman noted that "marijuana may precipitate a psychosis in an unstable disorganized personality" if the subject took doses he couldn't handle.[45] Gaskill agreed with this, noting that whereas psychopathic individuals who commonly smoke marijuana will often exhibit abnormal behavior without the drug, their tendency towards psychotic behavior is markedly increased by its use.[46]

Bromberg noted that toxic psychoses occurring from marijuana use involve disturbance of the sensorium accompanied by delusional and emotional reactions. He described cases in which symptoms lasted from a few days to up to a year or more.[47]

In Isbell's study, most of his subjects experienced altered time sense and both visual and auditory perceptual changes with an intake of 50 micrograms per kilogram of body weight. When Isbell increased this dose to 200 micrograms, all subjects underwent some psychotic reactions, including illusions, delusions, and hallucinations. When investigators used from one to eleven standard marijuana cigarettes, nine out of the 77 persons involved developed acute psychotic episodes. This occurred despite the fact that the experiment was performed in a controlled atmosphere where the subjects made an effort to "maintain."

This author does not mean to imply that low doses of mild pot will necessarily precipitate a psychotic reaction. What is shown is that trouble *may* occur when a sufficient or even a small amount is given to the psychosis-prone individual. Furthermore, in some cases the adverse reaction is directly related to the time period in which the drug is used. Louria notes the case of a sixteen-year-old boy who smoked pot for three years and was schizophrenic for the entire period. After quitting, however, he returned to work and his aberrant mental symptoms stopped. This occurred, incidentally, with no therapy other than convincing him that he should "quit the weed."[48]

Even one joint, Louria notes, can on occasion precipitate a psychosis in an unstable personality, "but for the most part psychosis is associated either with utilization of very large amounts over a short period of time or with chronic heavy use." The marijuana proponents can justifiably claim that if one smokes only one or two cigarettes a day of American type marijuana, psychotic reactions are rare. But for the heavy user, or the pothead who smokes almost constantly, the story is entirely different. "Once precipitated," Louria warns, "the psychosis usually improves in a period of several days to several months after marijuana use is stopped, but it is clear that on occasion it can last for a very long time."[49]

In 1969 Bartolucci reported a case of a thirty-year-old man from a middle-class background in Canada who had used pot to broaden his experience and refine his artistic sensitivity so that he could improve as a painter. His wife described him as an expansive and outgoing person with strong feelings, a man who needed to be involved in worthwhile causes.[50]

He had smoked marijuana for approximately a year before the psychiatrists saw him, and of late had been smoking daily to obtain euphoria, a state which, he felt, enabled him to work in a "personal way." He denied ever having used any other drug and his wife agreed with this statement. Apparently he was in good mental and physical health.

Three days before he came to the hospital he started smoking a new batch of weed with some friends, none of whom, significantly, had bad trips or reactions. After one or two joints he began to have unstructured visual hallucinations and shortly announced that he was Christ and had to die for the world. At first his wife tried to manage the situation herself, but two days later when his behavior was worse, she brought him to the hospital.

Arriving at the emergency room the man jumped from the

examining table and pounded the walls with his fist so hard that he developed a large blood clot in his hand. Twenty-four hours later, he was more cooperative, but still frightened and occasionally depressed. His speech was slurred and he used abstract and loose verbal comparisons. He continued to believe he was Christ and still had visual hallucinations.

On the third day of hospitalization he informed his doctor that he was turning into stone. He was sure this was so because he had had an erection the night before; this confirmed his beliefs that he was beginning to "stiffen." That evening he asked to be taken to a private room where he stripped himself and pounded his genital area.

Four days following he was still restless and emotionally labile, thumping on the tables and shouting at the nurses. This went on for several days until eight days later, when he seemed well enough to go home. Even then, he stated, he felt "incapable of human emotion." Fortunately this feeling abated. His progress was followed by his doctors for several weeks and their reports seemed to show steady improvement.

Reviewing this case the doctors made several observations. "Panic, resulting from a novel and frightening experience in a non-supportive setting seems highly improbable" in this instance, they said, "because the patient was with supportive members of his subculture when the episode occurred." Another explanation they considered was that the use of the drug had triggered a latent psychosis in one predisposed toward it. Yet, they said, "we elicited no evidence of prepsychotic characteristics and his family history (of mental disease) was negative."

It is interesting that the experience the man endured during his bad trip was somewhat like the trips he had enjoyed previously. This time it differed in that it was accompanied by simple visual hallucinations, wide mood swings, uncontrolled and impulsive behavior, loss of ego boundaries, and delusional ideas.

What caused the difference? Defenders of marijuana who encounter a case like this will often smile wisely, then change the subject. A more reasonable conclusion is to recognize the necessity of evaluating evidence that demonstrates, as the authors have noted here, that "adequately high doses of the active principles of marijuana can induce a psychotic reaction in almost anyone."

"Experienced smokers," Bartolucci noted, "seem to become able to control the effects of the drug by regulating the dosage so that only the desired and familiar effects are provoked. Nonetheless, even experienced smokers, like our patient, may go beyond their individual tolerance, possibly because of a progressive impairment in judgment which marijuana seems to provoke. This would lead," he said, "to unwanted and unusual symptoms which are probably primarily pharmacologically determined, although flavored by previous personality traits."[51]

In late 1969, Talbott and Teague reported their findings of twelve cases of acute psychosis associated with cannabis derivatives and environmental stress occurring in young soldiers stationed in Vietnam.[52] Grinspoon, whose recent article in *Scientific American* minimized the negative effects of pot, called this study "terrible," arguing that 50 percent of cannabis preparations seized in Vietnam are laced with opiates (which, incidentally, narcotize and sedate) and thus these reactions cannot be ascribed to marijuana alone.

He argues that Talbott's paper overlooks the fact that the use of pot may be protecting some American soldiers from psychosis. Furthermore, he stated, "the anxiety and sense of helplessness generated by the dangers of our time may be focused in some degree on marijuana, driving some people to protective immersion in the drug and arousing others to crusade against it."[53]

Talbott and Teague, however, saw things differently. "The environment of a war zone makes the symptomatology (of cannabis intoxication) potentially more dangerous," i.e., walking into a mine field or having a loaded weapon readily available. "Similarly," they admit, "the same environment may have an effect on the nature of the symptoms."[54]

The men Talbott saw were twelve soldiers between the ages of nineteen and twenty-six who had never smoked cannabis prior to their adverse reaction. Since most men who react badly to drugs in Vietnam are handled, as they are in the United States, by buddies who use time and patience for the sobering up, doctors seldom see other than those individuals who are totally out of control. Such was the case here.

"Physicians in Vietnam have been impressed by the severity and frequency of adverse reactions to smoking cannabis derivatives," they note, citing the published observations of Fidaleo,[55] Neiman,[56] Postel,[57] and Casper.[58] "During the early part of 1967," they stated, "we saw several cases of perplexing psychotic reactions which cleared in one to four days and a few which last a week or longer."[59]

To study adverse reactions to cannabis more fully, the authors made two independent examinations of the subjects. The clinical course of each soldier was followed closely by both physicians. This is what they found. In twelve men, only two of whom showed evidence of any previous mental or social problems, the usual first symptoms of adverse or undesirable reaction to use were burning and irritation of the respiratory tract accompanied by an urge to cough. Soon, thereafter, the men noted impaired coordination and difficulty with fine movements. Then, odd, irregular, and vague aching of the large muscles of the extremities, especially the legs, and eye irritation occurred.

"Impaired cognitive functioning [i.e., the ability to reason, to understand, to be aware and to perceive] was also present in each soldier," the authors noted. "This included impairment of orientation to either time or place; severe impairment of memory, most particularly of recent memory; impairment of intellectual functioning manifested by confusion, short attention span, and difficulty concentrating; impaired thinking with tangential and disjointed qualities; and impaired judgment."[60]

"The twelve exhibited liability of affect and marked anxiety and fearfulness. Ten showed paranoid symptoms including suspiciousness, referentiality and delusions or hallucinations. Expressed fear of overt homosexual assault on the patient was frequently a factor in bringing the soldier to the medical facility." These problems seemed to be short lived, however, and the men returned to active duty within one week.

The authors were far from "bluenosed" in their attitude towards pot. "Smoking marijuana for most persons is a pleasant, nonthreatening and egosyntonic experience," they admitted. "The degree of intoxication, pleasure and mystical experience is variable and depends on the individual's personality, the existing emotional set before and in regard to the experience, and the amount of marijuana smoked or swallowed."[61]

But these authors are in the field and see the undesirable things that occur. They continued, as do few popular writers, to take a close look at both sides. "Adverse reactions to marijuana," they state, "are also varied, but the experiences are generally unpleasant, threatening, and ego-dystonic. Symptoms include, anxiety, fear, tachycardia, dyspnea, crying, depression, suspicion, dissociation, depersonalization, disorientation, confusion, paranoid ideation, delusions, and auditory hallucinations."[62]

"Cannabis derivatives," they report, noting that cases which reach civilian hospitals and are misdiagnosed may be more numerous than suspected, "as a causal or precipitating agent, should be considered whenever a young person presents an acute toxic psychosis with paranoid features. Since possession of the drug is illegal, accurate histories may not be obtainable, but the physician must be alert to the possibility of marijuana psychosis in cases resembling acute schizophrenic reaction, acute paranoid psychosis, or acute toxic-metabolic psychosis."[63]

As we shall note in Chapter Eight, marijuana in the military is becoming a major problem. Much of this, understandably, is unpublicized. Enough has been written about the situation, however, to indicate it has reached critical proportions.

In mid 1969, this author was approached by an armed services defense council for assistance in defending a nineteen-year-old serviceman accused of homicide while under the influence of marijuana. The situation involved three men on guard duty in Vietnam who became bored with the inactivity and went up on pot for emotional relief. The serviceman in question became increasingly paranoid to the point where he was certain his buddies were trying to kill him. In what he believed was self-defense he took his .45 and shot them both dead. Defense was trying to show the man was innocent because he could not think properly under the influence of the drug.

As time progresses, more and more information concerning psychotic reactions is accumulating. Klee recently wrote a long case study of a twenty-six-year-old man with no previous history of mental illness, who developed an acute psychosis after smoking less than two marijuana cigarettes.[64] He was equally inept with alcohol. "Although some people appear to use marijuana with apparently little or no harm," Klee notes, "there can be no doubt that this drug, on occasion, can precipitate psychiatric disturbances. This case is only one of the more flagrant examples. There are many others to be observed in everyday clinical experience and still others in the literature. "Prolonged psychotic reactions can also be precipitated by cannabis," Klee notes, "as can depressions and apathy. There may also be consequences of other behavior often associated with the use of cannabis. . . ."[65]

Klee further observes that although research may fail to show immediate ill effects, only the irresponsible will conclude that marijuana is therefore totally safe. Referring to the Weil report, which has been frequently misinterpreted by some media, he notes, "It is not remarkable . . . that such subjects [17 healthy young males screened to eliminate mental or physical defect] smoking two marijuana cigarettes under controlled laboratory conditions, did not suffer extreme reactions. By a similar type of reasoning one might conclude from observing an average cocktail party that alcohol is innocuous."[66]

Six additional adverse mental reactions to cannabis were reported early in 1969 by Grossman in young Americans who were using ganja, a relatively potent form of Cannabis indica.[67] The reactions in general were similar to those described by Talbott and by most other investigators who clinically treat adverse reactions to cannabis. "As evidence of the psychotogenic capacity of substances such as LSD, STP and amphetamines increases, concern has been generated as to the possibility of similar complications arising from the use of cannabis products," Grossman says. "The need for more research in this area has been emphasized," he notes, citing various references, "and some recent reports may indicate that cannabis is not as benign as many of its supporters claim."

"Although current evidence by no means constitutes proof of a causal role for cannabis in emotional disturbance," he says, ". . . until there is further and definitive information as to the effects of cannabis products on the mental health of those who use them, a cautious attitude towards their widespread and unsupervised use is justified."[68]

Reports describing clinically observed adverse psychological effects secondary to the use of pot are becoming numerous. Johnson reported a case of a severe bad trip in a college student.[69] Perna cites the experience of a twenty-three-year-old in which, she feels, there was a causal relationship between his use of cannabis and subsequent delusions and psychosis.[70]

Keeler has reported numerous problems associated with the use of cannabis by students, citing, in one paper, eleven distinct disruptions in their value judgment and ability to relate to currently accepted reality.[71] Farnsworth has cited similar unfortunate experiences occurring in students under his care at Harvard

University, some of whom nearly committed suicide once their inhibitions were released and their previous intent fortified.[72]

One, a twenty-one-year-old woman, whose choice of male friends caused "fighting" with her mother, began to drink to excess, renounced her religion, and became promiscuous. "When she became fearful of the effects of drinking she began smoking marijuana regularly. She then became depressed. To combat her depression she used more and more marijuana and, on one occasion, after smoking an unusual amount, slashed her wrists and was admitted to a hospital. Under psychotherapy she improved, stopped using drugs and resumed effective academic work."

In another instance, "a nineteen-year-old man with high moral standards became depressed, used marijuana to combat an acute depressive episode, experienced 'black despair,' and then obtained sedative pills from a friend which he took in an attempt at suicide. After admission to a hospital and subsequent treatment for his depression, he improved and has resumed his studies."

Did marijuana "cause" the suicidal attempts? No. Did it play a role? Quite probably. Dr. Michael Peck, a staff psychologist at the Los Angeles Suicide Prevention Center, warns adults not to ignore the basic needs of the unhappy youngster; not to blame drug usage for loneliness and alienation. These conditions, not the drug per se, he feels, cause a youth to attempt to escape problems through suicide.[73] Yet drug use, particularly the abuse of reality-changing drugs, is a symbolic type of suicide in itself. "For the very young," notes Dr. Richard Seiden, "death is equated with running away or escaping an unbearable situation. Without the realization that death is final, a child measures his own life's value with a defective yardstick."[74]

The most frequent reason given by young children for their suicidal behavior is revenge on a parent. "If I die, then my parents will feel sorry, they think," states pediatrician Reginal S. Lourie, but "what they really want is parental love and attention."[75] And so the child reaches for some way out. But does he wish to die? More likely he tries to tell a hostile world through his actions that what he needs is help in order to live.

How critical is the problem? Suicide accounts for one death in 200,000 youths between the ages of 10 and 14. Between the ages of 15 and 19 the rate increases eight- to ten-fold. By age 20 to 24 the *completed* suicide rate doubles again. Twelve percent of all suicide attempts in the United States are made by adolescents. Ninety percent of these are made by teenage girls. It is significant, however, that fewer than one-tenth of these would-be suicides actually kill themselves.[76]

How hopeful is the situation if the youth becomes hung up on a mind-altering drug? What role specifically does cannabis play? One can't answer this, other than to offer opinion and observation, because the standards of laboratory "proof" cannot apply to these labile situations. But the trend described in cases such as those presented elsewhere by Farnsworth may be related to warnings offered by seasoned experimenters or observers in the field of cannabis investigation.

"A man will never escape from his destined physical and moral temperament," Baudelaire noted nearly a century ago. "Hashish will be a mirror of his impressions and private thoughts, a magnifying mirror, it is true, but only a mirror. . . ." The cannabis trip, he stated, "will always retain the private tonality of the individual. The man wanted the dream," he remarked regretfully," now the dream will govern the man."[77]

Hashish. "Good" grass. Adverse reactions from "mild" grass. How great is the difference? How can you be sure? Most trips are good? Probably! But when they turn sour, how can we justify the results? With this in mind, let's pose a hypothetical question. Did sixteen-year-old Joe kill himself because of the effects of cannabis? Or did the cannabis exaggerate pathological thoughts in his mind? Or did the weed have any influence at all? How do we know?

"The sharp increase in attempted suicide at puberty has been linked to the stresses and strains of adolescence particularly to conflicts over sexuality and dependency," notes psychologist Michael Peck. "Self-destruction may be precipitated by crisis in sexual identity or concern about possible homosexual tendencies, deeply disturbing to the adolescent."[78]

How about Joe? How do you ask him, now that he's gone?

THE PROPER MANAGEMENT OF BAD TRIPS

An increasing number of medical papers are attempting to advise others as to the proper management of bad drug trips.

Weil has recently dedicated one full paper to the complications of the use of cannabis, and while he properly stresses they are rare in comparison to the number of trips taken, the problem is of sufficient importance to devote time and space to its study.[79]

Weil's paper, primarily directed towards physicians, notes that proper medical response may well determine the seriousness and length of the reaction. In other words, a physician not acquainted with the management of bad trips may make the situation worse by mismanagement. The importance of proper diagnosis becomes more important as the number of marijuana users and the corresponding number of adverse reactions increase.

Weil, recognizing it is only the more severe reactions that reach a physician, divides adverse reactions into three categories for treatment purposes. The first, "simple depressive reactions" are more or less self-contained crises and will pass if the patient is reassured and encouraged. Weil, who seems less critical of cannabis than some, is impressed that the 20 patients he studied and reported in this particular paper took the weed as an excuse to become depressed, concluding that cannabis per se had nothing to do with the depressive reaction.

Weil's second category involves panic reactions, which he feels account for more than 75 percent of the reactions he has encountered. As previously noted, these seem to be caused by the individual's inability to "flow" with the trip, and are augmented if the subject feels threatened physically, mentally, or socially. The reactions vary from locale to locale, he notes. If marijuana is frequently used as a social lubricant in an area, the reactions should be less than in a situation where the experience is novel and unguided. Treatment of such reactions involves reassurance and interest and, in the case of physicians, proper diagnosis and the avoidance of contraindicated procedures.

Weil's third group consists of toxic psychoses, which he feels are temporary malfunctions of the frontal part of the brain, caused by the presence of marijuana toxins. Weil has encountered ten of these to the date of his paper and noted that, in his experience, they usually occurred from ingestion, not from smoking. The patients are delirious, have a high fever, are disoriented, confused, often prostrate, and have visual and auditory hallucinations. Weil thinks treatment here should be supportative with little or no medication. "However serious such a reaction may appear," he advises doctors, "the physician should remember that literature on cannabis does not report a single fatal case due to the drug." This is almost but not totally correct.

Weil also notes that adverse reactions can occur in patients with no history of mental disorder: some incur "flashbacks," some have delayed psychotic reactions to previously ingested hallucinogenic drugs. These, he notes, can be quite serious. In some cases, the delayed psychotic reactions have "clearly been triggered by acute marijuana intoxication," although, he states, "there is no way of knowing whether they would have happened anyway."

Taylor, Maurer, and Tinklenberg have also offered advice on the management of bad drug trips.[80] "A wide variation of mental states ranging in severity from mild apprehension to severe panic may be seen in persons undergoing bad trips," they note. "Perceptual changes, such as illusions and hallucinations, are usually present and can be terrifying. A person may feel that he is going to 'lose control' or 'never come back.' Severe feelings of depersonalization or even total loss of one's sense of identity may appear. Gross distortions of body image such as the sensation that one's 'brain is melting' may be present. But these same sensations that are experienced by one individual as extremely threatening may be experienced by another as mystical or beautiful."

Taylor and his associates are discussing bad trips on hallucinogens in general and not cannabis in particular, although the advice holds true for most such drugs. "Establishment of verbal contact with the minimum use of tranquilizers should be a fundamental rule in the management of 'bad trips'." They advise, ". . . reassurance and repetitive defining of reality often prove to be adequate treatment."

The group encourages the therapist, the buddy in the pad, or the doctor in the hospital to emphasize the fact that the distortions and frightening feelings of the experience are due to the drug and not to impending insanity. Furthermore, the subject should be reassured that this experience is only temporary and will shortly pass with no after-effects.

"For a panicked 'bad tripper'," Taylor notes, "it can be very reassuring to be repeatedly told his name, that he is in a hospital bed, and in such and such city. Concrete labeling," they state in their advice to doctors, "helps the patient reassemble his reality, allowing him to firmly establish that he is indeed a real person experiencing a drug-induced 'bad trip' that is time-limited."

"While a person 'comes down'," they warn, "he experiences a phasic 'in and out' alternation of mental clarity and confusion. This should be expected and predicted by the therapist. Reassurance should include making explicit this waxing and waning of awareness. The physician should make certain that a patient who evidently has come down is truly 'all the way down,' not just in a temporary or transient clear spell."

Margolis uses a more "pad" level approach to the subject, and while he keeps arguing that adverse reactions seldom occur, he nevertheless offers some interesting advice for those who find themselves exceptions.[81] "The first sign of depression or anxiety," he states, "is often a feeling of nausea." If this starts, he suggests, "simply begin thinking of something specific. Anything will do. Focus your mind on externals, or on a pleasant thought. The nausea will usually disappear."

". . . [I]t may be difficult to get yourself out of a bad trip," Margolis admits, "but [it] is relatively easy to help someone else. So, if you're going through a bad scene and you're alone, call up a friend and tell him what's wrong. Just talking about it will help tremendously."

How about the situation where someone is really in trouble? "You have two choices," Margolis says. "Let him go through the bad trip in the hopes that although he'll be very uncomfortable, he may gain some insight into what is causing him to be frightened or depressed; or, get him out of it."

Margolis, not a physician, at this point makes a suggestion that could result in death! "The first thing is to give him some tranquilizers," he states. In contrast, Weil and Taylor *both advise against unwarranted use of drugs in managing the bad trip.* Taylor's group noted that it is possible the phenothiazines, i.e., Thorazine-like drugs, which, incidentally, may precipitate some real problems on their own, may act like long-acting sedatives, rather than tranquilizers, and thus prolong the trip. To eliminate this, they have substituted short-acting barbiturates and have initially found them "promising."

Margolis notes that whatever is bothering the subject is not as terrible or as immediate as he believes; thus a friend can use suggestion to bring him out of it. Remind him, he suggests, that he has smoked a lot of grass and that weed distorts reality. Dis-tract him away from his thoughts. Tell him an exciting bit of news or gossip. Put on some pushy music or show him an intricate picture.

Another useful approach, he states, is to change the environment. Turn up the lights if the room is dark or vice versa. Take him for a walk or go into a different location. "Be interested in him," he says emphasizing a critical point, "don't ignore him, and keep up a steady stream of babbling." If he isn't interested in what you have to say, Margolis says, paralleling Taylor's advice, ". . . get him to talk about what is bothering him. He will usually do this fairly readily, especially if you convince him that by talking about it, he'll get through the bad feelings it's causing him."

"All you have to say," he assures, "is 'Look, you're not interested right now in anything except what's bothering you. I can get you out of it. Tell me what it is and we'll talk about it. Maybe it's the same hangup I've got'." You should, most of all, be calm, Margolis advises. Treat the problem logically. And if all this doesn't work, then call a mutual friend whom both user and buddy respect, preferably one who has a natural knack for making people feel better.

Most bad trips, Margolis states accurately, are self-limited. "Both good and bad emotional states may seem to be strong and external, but they are only transitory, lasting only until the stoned condition passes." He puts the time interval at three to four hours, which is a reasonable estimate for most trips—a point that is reassuring in itself. Sadly, Margolis overlooks the fact that in true bad trips, psychiatric care and/or hospitalization may be necessary. By failing to advise those who may rely solely on his book for advice in trying times of this important fact, he may have performed a real disservice to the pot-oriented counterculture.

So, "pot can't hurt you." Well, as a matter of fact the percentages may be in your favor. You as a reader at least now know some things you might not have considered before. You may be aided in making personal decisions. Having explored these areas, we can now turn to some of the arguments, the things people prefer to discuss, rather than study pharmacology. There are now five major areas of public debate and concern. These will be discussed one by one in the following chapter.

"No pot for me, thanks. I'll just get drunk like the
good Lord intended me to."

the
major
controversies

8

There are no whole truths;
    all truths are half truths.
It is trying to treat them as
    whole truths that plays the devil.
           ALFRED WHITEHEAD

*W*E HAVE LOOKED AT THE FACTS: Cannabis
is a weed with psychoactive properties in its resin. For some
3,000 years, men of various cultures have used it to heighten
perception and release inhibitions. It has been and still is a religious sacrament in the East. In America it currently seems to be
becoming the rallying symbol of the drug counterculture and
the turned-on generation. In this latter role cannabis has sparked
a widespread controversy in the United States. Indeed, it is this
debate that interests most people, whichever side they take,
and it is this controversy that will engage our attention in this
chapter.

The arguments raised for and against cannabis are legion.
Many of the specific questions are taken up in the appendix
(question-and-answer) section. But the major questions center

around five areas of concern, each having to do with the relation of cannabis to some other area of activity. Four of these controversies are chronic and are concerned with the cannabis-alcohol comparison, the cannabis-tobacco comparison, the relation of cannabis to crime, and the relation of cannabis to violence. In recent months a fifth problem has appeared: the use of cannabis by the United States Armed Forces. Let us look at each in turn.

CANNABIS AND ALCOHOL

The attempt to compare alcohol and cannabis has involved far more energy than it deserves. It is impractical to try to compare the two; pharmacologically, they are quite different. This difference has been helpful to debaters, because it is impossible to reach a conclusion, and thus the argument can continue while the important issues are avoided.

Alcohol *can* harm the body. After many decades of use, we now face the unavoidable fact that the abuse of alcohol can seriously damage the body, especially the liver and the brain. This fact does not deter the alcohol-using population from enjoying its drug. For many, the issue fails to register on their minds. One would think, therefore, that this group would be highly sympathetic to the pot-using segment of our nation, since the attitudes of the two groups tend to be nearly identical. Unfortunately, alcohol users lack such insight; they frequently deplore the abuse of cannabis by their offspring. Young people, on the other hand, point to the drug habits of their parents, and decry their hypocrisy. The result is an impasse. The winner, if any, in this controversy would have only a pyrrhic victory; the loser will not accede. Trying to equate alcohol and pot, in hopes of villifying one to the exclusion of the other, is a hopeless task. The adult who badgers his pot-using son, while he holds a martini in one hand and a cigarette in the other, has convinced only himself.

The cannabis-alcohol argument, as it relates to physical effects, is not all onesided. Contrary to popular opinion cannabis *does* cause physical harm. The drug is highly irritating to the respiratory system. Increasingly, reports are accumulating in the files of physicians treating pulmonary problems, to indicate that the use of pot aggravates pre-existing respiratory diseases *and* is capable of precipitating *new* ones. Cannabis use also seems to have an adverse effect on the body's immunity mechanisms. Scientists have some evidence of this, but with justifiable scientific caution, they are waiting to render a definitive opinion, until they have more proof. Street users are less hesitant. "Heck," a young potsmoker told this author, "most of us know it's hard to get over a cold, if in fact we don't catch more colds, when we're smoking grass. But we sort of accept this as a price to pay for the enjoyment we get."

The use of grass also produces adverse effects on the gastrointestinal system. There is now some evidence that it may affect the liver. It is not true, therefore, that pot can't hurt one physically.

Both alcohol and cannabis have psychological effects on the user. Both may directly affect the brain. Many pot enthusiasts attempt to confuse this issue by arguing that adverse psychological effects occurring in marijuana users happen because those users were unstable anyway. It is specious thinking to assume that a potent mind-altering substance cannot be held responsible for adverse effects because the user had pre-existing problems. That is to assume that the drugs in cannabis are pharmacologically inert, which of course, is not true. It can be argued that in many cases, marijuana use has only augmented pre-existing problems, but when this argument is used, it is seldom admitted that the pre-existing problems might never have become a handicap were it not for the drug's precipitation of the adverse effects.

If one is being logical, he will not argue which of two unrelated drugs is the most harmful. Instead, he will consider which drug increases the chance that a given personality will sustain adverse effects from the drug's use. "An argument about the relative dangers of alcohol and marijuana can get the discussion off on a wrong track," notes Samuel Grafton.[1] Alcohol is unquestionably a very dangerous drug. But that doesn't shed any light on marijuana. It took many, many years to discover the full and precise effects of alcohol abuse; controlled research on marijuana has scarcely begun. Yet the argument continues on two issues: first, that the drugs are comparable and therefore should be treated equally; second, that the effects of being drunk on booze can be related to the effects of a mild high on grass.

Even if the argument were honest and the drugs were compared at the same levels of intoxication, the highs are in no way similar. "A pot high is quite different from a liquor high," an observant user told *Time* magazine.[2] "Alcohol dulls the senses whereas pot sets them on edge. If a child were screaming in the next room, I'd take a drink not a joint. If I were sitting with an arm around Jane Fonda and she had just told me I had beautiful eyes, I'd light up. Drink is for tuning out. Pot is for tuning in . . . ."

As for trying to compare the drugs pharmacologically, Wilson notes, "It is a pharmacological principle that many fallacies may arise if drugs whose mechanisms of action are known to be different are compared from quantitative and qualitative aspects . . . comparisons are [usually] made between the pharmacological and toxicological effects of cannabis and alcohol, cannabis and heroin, and cannabis and tobacco. Such comparisons are scientifically invalid and are not based on any acceptable pharmacological methods of comparison."[3]

Grinspoon, in defense of cannabis, notes quite accurately that "the habit called social drinking is considered as American as apple pie, and it receives about as much public acceptance," despite the fact that insurance statistics indicate that social drinkers have "considerably higher than average mortality rates from all the leading causes of death: diseases of the heart and circulatory system, cancer, diseases of the digestive system, homicides, suicides, and motor vehicle and other accidents."[4] Grinspoon also notes that the "still powerful vestige of the Protestant ethic" in the U.S. "condemns marijuana as an opiate used solely for the pursuit of pleasure (whereas alcohol is accepted because it lubricates the wheels of commerce and catalyzes social intercourse.)"[5]

A number of investigators have noted that as youths in late adolescence and in the early twenties turn to marijuana as a socio-relaxant, their intake of alcohol drops. This was particularly noticeable in the Haight-Ashbury section of San Francisco among so-called "hippie" advocates of pot.[6] The correlation seems, at times, to disturb the alcoholic beverage industry, which recently used its public relations experts to produce a bulletin on the "facts" about pot and booze.[7] Here is part of their analysis of the situation: "Youngsters see their parents, adults see their friends, use alcoholic beverages with enjoyment and without harmful effect. To suggest, therefore, that using marijuana is no more dangerous than drinking, rather than discouraging drinking, will only serve to encourage use of marijuana."[8]

In this interesting concept the alcohol industry is correct but for a reason not their own. Seeing the havoc wrecked on this nation by alcohol, and often failing to see comparable effects from the use of pot, youth may indeed tend to put one down in favor of the other. If they do, the alcohol industry will feel the effects. To counter these effects they offer arguments such as these:

"Those who suggest that using marijuana is no more harmful than drinking are doing a dangerous disservice to the public, particularly to the youth of this country."[9] Roughly translated this means, "Hey man, you're hurting my business . . . Cool it."

Actually, the alcohol industry has little to worry about. From what we know about the youthful abuser of heroin, amphetamines, marijuana, and other drugs, he tends (if he continues his drug abuse pattern) to become the alcoholic of the age forty to fifty group. Alcohol usually serves as the final common pathway for drug dependency. Thus, if those in the alcohol industry will only bide their time, the potheads of today may be among their heaviest customers within a few decades.

"There's neither social nor scientific basis on which to equate the use of marijuana with that of alcoholic beverages, the bulletin continues."[10] Scientifically, the comparison is inaccurate, but socially, the problems are similar. With caution and reasonably good sense, casual use of either drug seems to produce minimal effects. If one gets stoned on either, trouble can occur.

"Beverage alcohol plays an important role in the lives of many Americans. It is often considered essential for hospitality and its use as a 'social lubricant' is well known,"[11] says the bulletin.

If the use of alcohol is considered essential, it is because of a continued multimillion dollar campaign to make the public dependent on it. As for using alcohol as a "social lubricant," one of the easiest ways to compound one's problems is to get "lubed" at the wrong time with the wrong people. To defend one of these drugs over the other, therefore, or to deny that social use of either without reasonable precaution is similar, is the height of rationalization.

The alcohol-cannabis argument cannot be ignored, however,

because it is a mainstay of the currently popular game of "expert witness." To examine the effects of the argument on youth, let us look at the testimony of Dr. David E. Smith, Assistant Clinical Professor of Toxicology at the San Francisco Medical Center of the University of California and director of the Haight-Ashbury Clinic in San Francisco. Dr. Smith is probably in closer contact with socially dissociated and drug-using youth than any other physician in the United States. In 1968, he testified before a California State Assembly committee[12] that alcohol is as dangerous as marijuana and marijuana as dangerous as alcohol. Further, he noted that the alcohol argument has caused many young people to distrust all drug information given them by authorities; they believe the authorities follow a double standard when it comes to alcohol versus cannabis. Some of the original Haight-Ashbury users went so far as to suspect that news releases on the chromosomal destructive effects of LSD were nothing more than a government plot to keep them from enjoying their drug.

Dr. Smith noted that, at its zenith, the use of drugs in the "Hashbury" was so widespread that forty percent of the people he interviewed admitted they had swallowed pills without having any idea what they were. Ninety five percent said they had used cannabis; ninety percent said they used it regularly. In this admittedly drug-oriented community eighty percent of the young people said that they were drinking alcohol when they arrived. After a time only fiften percent continued to drink it. The others considered it a dangerous drug. The group involved was between ages fifteen and twenty-five, with a median age of twenty years. Those who continued to drink, and in many cases therefore violated the alcohol laws, were rarely arrested for this offense, since police seemed primarily interested in apprehending cannabis and other drug violators. Nevertheless, alcohol consumption was not an important part of the activity of the community in the Haight-Ashbury district during its peak years as America's drug use center. Neither is it the drug chosen today in those communities which "splintered" away from the original "Hashbury" concept.

According to Dr. Smith, the legality of alcohol versus the illegality of cannabis has created hostility and resentment among cannabis users. Many drug-using youths today consider themselves a minority that is being set upon by members of the Establishment intent upon retaining alcohol and tobacco for themselves, while denying the use of cannabis to others.

Even more interesting are recent findings which suggest that the use of alcohol by parents may be a critical factor in precipitating the abuse of other drugs by their children. According to Jim Velleman and Ted Lawrence, who conducted a survey among upper-middle-class high school students in Port Washington, Long Island, New York, parents' drinking habits not only influenced the drug habits of their children, but the number of drinks the parents took and the number of times they got drunk were especially important. They found that "those who said their mothers had ever been drunk had a significantly greater tendency to be drug users than those whose mothers had never been drunk."[13] These findings coincide with those noted by Smith in the "Hashbury," a community where members also often rebelled against their parents and backgrounds through a change in life style and the use of drugs.

Can alcohol be defended in our society? There are some arguments in its favor. It has significant industrial and medicinal applications, whereas cannabis, at the moment, has little or none. In addition, properly or improperly, it has been chosen by the incumbent adult majority as a pharmacological escape mechanism. We care enough about it to endure immense social and economic costs and to contend with the problems it produces.

The cost of this luxury is high. Some seventy million Americans drink regularly; nine million of these are alcoholic. If one looks down a row to the fifteenth person in an average audience, Dr. Max Hayman recently noted, "that person will be an alcoholic.[14] If one counts down to the fifth person, this one's life will be adversely affected in one way or another by an alcoholic. If you now look at the intervening persons, the fourth will be an abstainer and the rest will drink varying amounts of liquor. Again, every fifth person will be a heavy drinker, and if the audience is composed of doctors, one in 100 will be lost to the profession because of drinking. Furthermore an unknown number will be handicapped in their work because of drinking."

One out of three arrests is for drunkenness; one out of four male admissions to mental hospitals is for alcoholism.[15] The chance is that one out of every ten cars one passes will be driven by a drunken driver. The National Safety Council estimates that liquor causes property damage on the highways in excess of four billion dollars a year. Approximately 30,000 people die each year in auto accidents related to alcohol. Absenteeism due to alcohol costs industry over eight billion dollars a year. Furthermore, seventy-five percent of the domestic-relations actions brought into court have alcoholism as one of the contributing factors.

Alcohol is a depressant of the central nervous system. Chemically, it produces psychological dependence, tolerance, physical dependence, and acute withdrawal symptoms in the addicted.

These are all facts. To deny or distort them is to confirm the charges of hypocrisy and double-dealing so often made by the pro-cannabis forces. But it does not automatically follow from these facts that alcohol constitutes a greater social danger than marijuana, or that the general comparison of alcohol and marijuana is meaningful and logically compelling.

We need not anticipate a sudden upsurge in the membership of the WCTU by reform-minded hippies, because the real reason for the drug community's alcohol attack and comparison has little to do with concern for alcoholism or its evils. It is a case of special pleading and question-begging. The attack on alcohol implicitly acknowledges the evils of cannabis and goes on to urge that we let two wrongs make a right. The fact is that alcoholism is a different problem with an entirely different ethos and history. What to do about alcoholism cannot be discussed here, but we should understand that legalization of cannabis will in no way alleviate the problems of alcoholism. It may, in fact, ultimately compound the alcohol problem as pot users grow older and seek the common denominator (alcohol) of the American drug scene.

It is an interesting fact that alcohol and cannabis have rarely coexisted in the same culture. In the East, where alcohol has long been frowned upon or outlawed, cannabis has been a religious sacrament. In the West, alcohol, in the form of sacramental wine, has been tied with religious activities. Cannabis has always been alien to the Judeo-Christian world. In this sense our society has been opposed to the use of cannabis, often without realizing why, on purely religious grounds.

H. B. Murphy makes another point as to why cannabis is so regularly banned in countries where alcohol is permitted.

One of the reasons, he feels, is the positive value placed on action, and the hostility toward passivity. "In Anglo-Saxon cultures," Murphy says, "inaction is looked down on and often feared, whereas overactivity, aided by alcohol or independent of alcohol, is considerably tolerated despite the social disturbance produced. It may be that we can ban cannabis simply because the people who use it, or would do so, carry little weight in social matters and are relatively easy to control; whereas the alcohol user often carries plenty of weight in social matters and is difficult to control, as the United States prohibition era showed. It has yet to be shown, however, that the one is more socially or personally disruptive than the other."[16]

Murphy's statement is largely true, and has not been denied in this study, but perhaps it should be rephrased to induce the recognition that one drug is *as* socially and personally disruptive as the other. The question is whether we, as a nation, can afford a second drug catastrophe. If we had never known the pleasant effects of alcohol, it would have been easier to enforce the Eighteenth Amendment (the Volstead Act). But we were fully aware of these effects many years before Americans became upset about the adverse effects of alcoholism, just as people in the East were aware of the pleasures of cannabis long before the present restrictive laws were passed outlawing cannabis use in any major country in the world. One can expect, therefore, that enforcement of these anti-cannabis laws in the Orient will meet with the same resistance that prohibition encountered in the United States.

The "two wrongs" philosophy is not properly applicable to the cannabis-alcohol argument concerning unequal attitudes toward the two drugs. The ideal and reasonable approach is not to legalize pot but to prohibit the abuse of alcohol. Try it. That's the whole point. Two wrongs in legislation may not make a right, but neither does the presence of one wrong, now no longer correctable, justify committing the same type of error again merely because the current situation cannot be justified in debate.

We cannot excuse alcohol, but neither should we forget that the comparison argument is disingenuous at best and certainly not logically compelling. But since the comparison will repeatedly be made, it is important to bear in mind that, similar as some of the effects of alcohol and cannabis are, there are others that are quite dissimilar. Such dissimilarities do not strengthen the case for cannabis. Let us also remember that we have abundant evidence on the effects of alcohol and that we know with some certainty the full range of these effects. Such is not the case with cannabis. What evidence we have in the United States, and it is grim enough, is based on the use of relatively mild forms of cannabis. There is no reason to assume, if the cannabis habit spreads through legalization or other means, that the only types of cannabis that will be used are mexicana, and, occasionally, americana. There is every reason to suppose that there would be a special premium on *Cannabis indica*, Vietnamese grass, and other more potent varieties, much as there is on the more potent forms of alcohol. So far, we have been in the "beer and wine" stage of cannabis use. The "whiskey" stage is likely to prove even more disturbing.

CANNABIS AND TOBACCO

Pro-cannabis people often compare marijuana to tobacco for the same reasons they compare it to alcohol. Many of the same rebuttals apply.

The pro-cannabis case is stated by writer Antoni Gollan: "There is growing speculation within medical circles that cannabis may be no more dangerous than tobacco or liquor. These two substances are widely used in the United States." He continues: "We smoke, many of us, cigarettes conveniently packaged by R. J. Reynolds, P. Lorrillard and the gang. We continue to inhale nicotine fumes despite the reported cancerous malignancies, destruction of lung cells, heart disease—despite evidence that smoking may interrupt life, and cancel the added years offered by the last half-century of medical science."

Gollan also points to the quasi-addictive nature of tobacco. "Smokers," he says, "develop psychological dependence on, and mild physical addiction to cigarettes. Ever try to quit smoking? The ordeal demands rigid self-discipline, and the withdrawal symptoms are nervousness and irritability."[17] But the chances of outlawing smoking, Gollan believes, are slim. He quotes U. S. Surgeon General Dr. William H. Stewart: "With forty percent of the population smoking, I don't think the public would stand up for a ban. We had one experience with Prohibition and I think it would, based on that experience, have the same kind of result."[18]

Now, again it is necessary to speak plainly about tobacco. It is a problem, although of a quite different nature from cannabis. Senator Robert F. Kennedy, speaking to the World Conference on Smoking and Health, on September 11, 1967, delivered a mass of statistics about the evils of tobacco: over a quarter of a million premature deaths each year are attributed to diseases associated with cigarette smoking; one-third of all male deaths between the ages of thirty-five and sixty come from diseases associated with cigarette smoking. Eleven million other persons have chronic diseases in the cigarette-smoking population. Death from lung cancer is increasing almost geometrically—from about 2,500 in 1930, shortly after smoking started becoming a national habit, to 50,000 today. If present rates continue, one-seventh of all Americans now alive—about twenty-eight million people—will die prematurely of diseases associated with cigarette smoking.

And there are many more statistics of the same sort. Senator Kennedy asserted that cigarettes would long since have been banned were it not for the power of the tobacco industry. He said: "If the cigarette industry's economic power were as miniscule as that of the marijuana industry, cigarettes would surely be illegal now and their sale subject to severe penalty as a health hazard." He concluded: "The cigarette companies have demonstrated a total inattention to public responsibility. But it is also a reflection on our society, on all of us, that cigarette smoking has been permitted to continue in our various countries. There is no reason for another generation of mankind to end up disabled and the victim of premature death. We must act and act now."[19]

It should be clear, as it should have been in the case of alcohol, that not all of the Establishment has a special interest in maintaining a privileged status for tobacco. But more important, it should be clear that the evil effects of tobacco do not excuse the use of marijuana. The same illogic that couples alcohol abuse with an appeal to legalize marijuana is operating in the case of tobacco, although the links are even more tenuous and the parallels more farfetched.

The ill effects of tobacco use are primarily medical, those of cannabis primarily social, although cannabis enjoys the distinction of having certain medical ill effects as well. Apart from the fact that most cannabis used in the United States is smoked, there seems, on the surface, to be little connection between marijuana and tobacco usage. Interestingly, some experts argue that cigarette smoking may lead to the use of marijuana. One of these, Tinklenberg,[20] cites two reasons for his stand. First, we have some direct systematic evidence to support the contention that tobacco smoking may encourage the use of pot. Second, the principle of modality generalization should apply as it does in the case of other psychoactive drugs. That is, if an individual has learned to derive pleasure from smoking one drug, it is likely that he will use other drugs by smoking them.

Where the tobacco-cannabis argument is raised, it is important to note the following comparisons of the two drugs: The tobacco smoker may suffer a lethal influence on his physical health; the cannabis smoker may suffer an insidious devastation of his mind and the development of an amotivational syndrome. Further, there is rarely a severe intoxication with tobacco; the effects are cumulative and ultimately chronic. Cannabis, however, presents an acute toxicity syndrome that manifests its results both immediately and cumulatively.

Max Miller notes some of these differences in his excellent film "Marijuana." No one has ever dropped out of school because of his addiction to tobacco, he says; no one who just smoked a cigarette ever forgot he was driving a car and began tripping on a cloud or a flashing light in the distance; and no cigarette salesman ever tried to induce a buyer to take up the heroin needle. Further, as Miller notes, one can smoke cigarettes and do many other useful and productive things even while smoking. Marijuana, however, absorbs the full time and attention of the user, at least while he is using, and sometimes the effects recur when he is not using.[21]

Tobacco interests, whether commercial or political, have much in common with the rest of the drug traffic. Tobacco has the advantage of being legal, and thus avoids the penalties involved in other types of dangerous drug peddling. Selling techniques, however, are so similar that they make one wonder who learned from whom. For pleasure and profit only, this industry aims its product at a susceptible youth, knowing that each kid hooked on its drug means a continuing income. The same techniques employed by other peddlers are used, except that the tobacco industries' seductive attempts are polished to a fine shine by Madison Avenue.

Essentially the tobacco industry's well-known approach is to associate its product with clean air, sports, and romance. All current and increasing medical reports condemning the product are dismissed as inadequate, immaterial, or non-existent. If the anti-tobacco pressure mounts too rapidly, as at the present time, economic pressure and political influence are used.

The government spends small amounts of public money in an effort to "educate" the populace not to smoke. At the same time it spends millions to subsidize the tobacco industry and keep it in good economic condition. The industry, of course, has not ignored pot. *Business Week* of September 6, 1969, noted that the tobacco companies have shown an increasing interest in the possibility of legalized cannabis.[22] The companies deny such an interest, but then, they also deny that any evidence links tobacco smoking with cancer.

Despite the irony of the United States Government's choosing to subsidize a product which its Surgeon General Jesse L. Steinfeld calls a "dirty, smelly, foul, chronic form of suicide,"[23] one should not succumb to the temptation to confuse tobacco with cannabis. Fundamentally, the two problems, tobacco and cannabis use, are different not in degree but in kind. Those who compare the two are darkening counsel, usually to gain the tactical advantage of obliging one's opponent in the debate to go on the defensive.

CANNABIS AND CRIME

At this point the initiative is taken by the anti-cannabis forces. The arguments relating to alcohol and tobacco are essentially pro-cannabis arguments designed to excuse one evil on the grounds of the acceptance of others. The arguments relating to cannabis and crime, (and cannabis and violence, which is discussed later), are essentially designed to strengthen the case against marijuana on the grounds of unsavory associations. Both pro- and anti-cannabis arguments, then are forms of guilt (or innocence) by association, with all of the dangers implicit in such argumentation. In the case of cannabis vis-à-vis liquor and tobacco, we have seen that innocence by association is not in fact proven at all, that actually the pro-cannabis spokesmen virtually admit that cannabis is undesirable and either rest content with saying, "so are alcohol and tobacco," or seek to take the offensive and argue that the existence of other evils excuses this one. We must be just as searching in our examination of the anti-cannabis arguments regarding crime and violence.

First the crime argument. Does the use of cannabis cause a person to become a criminal? To be quite clear, let us exclude from the definition of criminality, in this instance, any violation of anti-cannabis laws. Although such violations are criminal in the United States, the charge of criminality as it relates to the argument of cannabis association here has to do with crimes of violence—murder, rape, assault—and with theft. Let us also ask what is meant by "cause." Direct causal relationships are very difficult to prove. In each specific case, we must ask whether the criminal activity actually resulted from cannabis use. Then we must determine whether any association established is sufficiently widespread and frequent to justify a categorical conclusion as to a causal relationship.

Attorney Gene Haislip has argued that cannabis may stimulate criminal activity in several ways: (1) it may be used by certain criminals to fortify their courage prior to committing crimes; (2) chronic use of cannabis (usually hashish) may produce general mental derangement and demoralization leading to criminal activity; (3) pot use may cause marginally-adjusted persons to lower their inhibitions and behave in an aggressive, antisocial manner; and (4) cannabis may cause panic, confusion, or anger in otherwise normal persons who react adversely, and then behave criminally as a consequence of their mental dislocation.[24]

It is difficult to tell how many persons actually indulge in crime either aided or caused by the use of cannabis. Police files are full of cases that suggest such an association; yet one must always question whether the use of the drug was an adjunct, rather than the cause of the problem. Police and law enforcement authorities generally take the hard line that there is a causal relationship between marijuana and crime, and that the two are in any case very frequently associated.

From the medical standpoint, Murphy has itemized three situations in which cannabis may contribute to antisocial behavior, i.e., violence and criminality.[25] The first may occur when a subject unaccustomed to cannabis develops panic in response to the hallucinatory experiences caused by the drug, and in his panic may attack any object in sight. The second situation may occur during the phase of hypersensitivity and psychomotor activity when the user's reactions to unpleasant external stimuli may be stronger than usual. The third condition may occur when a person takes the drug deliberately to release repressed feelings of hostility. It should also be noted here, however, that cannabis, being unpredictable, may sedate rather than encourage hostility and violence.

Inspector Burnell Blanchard, formerly of the California Attorney General's Bureau of Narcotic Enforcement, argues insistently that the connection between cannabis and crime is not coincidental.[26] Ten years ago, Blanchard was involved in the case of an East Los Angeles gang that set fires by tossing Molotov cocktails indiscriminately at residences and business establishments. When the gang was broken up, police learned that the gang leader, known as "Duke," had drawn up elaborate plans to set a spectacular holocaust to totally destroy Los Angeles County General Hospital. The connection with cannabis was this: Duke and his gang regularly became intoxicated with marijuana before their raids. It stilled the inhibitions of those members who were sadistically violent and enabled them to carry out Duke's orders without qualms. Further, it intensified for them the exciting sensations of noise, sirens, burning fires, and general chaos that surrounded the blazes they set.

Such encounters with cannabis are extremely frequent in police work. When the police hear that "only a few" users become involved with crime, they wonder how they keep meeting that few so constantly. And in truth, there is a considerable gap between the experiences of the sociologist or psychiatrist, and those of the police on the street. It may not be so much that one or the other is wrong as that they move in different circles.

Pro-cannabis sociologist Erich Goode expresses a different view regarding this split in consciousness between police and sociologists. In a recently-published book that is highly favorable to marijuana (and was paid for in part by a U.S. government research grant),[27] he observes:

As a student of deviant or criminal behavior, the sociologist should be *at least* as acquainted as the policeman with street-level crimes, since he has access to crimes that the policeman discovers only by accident. In fact, the sociologist is in a far better position to see an accurate picture of the criminogenic effects of marijuana than the policeman, because he is around marijuana users (or should be, if he is engaged in doing research on marijuana use) all the time, when they are engaged in activities of *all* types—including crime.

The policeman, on the other hand, is *only* concerned with the criminal aspect of marijuana use, and this fact alone would necessarily exaggerate its importance. That is, after all, the only thing he sees; that is what he is *supposed* to see. The policeman sees a visible tip of a very deep iceberg, most of which is hidden from view—at least hidden from the view of the policeman. He is privileged to see only a highly biased segment of a highly complex phenomenon. Crimes, and especially violent crimes, are much more visible than noncriminal activity, and the policeman sees that segment which is most visible. We would therefore think that crime occurs among users much more than it actually does.

In addition, those users who happen to get themselves arrested for marijuana crimes (as well as for other crimes that accidentally happen to reveal marijuana possession) are more likely to be involved in other criminal activity as well. They are individuals who are likely to be less discreet about their use. They attract public attention and sanction, making them more likely to be the kind of person who attracts the attention and suspicion of the police about all kinds of activities, including non drug crimes.[28]

Goode philosophizes that police think the crime rate among users is much higher than it is because police are not in a position to see things as they really are. The police view, he states, "is highly partial and unrepresentative." In contrast, Goode believes, "the sociologist, who invades the privacy of the user and delves into any and all aspects of his life, has the chance to develop a more balanced view."[29]

It might be well to pause for a moment and reflect on this rather surprisingly compartmentalized bit of rationalization. Two disciplines are in question here: the police, who Goode seems to feel are uninformed, and the sociologist, whom he seems to laud as all-seeing and understanding. However, he overlooks the critical role of the police undercover agent, who "invades" the private lives of users and "delves" into any and all aspects of their lives more in a few short months of intensive undercover investigation than most sociologists studying marijuana could do in a lifetime (unless, of course, the sociologist in question belonged to the subculture).

To assume that many if not most enforcement officers are unaware of the change of the character of American drug users is to assume that the police are hopelessly isolated from social reality. On the contrary, police may be opinionated, but they are neither isolated nor uninformed. Some sociologists may not realize, as they investigate the private lives of drug users, that they are associating with police undercover agents. Such agents are not only capable of discerning the changing tempo of the drug scene, but they have become increasingly concerned about something else: As social scientists continue to delve into the study of mind-altering drugs, some become involved with the intriguing subculture. The immersion of some has become so deep as to make them almost undiscernable from active members of the subculture, itself. This observation is not made here in reference to any specific person, and certainly does not refer to Goode, who has performed a salutary service in communicating his observations involving the use of drugs by young Americans; it is made as a general statement about a situation that has social impact.

Police have noted with increasing alarm that some sociologists' association with the subculture may breed first awareness, then assent, and finally assimilation into the drug subculture. The situation has raised the question not only of how valuable the investigators' biased and often drug-influenced conclusions are to the scientific community, but has also caused concern that their observations may serve more to recruit youth to drug use than to encourage caution in such involvement.

For social scientists to make the assumption, therefore, that sociology knows all and that police are isolated, misguided legal puppets, is to make two assertions which are invalid: that sociologists are *that* well informed as to the total picture, and that police are *that* misinformed and isolated from the situation as a whole. The truth is that each discipline has much to learn from the other.

Ausubel said in 1958 that a fair summary of the available evidence "would be that very rarely do major crimes follow upon the use of [cannabis] and that, in instances where they do, the relationship is an indirect one."[30] Earlier, in 1945, Gaskill contended that "marijuana, like alcohol, does not necessarily produce abnormal behavior. The danger lies in the fact that immature and psychopathic persons use it to deaden their perception of reality, and when under its effects their inhibitions and judgment are impaired with consequent increase in abnormal behavior. . . . [Cannabis may act] as the determining factor turning the balance in the direction of asocial behavior rather than permitting the poorly integrated social conscience of such an individual to remain in control."[31]

Ausubel does concede that, in addition to releasing latent criminally associated traits, cannabis may contribute to premeditated crime when used to bolster courage prior to the act, such as the pattern described by Blanchard in the case of "Duke" and his gang. Ausubel notes, "Some of the more sensational instances of homicide and sexual assault attributed to marijuana intoxication are undoubtedly manifestations of transitory psychotic states induced by the drug." But he also says that "still another reason for the association of marijuana addiction and crime is the greater use of marijuana in slum-urban areas where delinquency rates tend to be high." In view of the variety of responses to cannabis, Ausubel is also obliged to note that "marijuana, by virtue of its stupefying effects, may sometimes inhibit the expression of aggressive impulses."[32]

From information available at this time, it seems impractical to attempt to indict cannabis as a general *cause* of crime. Whether or not it contributes to criminality apparently has to be decided in each individual case. Significantly, there seems to be a high incidence of what we must call unstable personalities who are attracted to cannabis *abuse*. This combination may result in the frequently high correlation that law enforcement authorities have noted between cannabis and crime.

CANNABIS AND VIOLENCE

This issue is very closely related to the debate on cannabis and crime, largely because our knowledge of most violent acts comes from police statistics and law enforcement information. The difference between the two questions—cannabis and crime and cannabis and violence—is chiefly one of emphasis. The question of violence has more to do with whether physical injury is inflicted on other persons than with whether a cannabis user is engaging in such criminal acts as theft, arson, prostitution, or acts directed against society at large. Nevertheless, there is obviously a good deal of overlap.

The case for the connection between cannabis and violence or violent crime is one made by the anti-cannabis forces. Police and law enforcement authorities provide the information, basing their charges on the many documented criminal cases where marijuana was a factor. To indicate the nature of police charges, let us look at some typical cases from the files of the Los Angeles Police Department, compiled in a 1966 special survey of the relationship between marijuana and criminal behavior. The cases presented are a fraction of the hundreds collected for the study.[33]

Case 1

Officers received a call regarding a family dispute. The officers were met by the suspect's wife, who stated that she and her husband had had an argument and she had threatened to leave with the children. The suspect became violent and struck her several times in the face. When she fell down, he kicked her several times in the ribs. The suspect then dragged the victim to a staircase and pushed her down the stairs. Officers could smell the odor of marijuana coming from within the house in which the suspect had locked himself. After entry was made and the suspect arrested, officers found in the suspect's bedroom a quantity of Zig-zag paper and a pipe filled with marijuana.

Case 2

A victim reported to the police that she had been kidnapped and robbed during the early morning hours. She stated that a man had held a knife at her throat and forced her into his car. The suspect then tried to force the victim to smoke a marijuana cigarette but she refused. The suspect then removed $30 from the victim's purse and forced her out of the car. The arresting officers located the suspect's apartment and at the time of the arrest officers found a partially smoked marijuana cigarette in an ashtray and a large bag of marijuana in a closet.

Case 3

A landlady of an apartment house reported that one of her female tenants had fired two shots at her. The officers went to the suspect's apartment, knocked, and identified themselves; the suspect opened the door and pointed a .25 automatic pistol at them. After disarming the female, the officers heard the toilet flush and, upon entering the bathroom, observed the defendant's boyfriend attempting to dispose of a quantity of marijuana. When the female suspect was being booked, officers found two plastic bags containing marijuana in her purse.

Case 4

Radio car officers received a call regarding a disturbance at an apartment house. Upon their arrival, the manager related that a man had run up the stairs with a bumper jack in his hand and had entered an apartment. When the officers reached the apartment, they could hear a female inside screaming, "Don't kill me, George, please don't kill me." The officers knocked on the door and identified themselves, and the female cried, "Oh God, please come in, he's killing me." The officers forcibly entered and observed the suspect standing over the victim with the jack handle over his head, poised to strike. The suspect was taken into custody and a marijuana cigarette was found in his pocket. The suspect stated he had smoked at least four marijuana cigarettes that day.

Case 5

Officers received a radio call: "woman screaming." When they arrived, the officers were met by a man and a woman, each claiming he was the victim of assault by the other. Both parties showed evidence of injury. The female suspect stated, "I smoked two or three joints. He looked at me with a weird look in his eye and called me a profanity. I picked up the ice pick and hit him with it. I am high now." It was noted that the male had been stabbed three times. A search of the house disclosed marijuana debris in several ashtrays.

Case 6

Radio car officers answered a call to a playground regarding an assault suspect. The officers were told by the playground director that he had ordered the sixteen-year-old subject from the athletic field because of a disturbance he was causing. The playground director suspected the youngster was intoxicated because his voice was slurred, his eyes partially shut, and he was staggering. The subject had also become antagonistic, swore, and swung his fists at the director. Marijuana debris was found in the subject's pocket, and he then admitted he had smoked three marijuana cigarettes just prior to the altercation.

Case 7

Officers received a radio call that shots had been fired. Upon investigation it was discovered that the suspect had earlier been ejected from a bar for a disturbance. Fifteen minutes later he returned and fired several shots from a shotgun in the street outside the bar. When the patrons of the bar quickly emptied into the street, the suspect fired in their direction, striking one in the leg. Numerous shotguns, rifles, and pistols were found in the suspect's home. In the closet was found a large quantity of marijuana. The suspect admitted smoking marijuana that day and on numerous previous occasions.

Now, the argument in all of these cases is similar to that already examined in the cannabis-crime discussion. Police on the firing line are prone to assume a cause-and-effect relationships. Other persons may question the causal role cannabis plays in events like those just described. For instance, in Cases 1 through 4, there is no direct evidence that the subjects were under the influence of marijuana. In Case 5, one might well ask how often these people fought, before a conclusion can be reached on whether cannabis was an integral part of the chaos. In Case 6, it is reasonable to question whether adulterants might have been present in the "weed," since much of today's available supply of cannabis is contaminated or "burned." In Case 7, it should be determined what role, if any, alcohol consumption played.

One must also raise the question of what adverse or psychotic reactions can be caused by pot use. In America, these have thus far not been common enough to provide grounds for a general indictment of cannabis as a *cause* of violent behavior like that just described. But it is not impossible that cannabis use might have *facilitated* these antisocial actions.

In the final analysis, says attorney Gene Haislip,[34] the question is not in what manner cannabis caused the violence or the crime. Instead it is sociologically important to determine how many, if any, of the crimes would not have been committed if the individual had not been using cannabis at the time of the incident. Pro-cannabis forces demand more direct proof of crime or violence caused by cannabis than cases merely showing their frequent association can provide. In regard to such demands for "proof," Los Angeles surgeon William F. Quinn recently stated: "If I had to have all the statistics and reports you people need to make your decisions in order to arrive at a diagnosis, most of my patients would die of a ruptured appendix." Smiling at his audience of sociologists and psychiatrists, Dr. Quinn then added, "Fortunately for sick people, surgeons are more practical than that."[35]

To turn to the pro-cannabis replies on this issue, let us consider the testimony of author-student Stephen Abrams: "Another criticism that is frequently made is that cannabis tends to cause violence and crime. . . . I find this extremely difficult to believe." He observed a group of cannabis users at Oxford University and found no evidence of violence: "During the so-called 'crisis' the most violent activity that is likely to occur is uninhibited dancing. I have observed hundreds of persons under the influence of cannabis and have never seen a single act of violence committed."[36]

As in the case of some psychiatrists and sociologists, Abrams appears to move in different circles than the police. One man's observations are, in any case, hardly sufficient to generalize about the vast drug picture today, but it must also be borne in mind that Abrams and many other pro-cannabis commentators are confined in their observations to the college crowd; many who are attracted to marijuana do not fall in the category of Oxford University undergraduates.

According to the American Medical Association, pot use is "probably disproportionately higher among young persons with developing psychiatric problems than among those without them. Persons who use marijuana continually and as the symptomatic expression of psychological conflict, a means of gaining social acceptance, or a way of escaping painful experiences of anxiety or depression, may be said to be psychologically dependent upon the substance. Continuous use may be associated with the development of psychiatric illness, although few chronic users are admitted to psychiatric inpatient facilities." The AMA warns further: "It is likely that those who do become dependent on marijuana or other drugs are psychiatrically disturbed, and that drug use is but one of a complex of psychological and behavioral symptoms manifested by them."[37]

Now, let us review again what cannabis does to the mind: Release of inhibitions, alteration of perception and judgment, increased response to suggestion, production (in susceptible people) of illusions and hallucinations that predispose to antisocial behavior, impairment of memory, distortion of emotional responsiveness, irritability and confusion, and a predisposition to anxiety and paranoia as a possible result of various intellectual and sensory derangements. That particular catalog comes, in part, from the 1965 report of the Committee on Drug Dependence of the World Health Organization.

However much we qualify allegations about the relationship between cannabis and violence or crime, no amount of qualification can obscure the simple medical fact that marijuana can produce psychotic reactions, and that a psychotic state can release violence and precipitate criminal behavior. This is not to say that such a reaction will occur in every case—or even in most cases—but that it can and has happened. Because of the relative mildness of Mexican and American varieties of cannabis, we have seen very little of this kind of reaction in the U.S. But with the coming of more potent oriental varieties, such as hashish, we can look for more and more instances of psychosis and aggressiveness as a result of cannabis use.

One of the most interesting facets of the cannabis-violence controversy is the potential of pot use as an influential medium among young American revolutionaries. There are two sides to this question—first, that of the "ex-dope dealer" whose anti-pot diatribe from *The Berkeley Barb* has already been cited elsewhere. Quoting Bertrand Russell's observation that revolution succeeds only when the revolutionaries have more knowledge and skills than the old order, he says, " 'Staying high' on pot will not gain us knowledge or skills."[38]

On the other side, a young girl who had been a close friend of one of the Seattle Seven (who were convicted of conspiring to damage government property) has this to say:

I visited the commune with him one evening after school to see how "truly happy" people looked and acted. Some of the girls had long hair, some short. Some smiled, some didn't. The boys wore a variety of colors and styles. They all smoked—filter-tip cigarettes at first, and later marijuana.

"Grass helps you get over the hangup of legality," Lora said. "You smoke it, and you've broken your first law. And suddenly you realize that law is full of ——."

"And you're an outlaw," Beau added. "Not an American any-more."

"And you don't really care," another boy spoke up. "You discover you never were an American in the first place. You never did iden-tify with the money system. Now you identify with Angela Davis, and the Viet Cong and the Berrigan brothers."[39]

Obviously the connection between cannabis and violence or crime depends most of all on the individual user and, secondarily, on who is examining and evaluating his behavior. If the user is not prone to violence or crime and if he does not develop a drug-induced psychosis, he will not, except for the infraction of the narcotics laws, normally resort to violent or criminal behavior. If, on the other hand, he is one of those who are predisposed to antisocial behavior and violence, unfortunate things may happen when he is taking marijuana. This is the issue in determining whether to legalize cannabis or not.

CANNABIS AND THE MILITARY

Considerable controversy has arisen around the use of pot by servicemen in Vietnam since the first edition of this book ap-peared four years ago. At that time most of the information directed toward military use was to be found in two investiga-tions conducted in the Panama Canal Zone. As recently as Febru-ary, 1970, a major decision concerning cannabis legislation in the military was based on this dual 1928 report.[40]

The first study from the Panama Canal Zone was made about 1925 by a committee appointed to investigate the use of mari-juana and to recommend corrective procedures to be taken in the event that the committee found the use of the drug was pro-ducing detrimental effects on the troops. In essence, after study-ing the situation for nine months, the committee found that the use of marijuana was not habit forming and had no deleterious influence on the individual using it."[41]

The second Panama Study was carried out in 1931. In this study thirty-four soldiers were hospitalized, given marijuana grown at the Canal Zone Experimental Gardens to assure uniformity of the resin content, and their reactions were observed. Such a controlled environment study of cannabis or any other psychotropic has certain built-in disadvantages, which will be considered later in treating the La Guardia Report. In any event, the second Panama Study also came up with the observation that cannabis in the Canal Zone is a mild stimulant and intoxicant (apparently Panama Red was not growing there in those days), that it was not habit forming, that crime and antisocial behavior failed to result from its use, and that delinquencies caused by marijuana smoking which might result in the user's being court-martialed were negligible compared to problems caused by the use of alcohol by the troops.

A decade after these studies were printed, the editor of the *Military Surgeon* added his observations by expressing the opinion that "the legislation in relation to marijuana was ill-advised, that it branded as a menace and a crime a matter of trivial importance."[42] Perhaps this was true in 1925 and 1931 when few individuals were using it. Perhaps it was of no consequence to a country at peace and able to cope with poor judgment and decreased ability on the part of its soldiers. But what about times when soldiers are facing active combat?

In 1944 a team of two army medical officers, Captains Eli Marcovitz and Henry J. Myers, published their observations made on thirty-five confirmed marijuana abusers who came under their care during a period of seven months at an Army air force regional station hospital. Their findings were released in 1944 in *War Medicine*,[43] a publication of the American Medical Association.

Pointing out that marijuana "addiction" as a problem both in civil life and in the armed forces has been the subject of controversy and of various viewpoints and conclusions, Marcovitz and Myers objectively expressed their observations on some three dozen men referred to the neuropsychiatric service. Four principal factors brought these men to the attention of the authors: first, chronic physical complaints, usually headache; second, cannabis intoxication resulting in uncontrolled behavior patterns or a state approaching stupor; third, disciplinary or delinquency problems, such as demands for passes to go out and obtain marijuana; and fourth, arrests of users because of violence or self-mutilating actions.

The authors stress that their conclusions were based on a specialized unit of highly involved marijuana users, a group of servicemen with difficulties that brought them to the attention of the military or medical authorities. It happens that in one of the Panama Canal Zone studies, a similar group of thirty-four men was observed. The difference is that in Panama the men were in a controlled environment, behaving as good drug users are supposed to behave in a controlled study, whereas those studied by Marcovitz and Myers were picked for study because of their behavior in an open, or uncontrolled environment. The variability of personality factors must also be taken into consideration in all such studies. Cannabis is an unpredictable drug that produces unpredictable reactions in unpredictable people.

Marcovitz and Myers note that marijuana users:

present a serious problem in their failure to perform any useful duties, in breaches of discipline, in constant need for medical attention, in consistent failure to respond favorably to disciplinary measures or to attempts at rehabilitation and in their disruptive effect on the morale of their organization.

Thirty four [of the users studied] were Negroes, and one was of the white race. As a group, their backgrounds were heavily loaded with adverse familial, social and economic factors. Their histories were characterized by delinquent and criminal behavior and failure to develop any consistent patterns of productive work. In effect, they felt and acted like enemy aliens toward society.

The personality pictures of such addicts show a typical pattern of response to repeated situations of frustration and deprivation. This consists, on the one hand, of immediate and constant gratification of the need for sensual pleasure and for the feeling of omnipotence, as well as the need to overcome their unbearable anxiety. On the other hand, they show hostility and aggression toward others, especially to authority, with the neurotic repetitive creation of situations which lead to further suffering. The addictive smoking of marijuana serves simultaneously as a satisfaction of all these drives. It is but one aspect of a complex picture of maladjustment.

It is concluded that the problems of disposition of confirmed marijuana addicts of the type described here cannot be solved adequately by punishment, short term imprisonment or discharge from the service. It is recommended that government institutions be created to which such confirmed marijuana addicts may be committed for long term treatment and rehabilitation or for indefinite custody.

The authors' recommendations, of course, were not followed.

Use of cannabis by soldiers in wartime is a different matter from the situations described by previous studies. Late in 1967 a spokesman for the Department of Defense told reporters that the use of marijuana by American troops in Vietnam "is not considered a problem of a consequence."[44] Nevertheless, he added, because of the ready availability of cannabis in Vietnam and the implications of its use by troops, the government was keeping a close watch on the situation. Let's look at the marijuana situation in Vietnam then as compared with 1971.

The first significant evidence emerged in October, 1967, when John Steinbeck, IV,[45] son of the novelist, was arrested in Washington, D.C., on a narcotics charge. The youth informed the press that three-fourths of his comrades in Vietnam were marijuana smokers. The government denied the charge; nevertheless, between January, 1966, and November, 1967, some 1500 GI's in Vietnam had been found possessing or using cannabis.[46] Even then officials recognized this was a low figure since only some of the users were apprehended. The army refused to court-martial soldiers on this offense unless the marijuana used as evidence was checked out in laboratory tests. The nearest laboratory to Vietnam was in Japan. About that time Army psychiatrist Joel Kaplan attempted to have Vietnamese marijuana analyzed because an increasing number of complications seemed to be arising from its use. The military laboratory in Japan would not cooperate with this project because they limited their analyses to drugs involved in criminal activity. Stymied at this, Dr. Kaplan attempted to mail a sample home to his father, who was then editor of the *Army Medical Association Journal*. It was intercepted. The Army's response, for a time, was to contemplate court martialing Dr. Kaplan for violation of drug regulations.[47]

In November, 1967, troop commanders still insisted in their official communiqués that the use of marijuana was not affecting unit efficiency, although they admitted controls were being tightened. At that time, however, Brigadier General Harley Moore, Jr., was quoted as stating that marijuana parties among the troops "have become a problem."[48] About the same time a Department of Defense spokesman, noting arrest figures were representative of a very small percentage of American military strength in Vietnam, said that army statistics indicate that the problem in Vietnam was less serious than among young men in the same age group in the United States. In the same month *Newsweek*[49] magazine asked its correspondent, John Donnelley, for a report on the situation in Saigon. Donnelley replied, "In Da Nang, a serviceman can swap a $2 bottle of PX whiskey for five ounces [of cannabis] and bulk purchasing can reduce the cost of 'roll-your-own' reefers to as little as three cents each."

Donnelley's report further stated that:

> GIs smoke pot everywhere, not just in rear areas. One night in the central highlands, I watched ten GIs light up in a squad tent, while three North Vietnamese divisions lurked only a few miles away just across the Cambodian border. And it is not just soldiers and marines who smoke Mary Jane. It is said that there is not a ship on the Navy's Yankee Station where one cannot get a "joint," and in Saigon there are pot parties in posh villas, where giggling embassy secretaries trade puffs with their junior-official dates.

In December, 1967, despite the reassurance from higher echelons to the general public, military officials ordered an intensified crackdown on marijuana. The decision was precipitated by an army survey that showed one out of every two hundred men was smoking marijuana. "Those arrested," said the Associated Press release,[50] "have included military police, young officers, guards on duty and combat men." Although senior officers could not estimate the actual incidence of use, they did reveal that marijuana smoking ranked as the single largest major offense among American soldiers in Vietnam.

A bulletin issued by one army division informed its troops that the Viet Cong was supplying marijuana to GI's because they know it makes soldiers ineffective in combat. A 1st Cavalry (Airmobile) Division bulletin amplified just how ineffective the cannabis user could be by warning its men that marijuana decreases effectiveness and makes soldiers subject to "unpredictable and unusual actions such as shooting, grenade throwing, etc." The bulletin went on to state that the enemy was using pushers in an attempt to knock the fighting edge off American troops."[51]

Why are our fighting men turning to cannabis? "You have to realize," an army legal officer told Donnelley, "that in a single division here we have the equivalent of the teen-age and early twenties population of a city of 300,000 in the States." Thinking that one over, Donnelley mused, "What he was saying was that at home these youngsters are the Pot Generation, and despite (or perhaps because of) the dangers of combat, it is unrealistic to expect them to act any differently in Vietnam."[52]

How bad was the situation and how detrimental were the effects of cannabis on American fighting men in 1969? No one really knows. Brigadier General Harley Moore, Jr., U.S. Army Provost Marshal, has been quoted as saying he would not be surprised if some GI's were smoking marijuana under combat conditions.[53] Reports to this author from returning GI's tend to corroborate this remark. One youth observed a bit dryly, "At least they die happy when they go."

The implication of GIs' using cannabis in battle was particularly disturbing to authorities. As a Department of Defense spokesman noted in this connection, there can be severe consequences arising from a situation in which "a man who has a gun and may be required to use it—such as a sentry—is high on marijuana."[54]

The problem increased as time went by. Then in 1969 the Department of Defense grudgingly admitted there were some 3,500 cases of marijuana use in the entire U.S. Army. "I couldn't help but laugh at this," Dr. Kaplan mused later for a Senate Subcommittee hearing, "because we had at least 3,500 drug abusers in our own patient population in Nha Trang."[55] (In making this statement Kaplan defined a drug abuser as one who used "drugs heavily, day in and day out.")

In January, 1971, *U.S. News & World Report* painted an even darker picture. "About half of all servicemen in Vietnam are believed to have used or experimented with [all] drugs," it noted. "During 1970 more than 65,000 Army men—about one in six GI's in Vietnam at midyear—were habitual users. More than 11,000 were arrested. More than 1,000 Americans were hospitalized for drug abuse," the magazine continued, and "during the first eleven months of 1970, there were at least 93 confirmed drug deaths among American troops."[56]

In may of 1971, the same magazine reported on the situation in Vietnam. Under the headline, "Who's Pushing Heroin to GI's in Vietnam?", they ran this information: "The war against drug use by Americans in Vietnam is faring badly. Possible reason: Some top men in the Saigon regime may be in on the racket."[57]

Once again, the curious association of marijuana followed by heroin use appears on the scene. A study conducted in April, 1971, by members of several disciplines, concluded that "between ten and fifteen percent of American servicemen in Vietnam are users of heroin."[58]

"Some officials," the magazine continued, "place the number of drug *users* among American servicemen at as high as sixty percent. The pushers are almost all Vietnamese. The wholesale distributors certainly are Vietnamese and so are the customs inspectors at the airports, who pay up to $700 in bribes to officials to be appointed to jobs which normally pay only $30 per month. The drug apparatus," investigators claim, has reached "so high in the South Vietnamese Government that only President Thieu has the power to initiate and implement an effective program to stop the traffic."[59]

The government is now discovering it is involved with a new type of returning GI. From VA hospitals across the land comes word that this group has little interest in obtaining the government benefits normally accorded returning servicemen, for education and advancement in civilian life. Some reports on psychiatric cases among these men indicate increased tendencies toward suicide, drug and alcohol abuse, and alienation.[60]

For a while, some frightening drug-related attitudes seemed prevalent among servicemen. One was the attitude that "anything goes" if it can get one kicked out of the service. "Our Number One psychiatric problem," Army medical authorities recently lamented, "is the young man who is not convinced of his military obligation and is trying to get kicked out."[61] The underground press, fomenting revolution and encouraging destruction of the armed forces, encouraged this evasion by advising that one way to avoid military service was to "TURN ON."[62] The AWOL rate rose almost geometrically to the point where, according to the *Wall Street Journal*, at one time an average of 500 GI's were deserting the army each week. According to the underground papers, during the fiscal year ending June 30, 1969, about ten percent of the entire 1.5 million-man army went AWOL at one time or another.[63] In 1969, the U.S. Navy discharged more than 3,800 men for illegally using or pushing drugs. This number, according to Vice Adm. Charles K. Duncan, by no means represented all the drug users in the navy. Significantly, the Navy's drug problem is not centered in Vietnam. According to Duncan, "Our experience in drug abuse in Vietnam is not any higher than in other places such as Norfolk or San Diego."[64] Amplifying this point, *U.S. News & World Report,* in late January of 1971, noted that our troops in Germany may have an even poorer record of drug abuse and service discipline than those in Vietnam.[65]

What has happened to American Armed Forces? "The military establishment," states an editor of *Drugs and Drug Abuse Education Newsletter* in scathing terms, "accustomed to simpler ages when the need for it was immediate, clear and unchallenged, is finding itself in an unforeseen and little understood dilemma in an age when those called upon to fill its ranks view it as unneeded, unwanted, anachronistic, oppressive and serving a nefarious purpose in an irrelevant Southeast Asian battlefield."

"Its leaders," the writer continues, "are finding young soldiers ignoring their commands, undermining authority, and using heretofore unimagined legal gimmicks to keep them, or get them out of its grasp or—failing that—to weaken its power over their lives." As this has happened, he notes, stating that it has equally occurred in the military's sister institutions, "drugs have emerged as simultaneously the symbol, the cause, the effect and the scapegoat of the complex and often bewildering set of social phenomena which have accompanied their rise."

Acknowledging that alcohol abuse still remains the most serious problem, the editor complains that until recently the U.S. military authorities dealt with the drug problem by ignoring it. However, he notes, now the military is not only acknowledging its inability to handle the situation, but is "making uncharacteristic and unmilitary concessions to the foot soldier in an almost desperate attempt to deal with the drug use and the deeper problems of discontent it seems to represent."[66]

In its frantic attempt to reverse the situation, the military at first prosecuted offenders; then later, realizing the futility of such an approach, granted amnesty to users who agreed to take advantage of drug rehabilitation centers set up on military bases. The military instituted the amnesty program in late 1970. Six months later, at least in Europe, GI's were responding at the rate of only about 140 men per month, although it is thought that one in ten of the 185,000 troops there is a chronic user of hashish, marijuana, heroin, and various pills.[67]

A congressional investigatory committee concluded that one reason for the low response was the presence of a "widely held feeling among drug users, especially hashish smokers, [that] there is no wrong—physical, moral or otherwise—in such use and hence nothing to be rehabilitated from. Another problem is that many young junior officers wink at marijuana smoking among the men in their command. These individuals, while occupying positions of authority over the troops, shared many of the same values of the enlisted men," the committee reported, "particularly in regard to the smoking of marijuana as a social activity."

One of the big problems the armed forces face in trying to control the use of drugs and of pot, in particular, is the fact that these substances are so plentiful. The supply of pot, very good pot, is so great in Vietnam that it's literally available for the asking. Some of it is disguised in regular American cigarette packs so well that it's "virtually impossible to tell the difference," Talbott notes, "without either removing the filling from the cigarettes or smoking them. Vietnamese marijuana is reported by the Army Chemical Laboratory in Japan to be about twice as potent . . . as that normally sold or found in the United States." "In addition," Talbott states, "approximately fifty percent of the cannabis contraband seized in Vietnam contains opiates. Therefore, the quality of the cannabis derivatives used there is likely to produce a much stronger effect on the consumer."[68]

"The big problem," says Lt. Col. George Mitchell, a psychiatric consultant to the Army in Vietnam, "is the availability of the drug. In Saigon and other major cities," he says, "marijuana cigarettes can be purchased at bars catering to GI's or even at sidewalk souvenir stands. In forward areas, they're sold by laundresses, civilian KP's and other Vietnamese employed at military installations, and by the prostitutes and children who flock to all but the most remote bases."[69]

There is no doubt, notes *Medical World News*, that Vietnam's marijuana trade has sprung up almost entirely in response to GI demand since the American military buildup began in 1965. This, they note, is a paradox in that Vietnamese themselves do not use the drug. Additionally, large supplies of pot have been found in Viet Cong caches, possibly for use by Communist troops, but more likely for sale to American soldiers through middlemen.[70] Some people think that there is a "Red plot" to use cannabis to demoralize our troops, but there is a more practical reason: the VC are interested in cash profits, which they use to support their own war effort.

To fight this the U.S. command may now begin paying the South Vietnamese government a little less than one cent for every marijuana plant destroyed by South Vietnamese troops.[71] Dr. Joel Kaplan suggests that the Vietnamese, who almost never use marijuana themselves, should be pressured to stop the traffic in drugs. He notes that when American MP's wanted to raid an opium den recently, they needed to get permission from the Vietnamese civilian police first. By the time they arrived the papasans had been warned, the dens closed and any GI's buying there long gone.[72]

One interesting aspect of the potential of cannabis products to marble thinking and alter motivation came to light when the Army briefly admitted it had been studying THC as an "anti-personnel" drug. Over the years, military research has given the drug scene considerable impetus, a fact usually denied by the Army. It was the Armed Forces which turned American troops on to amphetamines during World War II, just as British, Japanese and German troops were "turned on" to the same drugs by their respective governments. One of the Armed Forces' efforts to produce anti-personnel substances gave birth to the mescaline-amphetamine combination which is better known as STP (4-methyl-2, 5-dimethoxy-alpha-methylphen-ethylamine). Prior to that they spent some fifteen years of research on LSD. At the moment it seems the Armed Forces has decided that the effects of psychedelic drugs are too unpredictable and therefore unusable for psychological or chemical warfare.[73]

The idea of using THC as an anti-personnel drug, and research into this subject by the Arthur D. Little Co. of Cambridge, Mass., struck some scientists as whimsical. At first the concept was to develop a drug that would develop a temporary psychosis in the enemy (assuming that only the enemy would drink contaminated water and eat contaminated foodstuffs). Then, apparently, as the sedative effects of cannabis became better understood, one investigator quipped, "Wouldn't it be nice to have a happiness pill so the enemy wouldn't feel like fighting any more and surround us with kisses and flowers?"[74]

Opinions concerning the effects of using marijuana in Vietnam are intensely varied. Writing in *Playboy*, an army captain, admitting that the use of the weed in his company was "close to 100 percent," said, "I have never ordered a man arrested for this offense. Why should I put a blot on the permanent record of a brave fighting man just because he amuses himself, during his brief respites from battle, with a harmless herb?"[75]

The compassionate Captain may have been aware that in 'Nam it can be extremely dangerous to "fink" on a pot-using buddy. Some of the men suspect the army has sent in spies from the CID, "at least, that's what most of us think," a youth complained—so much so that "we're all slowly becoming paranoid." "Everybody smokes pot here," he said, "and everybody wants to 'get' the CID men before they get us. The saddest part of the whole mess is that those we suspect may be as innocent as we are."[76]

A former Marine sergeant complained before a Senate hearing that his attempts to stamp out marijuana use among his men almost got him killed. "I was blown up by my own men," he complained, "who rolled a grenade under my bunk as I slept. Marijuana," he said, "was everywhere you looked and Marines smoking pot just couldn't do their jobs."[77] (The sergeant was lucky to be alive. In 1970, more than 209 incidents of lethal "fragging" were reported in Vietnam.[78])

"I cannot understand the narrowmindedness of American officials when it comes to pot smoking in Vietnam," a woman reader wrote *Playboy*.[79] Noting the boys were fighting for outdated ideals at the behest of old men who sat back in comfortable leather chairs to run their bulletin board war, she asked, "Who can expect these young boys to live under such conditions without the mind releasing help of marijuana, when the plant is so available there? The officers should be glad their men can remove their traumas and anxieties for a few hours and thus be able to face a new day of fighting."

Seven irate servicemen answered her letter. They were not old crocks in leather chairs, they said, but men who for the most part were well-disciplined soldiers who relied on "quick reactions and thinking to save themselves and their buddies from Viet Cong and North Vietnamese booby traps and ambushes." If this woman's "mind releasers" "hinder a man from recognizing the significance of a clump of grass or a misplaced tree limb, he will lose something far more vital than the 'trauma and anxieties" that pot alleviates," they noted. "On guard or on the move, a man must be fully aware of things as they are and his 'traumas and anxieties' help him stay alert and think about every move he makes."[80]

In a wry summary, which demonstrates that pot smoking may be as dangerous a social activity as being a "fink" who objects to it, these men remark, "Pot smoking among the troops is a problem, but usually not for long. Once the men in the platoon realize that they can't trust a man to be a soldier all the time, they find a way to remedy the situation. We've had men hospitalized for "slipping on a bar of soap" after they were found by their buddies to be asleep on guard. Marijuana has no place where soldiers have to rely on each other 24 hours a day to stay alive."

Agreeing, another soldier wrote, "If I am sent to Vietnam and someone smokes pot while on patrol with me, I will put a bullet in his head. I am not going to allow some messed-up GI to jeopardize my life."[81] Another, with a different viewpoint, said, "I believe that marijuana should be legalized and I'm in Vietnam to defend my right to vote on that belief when it gets on the ballot."[82] These two comments indicate that the "generation gap" may not be among the old and young after all. The biggest gap seems to be between the young who are conservative and those who are ultra-liberal.

How simple is the use of grass in Asia? "Marijuana was the most popular drug in Vietnam," psychiatrist Joel Kaplan recently told *Look* magazine.[93] "I came to feel that it is much more dangerous than what we've been led to believe, in terms of chronic illnesses, toxic psychosis and impaired performance. If marijuana were legalized here the potent varieties from places like Vietnam would be introduced and you'd see what we saw in Vietnam."

How mild can a marijuana cigarette be? A Navy hospital corpsman, assigned to a Marine infantry unit in Vietnam, wrote *Playboy* that he had had opportunity to see the effects of using pot. "For example," he said, "during a recent mortar attack, two Marines, both high on pot, decided they'd sit outside their protective bunker to watch the fireworks. They were both wounded, one of them seriously, and they endangered the life of a corpsman who had to leave his shelter to treat them and who, incidentally, was also wounded. I don't condemn pot," the youth said, "but in Vietnam it 'may be hazardous to your health'."[84]

Physician Joel Kaplan, relating his observations, said that when a guy got stoned he was unable to do his job. "We learned of men on patrol who missed ambushes and got themselves or their buddies killed. They thought their reactions were better under pot, but in fact, they were missing what they should have seen or seeing what wasn't there. I heard of one pot-smoking soldier," he continued, "who, when he was at base camp, picked up his weapon and, convinced that everybody around him was Vietcong, shot a colonel and several enlisted men coming to take his weapon away."

"One man," he continued, "told me he had been smoking pot while on guard near the DMZ. He decided to make peace with the Vietcong, took off his shoes and tried to walk across the barbed wire. His friends pulled him back and he was taken off guard duty."[85]

In contrast to this depressing picture, other GI's interviewed in Vietnam have a more optimistic viewpoint. "Too much is being made about marijuana," Sgt. Glenn L. Young, age 25, told a *U.S. News & World Report* reporter.[86] "Sure guys smoke it, and some of them smoke it all the time. Boredom is the worst thing. . . . To an outsider there appears to be a conspiracy of silence on the drug issue. No one wants to inform on a buddy—not if he doesn't endanger anyone's life." There is a definite impression that "pot" is less of a problem than statistics show, the reporter concluded, "—that the vast majority of men smoke only once in a while for kicks."

The Armed Forces are now doing their best to re-educate and rehabilitate youths who have become deeply involved with drugs. They face heavy opposition from anarchic and defeatist forces. The underground press in particular does its best to invalidate any attempts on the part of the government to warn youth about the potential adverse effects of pot. This information, coming from a hated authoritarian figure, is greeted with hoots and laughter by those in the drug subculture who have yet to see or admit having seen an adverse reaction to the smoking of grass. Working with minds already rendered susceptible to suggestion, the underground uses every technique available to promote the idea that "pot is cool."

Recently the Army came out with a bulletin intended to outline some potential dangers involved in using pot, particularly Vietnamese grass. The underground press' response was ridicule and laughter. "The United States Army through the United States Information Office has recently issued a pamphlet of which you, the reader, should be aware. It may make you straight," the underground writer says with tongue in cheek. "It may make you laugh straight into tears." From this point on the writer repeats almost verbatim the highlights of the pamphlet. He need say nothing more to cause his readers to chuckle and disbelieve everything the pamphlet says.[87]

MARIJUANA AT MY LAI

One morbid controversy arising from the Vietnam war revolves around the role of marijuana use in the My Lai (code name Pinkville) slayings. Dr. Myron Feld, basing his comments on studies of 2,041 Vietnam veterans over the past 2½ years, told the Society of Biological Psychiatry in May of 1970 that he feels the heavy use of superstrong Vietnamese marijuana by soldiers in Southeast Asia has played a heavy role not only in excess killings in the war but also as a causative factor in the high rate of mental illness among veterans.[88]

The comments of a GI to a *U.S. News & World Report* researcher are interesting here: "Out here in the field," he said, "is not the place to smoke that stuff. It sounds corny, but we all know we've got to be alert or 'Dink' will get us. So we keep a watch on each other when we're out on patrol."[89] Feld offers a sharp contrast to the soldier's remarks. "Our troops find it necessary to enter combat under the influence of drugs and further to continue their use on return to the United States," he said. Three-fourths of U.S. combat troops use drugs, he told his colleagues, mostly marijuana that is twice as powerful as the kind available in this country. He further indicated that many soldiers go into battle in a drug-induced fog that endangers their lives and the lives of their buddies as well as keeping them from seeing killing as a reality.[90]

One of the factors in this war, noted with some pride by government officials, is that the number of psychiatric casualties from Vietnam are much less than those from previous wars. Feld punctures the seemingly bright side of this observation by noting that most of the mental illness is currently showing up after discharge. Much of the cause of this he places on the use of drugs, LSD, and amphetamines as well as marijuana. When Feld worked as chief of psychiatry at Long Beach Veterans' Hospital, he noted that half of his patients were combat veterans from Vietnam, a number far in excess of those from other wars. The treatment of these men is complicated by the fact that their heavy drug use makes it hard to manage them with tranquilizers normally employed for mental patients, so electric shock therapy must be used, instead.

Feld also noted that Vietnam veterans seem to lack "combat dreams" that so often plague returning servicemen. He suggests that the use of drugs causes this lack. "They were in a dream-like state already while participating in battle so that it has never entered their waking personality. It is not treated as a reality."

Many drug experts believe that marijuana users are not prone to violent acts, but instead develop feelings of languid well-being. Feld disagrees, noting that the type of grass used in Vietnam is "superstrong." Feld also observes that only one-third of World War II troops and one-half of Korean war troops fired their guns in battle. "In this war they can't stop them from firing," he states, and then asks the eternal question: "What role do drugs play in these different occurrences?"

The answer to this question may not be as obscure as it seems, if one will put aside what he wishes to believe and face reality instead. Noting whimsically that the Vietnam war is the first in which the Army has been more concerned with marijuana than with venereal disease, psychiatrist John A. Talbott observes that soldiers with pot reactions seem to be quite similar in personality to those World War II soldiers who developed psychoses attributed to combat fatigue.[91]

Twenty-five years ago Freedman studied 310 enlisted men in the Army who were clinically examined by the Mental Hygiene Division of the Army Service Forces Training Center because, among other reasons, they had used marijuana.[92] These men, who had been in military service for an average of fifteen months, he noted, "were seen because they were having difficulty meeting Army requirements at the time they were referred for evaluation. Their use of marijuana," he said, "was but one factor which was revealed as a study of their total personalities developed. The causative factors of their Army maladjustment were found to be multiple. These causes were seen in the combination of limitations both within their personalities and environmental frustrations which were not conducive to healthy basic personality formation. The evidence of emotional conflict prior to indulgence in marijuana, even in those cases where community standards of behavior are violated, is clearly revealed in the material presented."

The question we may be discussing here, then, is not "does marijuana *cause* many of these problems?" More likely the question is, "Does it precipitate problems that might not have occurred?" or, "Does it make the problems worse?" or conversely, "Does it help the individual with emotional conflicts?"

"There's no general agreement among medical officers as to how much, if at all, marijuana usage affects a soldier's combat performance," *Medical World News* observes. "One Army psychiatrist suggests that marijuana smoking may serve a militarily useful purpose in reducing emotional tension and countering combat fatigue." This doctor admits, however, that "a 'high' might be a handicap in battle," but holds that combat soldier's intense will to survive makes it unlikely that they would light up when action was imminent.[93]

In contrast to this, statements reaching this author indicate that some soldiers think that their lives were saved by the fact that they did "light up" during battle. "Too many guys get jumpy when a sniper's around or the fire gets too heavy and they move too quick and get hit," a youth said recently. "If a guy tokes up he calms down and sort of just lays there where nobody can see him and pretty soon the battle's over and he can get up and get out with no scratches."

The question is, who wants to fight this war? "It's strictly shit," a returning survivor recently said. "We got three new commandments hanging over our heads all the time: Thou shalt not win, Thou shalt not hurt thine enemy, and Thou shalt not return too soon and upset the economy."

It is generally overlooked that the attitudes and responses evidenced in the war zone, especially among drug-using youth with marbled inhibitions, may well be continued here in the States and with the same violent results. Following an upheaval in San Francisco when the SFPD tactical squad inadvisably roughed up a priest who was trying to get his longhaired sheep off the streets, a young Vietnam veteran bitterly told this author, "The day of the pig is just about over. They taught us how to kill and they gave us the knowhow to do it and we haven't forgot. One day soon these streets will run with pig blood."

The thing that is so critically different about today's soldier, two experts in military psychiatry recently stated, is that he has no reluctance to kill. "We've known for some time that we've been unlocking something in the American boy that wasn't going to be pleasant," Dr. Benjamin Boshes, chairman of North-western University medical school's department of psychiatry,[94] said recently. The physician had had experience before in both North Africa and Italy and thus his observations were rhetorical. "In World War II," he said, "the American boy was a person who didn't want to hurt anybody—who didn't want to kill. Now we've produced a different sort of man."

Agreeing, former chief psychiatrist for the Army, Dr. Albert J. Glass, referring specifically to the My Lai massacre, said this activity represented a new phenomenon. Noting that in previous wars many American soldiers would not fire their rifles in combat, he observed that today military commanders have a new problem: conservation of ammunition.[95]

What really happened at My Lai? We may never know. Says former military psychiatrist Dr. Lewis Kurke, "Pinkville [i.e., the My Lai massacre] has been described as in some way sick or ill behavior. I think," he said, "it probably has more to do with the peculiarities of this new kind of warfare we're in. I don't think we've ever operated against civilians before in an ambiguous situation where the civilians seem to be intermittently indistinguishable from fighting forces. And this is the dilemma of the soldier who is in a situation where the definitions are made in the same chain of command through which orders are transmitted."[96]

Soldiers, most of them late adolescent or in their early twenties, had seen civilians return their proffered hand of friendship by placing a grenade in it. This was true of old men, women and children. When they were told to "wipe out" My Lai, Dr. Kurke notes, "The definition these men had was: 'This is a village that sheltered North Vietnamese soldiers who had been shelling our people. They are enemies apt to kill us and we must kill them'."

Did drug use influence the troops involved in the My Lai massacre? The government released a statement through Assistant Defense Secretary for Public Affairs Daniel Z. Henkin that the Army had thoroughly investigated the use of marijuana at My Lai and, in a manner of speech strongly resembling the sociological section of the La Guardia report, said the army "developed no evidence that any member of the units in the Song My [My Lai area] operation was under the influence of marijuana or narcotics."[97]

In contrast former Army Sgt. Charles West of Chicago told a Senate Subcommittee that an estimated sixty percent of the men in C Company had smoked marijuana at least once and that some had used it the night before the alleged massacre.[98] West, incidentally, was a squad leader in C Company. Related to this testimony, psychiatrists James W. Teague of Los Angeles and Albert A. LaVerne of New York told the same subcommittee that if men had smoked marijuana a few hours before or during the My Lai incident, it would have influenced their actions.[99] Significantly, a Pentagon task force studying this problem came up with the advice that while "there is no evidence that drug use has had an adverse effect on unit readiness in Vietnam it is suggested that soldiers be considered voluntarily incapacitated for duty for 12-36 hours after using marijuana."[100]

The cautious statement of the Pentagon committee may be grossly underestimated. "Contrary to many popular opinions held here in the United States," La Verne told the Senate Subcommittee, marijuana "could cause people to become fearful, paranoid, extremely angry and lead, in a number of cases, to acts of murder, rape and aggravated assault."[101]

Said psychiatrist James Teague, Vietnam veteran, at the same hearing, "I used to think that marijuana was not a dangerous drug. Now I believe that it can be. It would be a good idea if a lot of American psychiatrists were given a chance to see the drug at work in Vietnam. . . ."[102] Adding to this observation was the testimony of former Spec. 4 Donald L. Ridenhour of California, whose letters to officials touched off the My Lai inquiry. Ridenhour testified that many men he served with in Vietnam used marijuana.[103] Ten to fifteen percent in his forty-man helicopter section used pot, and a 150-man, long-range reconnaissance patrol with which he served for seven months, had a seventy to eighty percent use factor (though the majority of this seemed to be casual use).

Jon Steinberg, age 25, a former Spec. 5 who researched this problem for the Army, estimates that the use of drugs by soldiers in South Vietnam is reducing the Army's effectiveness.[104] A study of 1,064 soldiers in the 173rd Airborne Brigade, by Dr. John J. Treanor, tends to support Steinberg's observation. The study, done in February, 1970, found that of 494 field soldiers questioned in a special section of the investigation, 173, thirty-five percent, said thay smoked pot once or more a week, and 94, nineteen percent, said they smoked it just about every day or "more often than once a day."[105]

Contrary to the widely held opinion that most marijuana smoking is done among soldiers in large, rear-area base camps, the study found that nearly two-thirds of the soldiers who admitted smoking marijuana were stationed at forward base camps, and spent most of their time on "field duty" or combat and pacification operations in the countryside. The interesting thing about the 173rd Airborne was that it contained a higher than usual number of career-oriented personnel. Of the total sample, which represented about one-sixth of the men assigned to the brigade (6,000), 32 percent had never used pot, 37 percent had used it occasionally, then no more, 15 percent said they used it once a week, and 16 percent daily or more.

Treanor found that 89 percent of the regular users were under age 25 and that use decreased as responsibility and rank increased. Most of the youths were dissatisfied with their jobs and nearly half had requested transfers. Treanor also discovered that among regular users the majority had started smoking pot before they came to Vietnam. Significant findings in other investigations show that nearly 90 percent of the Army's court-martialed soldiers aged 18 to 24 smoked marijuana before they entered the service.

"We have not yet seen the brilliant young man of higher education using marijuana to express his disgust with our hypocritical society," the physician said. "What we have seen clinically is a majority of rather incapable, frustrated, poorly educated . . . personalities complicating the many problems they already have by becoming involved with the use of marijuana." If Treanor's statistics are a criterion by which we can extrapolate the forthcoming civilian problems, we come back again to the same conclusion. Many youths can play with pot, even use it, and because of pre-existing personality stability may not be harmed. But some will be damaged. If the Army statistics have meaning, this "some" may be twenty percent.

"There is mounting concern in the Pentagon," *Medical World News* notes,[106] "over the use of the drug [marijuana] in the Armed Forces. About nine out of ten men court martialed for offenses in Vietnam are reported to have been on the weed before joining the service. But the problem is larger than that. Many who return from Vietnam are users. Reports from Washington indicate that the Pentagon is attempting to trace and crack down on returning servicemen who have not given up the drug."

Noting a marked increase in the number of soldiers dying from overdose of hard narcotics and stimulant-depressant combinations, the Army suddenly reversed its public relations releases of August, 1970 and in October of that year labeled drug abuse "a matter of grave concern." Former Senator Thomas J. Dodd was sharply critical of the military's approach of punishing drug users instead of trying to stop the traffic in narcotics, which has seemingly lined the pockets of people who accept our help and allegedly are our friends. He says the Defense Department "does not really know and may never know much about drug addiction because drug addicts who admit their affliction are court martialed or receive a dishonorable discharge or are dealt with in other ways reminiscent of medieval treatment for the insane."[107]

Dodd notes that when the military treats drug users by simply discharging them, it is releasing upon the United States a drug problem which neither the military nor the civilian population can properly manage. Based on available statistics, Dodd notes, more than a million drug users are either already out of the military or are ready "to come home to continue their habit." It is fortunate, in a sense, that marijuana is the drug which most of these youth are involved. But as has been persistently the case, involvement with one pleasurable drug and dependence on it may lead to experimentation with other drugs for additional or different effects. "As the war in Vietnam slows down," states Air Force Lt. Col. Richard C. Froede, "narcotic drug addiction and addict deaths in the Armed Forces will increase." It did so after World War II and also after Korea.[108]

This time, however, there is a difference. Added to the hard drugs is a substance most youths have been taught "can't hurt you" and is the ideal stuff for socio-recreation. Times are indeed a changin', as Bob Dylan long ago noted. This time when the boys come home, a new girl will have replaced Lili Marlene and the Mademoiselle from Armentières. Her name is Mary Jane. We have only begun to hear about her.

"Let's see, that's one 'yes,' four 'no' and seventeen 'Like, man, who needs it?'"

the
literature
of
cannabis
use

9

Literature is a phase of life. If one is afraid of it, the
    situation is irremediable;
If one approaches it familiarly what one says of it is
    worthless.

—PICKING AND CHOOSING

ONE OF THE PRINCIPLE ARGUMENTS of-
fered by pro-cannabis enthusiasts to "prove" that marijuana has
never been indicted as a dangerous drug is that no valid studies
have appeared in medical literature which offer sufficient evidence to warrant avoiding the use of cannabis. This is another
of the marijuana myths. The reason most people believe it is
that it is continually reiterated, and repetition breeds conviction.
The same is true of the refrain, "Pot can't hurt you." In fact, both
comments are loaded with error.

Dr. Oliver Byrd at Stanford University[1] is currently wading
through some 2000 of these "non-existent" studies, the majority
of which overwhelmingly warn against marijuana use or urge
caution in evaluating it. The bibliography was obtained from the
United Nations, which has catalogued the material for those

who wish to peruse it. In America, a similar though less extensive bibliography can be obtained through STASH.[2]

It is true, of course, that there has been a publications gap over the past twenty years as far as new observations on cannabis are concerned. There was a rash of articles on cannabis in the eighteen hundreds, then a slacking off until the mid 1960's when it started again. Perhaps this was due to the fact that observers, after publishing so much on the subject, felt it was adequately covered and moved on to study other problems. The new generation, however, particularly in the English-speaking countries, seems intent on reviving the situation again, negating all that has been observed and finding out the hard way what has been noted from experience by previous generations in many different cultures and countries.

As a matter of interest, previous studies on this subject have appeared in most of the major languages. By 1968, one could study the following material: 936 articles in English, 386 in French, 206 in German, 106 in Portuguese, 74 in Spanish, 45 in the Slavic languages, 33 in Italian, 12 in Latin, 8 in Dutch, 8 in Turkish, 7 in Russian, 3 in Greek, 3 in Norwegian, 2 in Swedish, and 31 in miscellaneous other languages. Much more has been written since then.

The interesting thing about this material is that so few authors have anything good to say in favor of using cannabis. Those who do, however, are quoted and requoted as though the opinions they express represent the majority view. In truth, the few articles that do express favorable opinions on cannabis are in the smallest minority. Although a few others exist, there are three classic studies the procannabis people frequently refer to: the Indian Hemp Commission Report published in 1894,[3] a paper that appeared in the *Military Surgeon*[4] dealing with observations begun in the Panama Canal Zone in 1925 and published in 1933, and the so-called La Guardia Report published in 1944.[5]

Speaking of these reports, HEW told Congress this: "The Indian Hemp Commission Report, for example, although a careful, systematic study for its day (the 1890's), can hardly be regarded as meeting modern epidemiological research standards. Subsequent studies such as those of the group appointed by the then Mayor La Guardia in New York City can also be easily faulted for their scientific deficiences."[6]

The report of the Indian Hemp Commission was quite permissive in its findings. It stated that no evidence existed which indicated the use of cannabis caused mental or moral injuries, that it was not associated with disease, and that it caused few, if any, effects different from indulgence in alcohol. While one could spend much time dissecting and commenting on the findings in this comprehensive report, it should be sufficient for our purposes to note that in 1953 the Indian government decided it had had enough of the effects of cannabis on its culture, and authorized a phasing-out program designed to eliminate the use of cannabis in India as quickly as possible.

In recent years a plethora of pro-cannabis articles has appeared in the public press, but medical literature in general, with a few outstanding exceptions, tends to be conservative in its attitude towards pot. Grinspoon,[7] whose comprehensive review of marijuana in 1969 discounted the opinion that cannabis is dangerous, and who indicated that "the anxiety and sense of helplessness generated by the dangers of our time may be focused in some degree on marijuana, driving some people to protective immersion in the drug and arousing others to a crusade against it," has offered an explanation for the attitudes expressed in medical literature. Calling the Talbott[8] report, which is far from radical, a "terrible study," he announced that his conservative article was "another instance in which the *Journal of the American Medical Association* picks papers on this subject which only take a very negative stand."[9]

Harvard psychobiologist Peter Dews asserts a more conservative viewpoint, however, concerning the "open arms" attitudes toward cannabis.[10] "Our government is assuming increasingly the responsibility of consumer protection," he notes. "Instead of *caveat emptor*, or, at most, mandatory warnings, government agencies are now under great pressure to remove from the market agents and devices whose safety has been questioned." Referring to the situation in which the government pulled cyclamates off the market (although in contrast to cannabis, there was no clear evidence that any human had ever been harmed by such sugar substitutes), he explains that our current society is heading toward a socialistic attitude in which people not only expect to take care of their neighbors; they also expect the government to be responsible.

"The evidence on the safety of marijuana," he warns, "is of

two kinds, laboratory and sociological. The laboratory evidence is fragmentary. We know the acute toxicity is vanishingly small, but the public information on chronic toxicity is far short of what the Food and Drug Administration requires for approving a drug even for therapeutic use; and it is, rightly, much, much harder to win approval for an agent to be taken by healthy people with no possibility of direct therapeutic benefit. Thousands of people," he reasons, "are killed annually by drugs taken for therapeutic purposes, but only a tiny proportion of the physicians who prescribed them are charged with wrongdoing; in contrast it is said that he who gives a drug to a healthy subject, (for example, for scientific purposes) and kills him is liable for murder." Where marijuana is concerned, he notes, "it has not been shown that [it] has even any indirect benefits to health."

The tendency today is to consider that anything old is passé and irrelevant. Members of the avant-garde reject the lessons of history, especially where pot is concerned, although almost every observation fundamental to civilization is based on records of the ancients. As a result of dismissing these sources, they have pinned themselves down to less than a dozen papers which they can interpret as being "acceptable" and, as we shall note shortly where the La Guardia report is concerned, they distort and misquote most of these in order to fortify their position.

Is it true that almost nothing has been written about pot? Hardly! It must be admitted, however, that many of the observations were made by practitioners who reported their own experiences without the benefit of laboratory evaluation. If only one or two had done this, it might be easy to ignore the accumulated literature. But the fact that many men have reported similar findings should prompt the prudent man to "play it cool" until he is certain there is reasonable safety in using marijuana. We seem to grant pot a certain freedom we have been unwilling to give any other drug in the history of pharmacology. If we had but a tenth of the adverse information about any other chemical that we have on pot, we would probably ban the other substance for all time.

If one peruses the medical literature, he finds that instead of a dearth, there is a plethora of information. We are told so often these articles do not exist that it's actually fun to discover them. Take the 1800's, for instance. In the late part of that century, authors reported the following things: a thirty-one-year-old

woman who was "successfully" treated for asthma with cannabis, but when she changed to a new supply, she developed pain,
swollen tongue and other adverse symptoms so that the medicine had to be stopped;[11] the warning that while small doses of
cannabis could be medically useful, large doses could cause
facial edema, weakness and tremor, mental feebleness, and
emaciation,[12] an accidental poisoning by 7½ drops of tincture of cannabis in a thirty-year-old woman who experienced
drowsiness, dimmed vision, great thirst, rapid pulse and dry
mouth. The author of this report felt the case was an "idiosyncrasy."[13]

The instance of a nineteen-year-old girl who became very
dizzy from taking ¾ of a grain of cannabis was also reported, and
her reaction caused the doctor to note that some people are quite
sensitive to small doses of cannabis;[14] a sixty-eight-year-old
woman experienced what were then thought to be "typical"
symptoms of cannabis poisoning from ⅞ of a grain, i.e., high
temperature, sensory distortions, and a slight dilatation of the
pupils.[15] Minter records an adverse reaction in a twenty-three-
year-old man who developed a dry, swollen tongue, hallucinations, air hunger, and a feeble, rapid pulse.[16] Palgrave reports
another case of poisoning by Cannabis indica.[17] Walker became
concerned enough to ask that some standardization of dosage be
found because of the cases of poisoning he observed.[18] Williams experienced an overdose of cannabis due to a 1½ teaspoonful dose of tincture; the patient had hallucinations, fast pulse,
and weakness.[19] Brown discusses the case of a druggist's clerk
who took 6 grains over the period of an hour and a half to see
what would happen. (What happened was nervousness, dizziness, an irresistible urge to run and to urinate, and finally, violent
convulsions.)[20]

Campbell tells of a youth who took 6 grains of extract, then
developed feelings of heaviness, uncontrolled laughter, double
consciousness, and "something" resembling *petit mal* seizures.
It was several days before he returned to normal.[21] Prentiss records the precipitation of hallucinations in a thirty-four-year-old
doctor who took 5 drops of tincture (then made by Parke-
Davis), with no bad continuing effects.[22] A case is reported of a
thirty-three-year-old woman who used cannabis for migraine
and developed a disturbed psychological state and a creeping
sensation in the limbs.[23] Simpson described the ill effects of

cannabis in *Native Poisons of India*.[24] In another instance, a physician personally took a teaspoonful of tincture, developed anxiety, unpleasant thoughts, and an inability to walk.[25] Fisher reports a case of poisoning,[26] while Dallas notes an instance of voice loss following its use.[27]

Bentlif[28] records a case of cannabis poisoning, while Bicknell[29] notes that an ingestion of 3 grains caused headache, loss of motor control, increased pulse and respiration, visions, marked urine output, and violent convulsive movements of the upper extremities. Foulis[30] tells of two brothers (20 and 22) who took 40 minums of cannabis in an effort to provoke the dreams described in literature. Both had visual distortions, increased respiratory and pulse rates, and fears of death.

Strange[31] notes he assisted a woman in marked depression who was using cannabis as the therapeutic agent, while Fischlowitz[32] records an instance where his patient complained of tingling and uneasiness in his legs, a parched throat, a thick and leathery tongue, reddened conjunctivae, and rapid pulse and respiration. Baxter-Tyrie[33] lists another adverse series of reactions in a young woman, while Atlee[34] notes a similar problem in a twelve-year-old boy who used cannabis as a therapeutic agent.

Geiser[35] states that cannabis made one of his migraine patients violently ill; Hamaker[36] tells of the self-experiment by a physician who, after taking 41 drops of extract (made by Squibbs), developed distortion of time sense, abdominal discomfort, and increased pulse and respiration. Ireland[37] notes a case of toxic psychosis. Saxby[38] records an instance of a thirty-three-year-old man who swallowed 2 teaspoons of tincture, collapsed, and became unconscious. Wood[39] describes the variability of action of different cannabis extracts and notes that overdose "poisons." Robertson[40] also reports a case of toxic symptoms from using tincture in official doses. Tirard[41] tells of a forty-six-year-old man who took 2½ times the recommended dose and developed giddiness, palpitation, anxiety, and nervousness. (When he took the recommended dose his migraine disappeared and he felt well).

Marshall[42] notes the pharmacological effects of cannabis and tells of his personal experience with 0.15 gm. of cannabinol in which he experienced slurred speech, ataxia, fits of laughter, and alterations in subjective time. A case is also reported of a man who personally took 40 drops of tincture to relieve neuralgia and developed heaviness and numbness of the limbs, loss of sensation, and a fear of death, plus the "irresistible desire to commit suicide." When this subsided he became "ravenously hungry."[43]

Fielde[44] notes three personal experiences with the drug, in which he depersonalized and felt his body image had altered. Dinshaw[45] reports another case of complete loss of voice, with recovery. Kelley[46] describes a sixty-year-old woman who took cannabis for rheumatism and developed giddiness, cold extremities, and auditory and visual hallucinations. Laurence[47] tells of ill effects from the use of bhang in the Native Indian Army. Marshall[48] reports his subjective reactions subsequent to taking 0.1 gm. of cannabinol; he experienced slurred speech, ataxia, fits of laughter, and alterations in subjective time. Bell[49] and Tull-Walsh[50] discuss case reports that show the ability of the drug to produce "insanity." Clarke tells of his own experience with the drug, during which he lost the use of one arm for a half-hour.[51] Wood states the use of the tincture made from American plants caused a distortion of time sense, convulsions, and an intermittent loss of memory, but no aphrodisiac effects nor after-effects such as nausea, headache, or constipation.[52]

Sawtelle reports seeing adverse reactions to cannabis while treating neuralgia.[53] Rushin notes two cases of acute poisoning.[54] Clouston records the frequency of admissions to the Cairo Asylum of cannabis users.[55] Tull-Walsh[56] notes that the mentally stable can use cannabis with minimal effects, but that it may precipitate insanity when taken by highly neurotic or mentally unstable people, and that by all means it should never be taken with datura (Jimson weed).

And so it goes. Eleven additional cases were described from 1900 to 1930.[57-67] Sixteen similar reports appeared in medical literature during the 1930's.[68-83] Fourteen were written during the 1940's.[84-97] Nine appeared during the 1950's.[98-106] In 1960 interest in cannabis seemed to revive again. During that decade thirty-two articles were printed in medical literature, the majority urging caution in the use of cannabis and/or listing adverse effects.[107-139] This summary of the literature scans only the English language publications; many others appeared in non-English magazines and books.

Nothing has been written concerning the adverse effects of

pot? The bibliography tends to dispute this. Well, we might be told, these weren't valid laboratory findings and therefore can't be considered as "proof." To believe this one would have to assume that the mass of physicians who have reported these findings were either incompetent to make observations or intellectually dishonest. This argument might be offered, though not honestly, against material written prior to the 1930's, but can one make the same derogations against medical authors writing *after* the '30's, who are alive and quite capable of defending themselves?

The student who is trying to make up his mind concerning the relative safety of pot should ask himself this, then, when he comes across the reassurance of "experts" who state there is no evidence of harm or that anything written is invalid because of the lack of expertise on the part of the writer: has the "expert" recognized at least *some* of the evidence above? If not, he is either at odds with the majority of medical opinion or toying with intellectual dishonesty.

One thing seems sure, considering the current trend to "report" observations on cannabis. If the above or even half the above were pro-pot, the headlines couldn't be big enough to spread the news. This, then, is the purpose of this book: to call to the attention of the reader that all is not safe with pot and that these observations have valid medical backing. When cannabis has been given sufficient time and exposure in other civilizations it has frequently been condemned as unsafe and unacceptable for general consumption. It has shown itself historically to be a menace to those whose personalities cannot handle it; it has proved to be a cause of adverse reactions even in the experienced user, and it can cause and/or precipitate incapacitating psychotic episodes.

THE LA GUARDIA REPORT: SOCIOLOGICAL STUDY

One major marijuana study of the past was not done hastily. It was performed by a panel of experts, clinically at least, comprised of truly respected names in medicine. The report came about because at the time of the passage of the Marijuana Tax Act of 1937 the country was caught up in a wave of hysteria concerning the effects of marijuana, particularly as it related to youth.

Fascinating organizations such as the International Narcotic Education Association were publishing diatribes in the guise of "information" that fanned the press and paled the red corpuscles of the readers. "The habitual use of this narcotic poison," one of their publications intoned, ". . . leads to physical wreckage and mental decay. . . . Marijuana sometimes gives man the lust to kill unreasonably and without motive. Many cases of assault, rape, robbery, and murder are traced to the use of marijuana."[140]

On December 28, 1940, the New York *Daily Worker,* in its health advice column, informed its readers that smoking the weed caused "the face to become bloated, the eyes bloodshot, the limbs weak and trembling and the mind [to sink] into insanity. Robberies, thrill murders, sex crimes and other offenses result." The article went on to say, "the habit can be cured only by the most severe methods. The addict must be put into an institution, where the drug is gradually withdrawn . . . [and] kept there until he has enough willpower to withstand the temptation to again take to the weed."

With all this uproar many public officials had cause for concern. One of these was the mayor of New York City, F. H. La Guardia. As was his custom in matters of health, he asked for the assistance of the New York Academy of Medicine. The mayor was aware of the paper written concerning the use of marijuana by soldiers stationed in Panama and was impressed by the drug's "relative harmlessness."[141] La Guardia wanted factual information that would be a basic contribution to medicine and pharmacology. He also wanted to know how bad the situation was in his city.

The Academy came up with the suggestion of conducting a dual study, one part sociological, one part clinical. The sociological study was aimed at finding out the answers to these questions: (1) the extent of marijuana use in New York City, (2) its method of retail distribution, (3) the attitude of its users toward society, (4) its relationship to sex, (5) its relationship to crime, and (6) its relationship to juvenile delinquency. The clinical study was directed toward the determination, by means of controlled experiments, of the physiological and psychological effects of marijuana on different types of persons, its production or lack of production of mental deterioration, and the potential use of the drug in the treatment of other diseases or addictions.

When pro-cannabis people come together they always eulo-gize the "Report." In truth, the only thing they usually refer to is the sociological study, being quite careful to leave the im-pression that this is the sum total of the discoveries of the inves-tigators. They also assiduously avoid mentioning how the socio-logical section came to its conclusions, all of which are quite favorable toward the use of cannabis. For those who really want to know what happened, this author has a suggestion: read the report. The original is difficult to come by, but a copy is avail-able in Solomon's book, *The Marijuana Papers*.[142]

Since the pro-cannabis writers conveniently forgot to inform their readers how the sociological conclusions were arrived at, let us take a brief look at the procedures. The reader will prob-ably be just as amazed at what he finds as this author was after he had gone carefully through the whole report. Once again, if in doubt about the findings as presented here, read the La Guardia Report for yourself.

The sociological study begins with a brief review of the history and notes that there is much dissension concerning the potential of cannabis to produce harm to its users. The authors note briefly the publications of the International Narcotic Edu-cation Association and the article in the New York *Daily Worker*, lumping these zany observations with a section of Dr. Robert Walton's book on cannabis that was anything but zany. One of its chapters is "The Present Status of the Marijuana Vice in the United States," written by the Commissioner of Public Safety of New Orleans, Dr. Frank R. Gomila.[143] In this chapter Dr. Gomila refers to his city as being one of the first, if not the first, large city in the United States where the cannabis habit had become firmly established. He noted that reporters had not only heard about but had actually observed large numbers of school-boys buying and smoking reefers. In one instance a peddler opened shop under the street stairs to a girls' high school.

Inquiries revealed that school children of forty-four schools in New Orleans, only a few being high schools, smoked mari-juana. "The Director of Kingsley House for Boys," Gomila noted, "received many pleas from fathers of boys who had come under the influence [of cannabis] and were charged with petty crimes. After personally seeing these boys in an hysterical condition or on the well-known 'laughing jags,' the director termed the situ-ation decidedly grave."[144] As a matter of fact, the situation *was* grave in New Orleans and provided the impetus to legislators to pass the Marijuana Tax Law. This is another fact often "overlooked" by the pro-cannabis people.

The committee doing the sociological study of the La Guardia Report, armed with this information, then set about organizing a unit to study the problem in New York. They did not study the entire city of New York. Instead, they chose to look at a very limited segment of the city, the borough of Manhattan. All conclusions concerning the rest of New York City were based on what they observed there. The New York Police Department gave the committee four policemen and two policewomen, who did the leg work for the observers. The work was strictly undercover, investigative, and infiltrative, with the officers being instructed not to arrest anyone. While on duty the squad lived with and studied marijuana devotees and their habits, although users were presumably unaware of the official capacity of their companions.

The officers' observations concerning sale, use, and users' general emotional reactions were essentially the same as those previously noted in the literature, i.e., that users were congenial, that they were not "addicted" per se, and that cannabis was transmitted either from user to user or in "teapads" where users congregated. They found one could buy with minimal difficulty after proper introduction, and decided from observation that most marijuana was sold either in Harlem or in an area off Broadway between 42nd and 59th Streets.

The undercover agents talked to the users and then relayed the information to the committee, which studiously evaluated it. They found most users were unemployed, were aware of the laws, did not use the drug to challenge the laws per se, did not express remorse because they used the drug, and did not blame cannabis for their present personal difficulties. The users all felt the drug was harmless and enjoyed it because it produced a "high," which the committee defined as a feeling of adequacy and efficiency with the allaying of current mental conflicts.

The committee accepted the observations that users were not frustrated if they couldn't find a supply of cannabis, that each user had a limit, past which he would not go because it caused him anxiety, and that the use of cannabis did not lead to the use of hard narcotics. It is well to remember the committee's recognition, as it described the sources from which it has arrived at its conclusions, that "we have made extensive use of subjective data obtained from those who were actual smokers of marijuana and directly acquainted with its effects and those who were not smokers [i.e., police investigators] but, because of residence, occupation or other interests, were acquainted with the general subject." This last group also, apparently, included many individuals peripherally associated with users, although the committee did not designate who they were.[145]

A point of interest here is that pro-cannabis people so often decry the current papers and in particular papers written in past years in which the observations were based on patients in hospitals and jails because "the accounts were all subjective." Yet, by the committee's admission, all of the observations in this sociological section were derived from subjective opinions of users as, in many instances, they related their opinions to undercover agents.

The committee then investigated the possible link between sex and cannabis. The investigators acquired their information by visiting many teapads. "It is true," the committee states, "that lewd pictures decorated the walls," but none of the users was interested in them. The pictures just happened to be there. In fact, one police investigator found, to his embarrassment, that he was the only one in the crowd looking at them.

The investigators went to parties and watched jitterbugging, a form of dancing which the committee says "is highly suggestive and appears to be associated with erotic activity." They watched the dancers who were high and those who were not and decided that one group wasn't any more interested in sex than the other. They asked users if they ever associated sex and cannabis and were assured by the users that this rarely occurred. They went to houses of prostitution and were convinced by what they saw (although they didn't say what that was) that, even in those brothels that sometimes doubled as teapads, "the use of marijuana was not linked to sexuality."

On the basis of these findings by police investigators—who must have been the world's most efficient undercover men to be able to mingle with a group well-known for their high index of suspicion, ask personal questions, and peer at their activities —the committee came out with the statement that is considered by many to be the final conclusion on sex and cannabis by the La Guardia Report. "These observations," they said, "allow us to come to the conclusion that in the main marijuana was not used for direct sexual stimulation."[146]

The committee now came to the weighty question of the association of cannabis and crime. Part of their "evidence" consisted of talking to various law enforcement officers and being assured by these police that, speaking off the record and confidentially, "there is no proof that major crimes are associated with the practice of smoking marijuana." Having satisfied themselves that these officers had given them the information they wanted, they then in the next paragraph of their report paid them the following left-handed compliment: "The sale and use of marijuana is a problem engaging the vigilance of the New York Police Department. However, the number of officers available for such duty is limited. Officers specifically assigned to the Narcotics Division of the Police Department are acquainted with the problem, but the *majority of the officers are fundamentally without authoritative knowledge regarding this subject.*" (Italics added.)[147]

The committee then read a paper published by respected psychiatrist-in-charge of the Psychiatric Clinic of the Court of General Sessions, Dr. Walter Bromberg, in which he stated that in his experience with respect to marijuana and crime in the Court of General Sessions over a period of five and a half years, drugs generally do not initiate criminal careers. Based on the measurement of succession of arrests and convictions in this court, Dr. Bromberg postulated that the expectancy of major crimes following the use of cannabis in New York County would be small. The conclusions of the committee:

1. Marijuana is used extensively in the borough of Manhattan but the problem is not as acute as it is reported to be in other sections of the United States.

2. The introduction of marijuana into this area is recent compared with other localities.

3. The cost of marijuana is low and therefore within the purchasing power of most persons.

4. The distribution and use of marijuana is centered in Harlem.

5. The majority of marijuana smokers are Negroes and Latin Americans.

6. The consensus among marijuana smokers is that the use of the drug creates a definite feeling of adequacy.

7. The practice of smoking marijuana does not lead to addiction in the medical sense of the word.

8. The sale and distribution of marijuana is not under the control of any single organized group.

9. The use of marijuana does not lead to morphine or heroin or cocaine addiction and no effort is made to create a market for these narcotics by stimulating the practice of marijuana smoking.

10. Marijuana is not the determining factor in the commission of major crimes.[148]

The committee now directed its attention to one of the most serious problems—the potential relationship of marijuana to juvenile delinquency. Again they limited their study to the borough of Manhattan. Investigative techniques included: watching schools to see if students bought cannabis from peddlers, investigating parental complaints concerning marijuana usage by their children, interviewing school authorities, and studying statistics from various city bureaus and private agencies.

"Unknown to the school authorities," the committee states, "our investigators had under surveillance many of the schools in the borough of Manhattan. . . . We must admit that it would have been possible for such sales to have taken place during the time that our investigators were not on duty, but we came to the conclusion that there was no organized traffic on the part of peddlers in selling marijuana to the children of the schools we observed."[149]

"Interviews with school authorities," the committee stressed, "were very significant. . . ." And indeed they were, for they exhibit a naïveté of great magnitude exceeded only by the committee's capacity to accept as valid the ability of six policemen to observe adequately marijuana activity at any significant number of schools. As to school authorities, the committee interviewed authorities and/or observed thirty-nine schools. To the committee's satisfaction the principals of thirty-three schools said they had no problem. Or almost. Actually what they said was, "I have had no trouble. . . ." "I have had no contact with it. . . ." "[I] never found anything to indicate the use of it. . . ." "[I] suspected that a group of chronic truants were using marijuana but [I] was unable to obtain any direct evidence. . . ." "[I know] of no marijuana problem in the school. . . ." "[I] found no tangible evidence. . . ." And so on.

The most fascinating report was that made of School Number Two, which was characteristic of all those institutions under investigation "knew of no marijuana in the school." According to the committee report: "No. Two High School, predominantly white. The principal at first appeared to be evasive and did not readily volunteer information, but after repeatedly being pressed with the question stated that the school 'had not had any difficulty with the subject of marijuana'." One can only sympathize with this poor principal, her job possibly at stake, trying to out-maneuver a group of blue-ribbon officials from the mayor's committee who were trying to find something bad about the students in her school.

In one school where the principal finally admitted there might be a "few" instances of marijuana smoking, an assistant to the principal told the committee there had been some boys in the school who had "reefers" in their possession. On one occasion a few of the boys appeared to be intoxicated and when examined confessed to having smoked "reefers." The assistant further stated, "It was difficult to be sure if sleepy, perspiring, pallid looking boys were feeling the effects of marijuana or were just recovering from too much 'partying' or 'drinking'."

A number of principals who "had no contact with it" assured the committee they would notify them immediately if anything turned up. In each instance the committee reports, "During the period of the survey no such report was made."

In another instance where the principal had "no tangible evidence," she did report she believed the drug could be found if one wanted to get it. The committee "investigated thoroughly the suggestions made by the principal as to premises where marijuana might be sold but we were unable to gather any evidence of its sale." In another school the principal reported students claimed that cannabis was on sale in a nearby candy store. Once again the committee "investigated" and came up empty-handed. The pattern was generally repeated in the committee's investigation of schools. In one junior high school where a teacher testified that cannabis had been used and that she had sent home five students she believed to be "dopey" from cannabis, the committee tended to doubt the teacher's word and emphasized that students could be sent home without notification of the principal and without medical examination. The principal had, of course, testified there was no problem in his school.

The committee did not, however, believe everybody. At School Number 39, for instance, where the principal also reported there was no problem, the committee decided they thought he was wrong. "We are certain, however, that this school does to some extent present an acute problem for we have observed a few students smoking 'reefers' away from the school. We have reason to believe that some of them smoke it while at school. The girls attending this high school have a very low moral standard."

Why the committee took such a dislike to School Number 39 they did not say, but at School Number 32 they were quite willing to accept opinions of the staff. "Although rumor is widespread that 'reefer' smoking is common at this school, thorough investigation did not produce evidence of it at the time of our investigation. We did obtain information," the committee said, "which we consider authoritative, that in 1935 a man was offered the concession to sell marijuana cigarettes to the students of this school. He refused the offer. The principal of this school stated that there had never been any trouble as a result of marijuana smoking and he knew of no actual cases."[150]

On the basis of these observations, to which, incidentally, was added a review of the Children's Court records for 1939, the committee came to these conclusions:

1. Marijuana smoking is not widespread among school children.

2. Juvenile delinquency is not associated with the practice of smoking marijuana.

3. The publicity concerning the catastrophic effects of marijuana smoking in New York City is unfounded.[151]

There, briefly, is the part of the La Guardia Report so dear to the hearts of the pro-cannabis people, the part that is quoted and requoted ad infinitum. Further study of the sociological section is left to the reader. Now, let us take a brief look at the part that is not so often quoted but which is significant in that it was, until recently, the only major published clinical observation on a reasonably large number of marijuana smokers.

THE LA GUARDIA REPORT: CLINICAL STUDY

The clinical study was directed toward evaluating two main things: the pleasurable effects that account for the widespread use of cannabis, and the undesirable effects, "including those leading to criminal and other antisocial acts."[152] A number of things about the study can be criticized: it was carried on in a locked ward of Goldwater Memorial Hospital, and performed under the direct observation of guards from the Department of Corrections and the New York City Police Force. The participants were seventy-two prisoners from either Rikers or Hart Island penitentiaries or the House of Detention for Women, plus five paid volunteers who had had no previous experience with cannabis. Only one of these was considered to be a normal personality.[153]

The subjects numbered sixty-five males and seven females, with forty-eight having a history of smoking marijuana previously. The committee notes that there were two advantages in selecting subjects from this group. First, they could be kept under continuous observation and second, they constituted an excellent sample of the "typical" New York City user.

There were also some disadvantages. Being under constant observation and in custody, the subjects were in no position to try anything original. This meant they did not dare permit themselves to become so high on cannabis they could not control their activities. Secondly, at least forty-eight of the group were "street smart": they knew that the best way to get along in jail is to cooperate and give the "man" what he wants. The group had an average IQ of nearly one hundred and they knew from experience that they could not get out of line without retribution. Even so, the clinical study reveals a number of important findings that are seldom referred to by the pro-cannabis people. These findings, chosen here at random from the report, can be read in their original context by those who wish to increase their knowledge on the techniques employed by the physicians who worked with this study.[154]

1. Different states of marijuana intoxication were precipitated by varying doses of the drug. These ranged from the usual euphoria and incoordination with smaller amounts, to feelings of discomfort and depression. One subject evidenced a state of depression with anxiety after taking the equivalent of four joints and a psychotic episode with a fear of death when he doubled this amount.

2. The subjects varied considerably in their general behavior after taking the drug. Quite commonly, they demonstrated a difficulty in focusing and in sustaining mental concentration.

3. The investigators did note that eroticism was reported in ten percent of the 150 instances in which marijuana was administered to the group. "The presence of nurses, attendants and other women associated with the study gave opportunity for frank expression of sexual stimulation, had this been marked."[155] The observers did not include in this observation the fact that the presence of guards also gave the subjects the opportunity for a slap on the head if they got too far out of line. On the other hand, some subjects did lose control and in isolated instances would loudly discharge flatus or urinate on the floor, while one man who had been previously arrested on three occasions for indecent exposure indulged in frank exhibitionism.

4. The general behavior of the group was interesting. They argued, but "the arguments never seemed to get anywhere, although they often dealt with important problems, and the illogical reasoning used was never recognized or returned by the person to whom it was addressed." The committee also noted, "it is obvious that under marijuana the subject laughs more readily and for longer time intervals. This is probably due both [to] the fact that things seem funnier to him and because when under the influence of the drug he is less inhibited." Further, the committee noted, "One forgot that these were actually adults with all the usual adult responsibilities. One could not help drawing the conclusion that they too had forgotten this for the time being."[156] But the committee report insisted that, "although urged to smoke more, no subject could be persuaded to take more than he knew or felt he could handle."

5. The problem of psychotic episodes has been mentioned before but is repeated briefly again because of its importance: "The conclusion seems warranted that given the potential personality make-up and the right time and environment, marijuana may bring on a true psychotic state."[157]

6. The more complex the activity engaged in under the influence of cannabis, the more the activity is affected. Simple functions such as tapping are affected only slightly, whereas complex functions such as hand-steadiness and reaction time "may be affected adversely to a considerable degree by the administration of both large and small doses of marijuana."[158]

7. Marijuana has a transitory adverse effect on mental functioning. The extent of the intellectual impairment, the time of onset, and its duration are all related to the amount of drug

taken. In general, the nonusers experienced greater intellectual impairment for longer periods of time than that experienced by those who had used cannabis before. Because speed and accuracy are affected, the user finds he has a falling off of ability. Indulgence in marijuana, however, does not appear to result in mental deterioration.[159]

8. Individuals under the influence of marijuana do not change their basic personality structure. They do, however, experience increased feelings of relaxation, disinhibition, and self-confidence, the latter tending to be expressed verbally more than physically. The disinhibition releases what is latent in the individual's thoughts and emotions but does not evoke responses that would be alien to him in the undrugged state. The use of marijuana releases not only pleasant reactions but also feelings of anxiety. Where personality is concerned, the people most likely to resort to the use of marijuana are those who have difficulty making satisfactory social contacts or experiencing emotional reactions.[160]

9. These subjects who were tested for attitude changes showed very little change of opinion toward family and community when they were under the influence of marijuana. The only very definite change was in their attitude toward the drug itself. Without marijuana only four out of fourteen subjects tested said they would tolerate the sale of marijuana. After they were up on the drug eight of them were in favor of this. Another significant reaction observed was that subjects who were up on marijuana were content to live in a community that was less orderly and well organized than they preferred when they were not influenced by the drug. This, the observers felt, might be due to the generally indifferent attitude and the lack of motor coordination caused by the effects of the drug.[161]

This, briefly, is a summary of the findings of the clinical study section of the La Guardia Report. It should be unnecessary at this stage to point out the relevance of these findings to the social aspects of cannabis use by those individuals who are marginally adjusted prior to coming under the drug's influence. Realization that it is this sort of person who is attracted to continued use of marijuana makes the observations of this study even more socially significant.

It is unfortunate that the La Guardia Report has been discounted by so many who apparently failed to read the significant findings of the clinical study. It is equally sad that the sociological findings are so often stressed when a survey of the techniques used to arrive at the final conclusions fails to stand critical scrutiny. This, however, has been the story of marijuana: confused, distorted, multifaceted, misunderstood, feared, exalted, misinterpreted. Perhaps, someday, a final study will be done to clear away all doubt in the minds of both proponents and opponents. As it stands at the moment, however, only a few writers of scientific standing have come out in favor of the use of the drug, and the literature in general is overwhelmingly critical, even condemnatory. Fortunately for man, all this discussion is limited to a unique plant with but a single genus and species. If there were more than one it is difficult to see how the world could survive the controversy.

RECENT PUBLICATIONS

Three varieties of publications are now beginning to appear in both lay and medical literature concerning the use of marijuana. The first category consists of formal research. This has been desperately needed. Fortunately it now seems to be proceeding with minimal restrictions for qualified personnel. The second group consists of case reports, frequently noting adverse reactions to the drug, but also noting, with increasing frequency, that low grade marijuana is not as harmful as was once thought. The third, primarily from sociological, psychological, political science, law, and psychiatric writers, usually covers the broad scan of cannabis use and frequently tends to question the validity of reports which indict cannabis as a potentially dangerous drug. It is not implied that all writers from these disciplines do this, but it has been noted that the majority of contemporary permissive and promarijuana observations have arisen among this third group.

As this book goes to press, two reports have appeared which are causing considerable comment. The first was reported in the April 12, 1971, issue of the *American Medical Association News,* and concerns the efforts of four scientists at Oxford University in England to study the effects of cannabis. The report is of interest in that it is apparently the only major laboratory study of marijuana being done as of this date in Britain. The observations, still to be officially reported by the Oxford investigators, are presented here because they differ so markedly from the comments of critics who state we have no proof that pot is a potentially harmful drug. Because it is unfinished, the only validity that can now be given to this report is that it is being conducted in a respected British institution by reputable scientists with the approval of their government and the majority of their peers, and that the American Medical Association has seen fit to publicize it as newsworthy.

According to William Paton, professor of pharmacology at Oxford University, the team has found "strong evidence that the drug is unsafe and in some cases may be highly dangerous."[162] The major question which remains to be decided, he says, is whether or not marijuana has a thalidomide-type effect on pregnant women. At this point, he comments, this possibility cannot be ruled out; there is a distinct possibility that women who regularly smoke marijuana may have a reduced fertility. It is also possible, he reports, that "regular marijuana use could lead to early abortion, to a change in the user's sex drive, and to damage to the liver."

The second contemporary report, by Kolansky and Moore, appeared in the April 19, 1971, issue of the *American Medical Association Journal*.[163] Within twenty-four hours of publication indignant rebuttals emerged from the four corners of the nation and from many points in between. The report centered around the study of thirty-eight young patients who were chronic users of marijuana. Their use, according to the authors, precipitated adverse psychological effects that ranged from mild ego decompensation to psychosis. "Clearly," the authors noted, "there is in our patients, a demonstration of an interruption of normal psychological adolescent growth processes following the use of marijuana."

The study began in 1965, when the authors, who specialize in child and adult psychiatry, noted a large increase in the number of patients whose psychiatric problems began shortly after they had started smoking marijuana. Although the two psychiatrists had treated and examined many marijuana smokers, they excluded from their study all patients who had a history or evidence of severe psychological problems prior to smoking marijuana, or who had used LSD, amphetamines or other drugs. In other words, they examined a collection of thirty-eight patients who had been, in their professional opinion as psychiatrists, in good mental health prior to their involvement with pot. They also excluded some neurotics whose symptoms became more severe after smoking marijuana. Still others eliminated were patients who had a marked predisposition to psychosis and who became psychotic after beginning to smoke pot. "Our purpose," the psychiatrists said, "was to report only the effects seen as a consequence of marijuana smoking in those not showing a predisposition to serious psychiatric problems."

With this goal in mind the psychiatrists chose youths ages thirteen to twenty-four (20 male, 18 female) for evaluation, treatment, and study. (They excluded a number of patients over the age of 24 who had similar problems in order to limit their attention to the adolescent group per se.) Most of the patients smoked marijuana two or more times weekly, and in general smoked two or more marijuana cigarettes each time. These patients, the investigators said, "consistently showed very poor social judgment, poor attention span, poor concentration, confusion, anxiety, depression, apathy, passivity, indifference, and often slowed and slurred speech."

The study reported that four of the youths, two male and two female, attempted suicide. Four males developed a marked psychosis, although they had no prior history of ego fragility, predisposition to psychosis, or family history of psychosis. Borderline states of ego decompensation were seen in twelve of the adolescents on trial for marijuana possession. (Many adolescents are placed on trial before the courts; it is questionable if so high a percentage of those tried react to this pressure with as great a decompensatory response as did these pot smokers.)

Six of the patients, ages 14 to 20, had symptoms that were not at first associated with marijuana: deterioration in schoolwork, inability to concentrate, gradual decrease in academic standing, apathy, indifference, passivity, and withdrawal from social activities. *When the patients stopped using marijuana, the adverse effects gradually disappeared and the patients resumed more normal behavior.*

The group had an unusual degree of promiscuity ranging from "sexual relations with several individuals of the opposite sex to relations with individuals of the same sex, individuals of both sexes, and sometimes, individuals of both sexes on the same evening." In the histories of all of these patients, the psychiatrists said, "we were struck by the loss of sexual inhibitions after short periods of marijuana smoking."

Kolansky and Moore had several goals in mind in presenting this report. One was to relate their observations on reactions occurring within *their* group of thirty-eight selected young patients. Another was to point out their hypothesis that one of the factors that led to the abuse of drugs by the youths in this group was the "equivocation" of their parents. The normal adolescent needs support and guided firmness from parents, the men advised, and if this is missing, the youth may turn increasingly to drugs.

As might be expected since it accepted and printed the report, organized medicine felt that the authors had done a commendable job of observation. Walter Wolman, secretary of the AMA's Council on Mental Health, said their report "exemplifies the kind of careful clinical study that needs to be made and reported in the literature in order that we can compile reliable documentation of the effects of marijuana in man."[164] In contrast, a professor of psychiatry, soon to release a book of his own on marijuana, told an inquiring reporter that he thought the authors and the AMA "should be put in jail" for publishing the paper.[165] He said he did not feel the study presented sufficient evidence to prove a direct connection between marijuana smoking and mental illness. This is an interesting reaction because Kolansky and Moore did not seem to be extrapolating their observations to marijuana smokers in general. They merely "told it like it was" in their experience, with thirty-eight individuals.

In fairness it should be noted that no report is perfect. Dr. Robert S. Wallerstein, chief of psychiatry at Mount Zion hospital in San Francisco and incoming president of the American Psychoanalytic Association, put it this way: "I'd give the old Scottish verdict, 'Not proven' [to the Kolansky-Moore report]. There is certainly important ground here for more scientific investigation, as to both the pharmacological and psychological effects of marijuana. And while this report raises important questions, it shouldn't be taken as nailing down one side or the other in a scientific controversy. Work like this should certainly be reported, but it should not form the basis for major policy decisions."[166]

Dr. Leo E. Hollister, marijuana researcher and associate professor of medicine at Stanford University, also raised some

objections, noting that the report offered little proof that marijuana actually *caused* the personality changes in the patients.
The patients did in fact become sexually permissive, he admitted; they did lose motivation, and they did become paranoid
in many cases. But these tendencies, he said, might well have
started before marijuana use began, and marijuana use might
well have been part of the deteriorating psychological
pattern.[167]

Yet, fascinating though the Kolansky-Moore report may be,
there is reason to be cautious in assigning the clinical effects
observed to marijuana alone. Dr. Norman Zinberg, professor of
psychiatry at Harvard, known for his criticism of marijuana conservatives, expresses worry that articles such as the Kolansky-
Moore report may be exploited as "proof" that marijuana does
cause mental illness.

Efforts are at last slowly succeeding, he warned, to unsnarl
the legal bind that makes potential felons of all young people
who use even small amounts of marijuana. "Now," he said, "I
can foresee a rightwing reaction against these efforts. I see
strong forces pressing for strong, repressive penalties and seiz-
ing on suggestive reports of damage as if the case were
proven."[168]

Once again, the spectre of repressive law enters this picture.
Once again, behavioral scientists are expressing more concern
about the negative effects of the law than about the drug itself.
And once again, we are reminded that if we are ever to better
understand the effects of this controversial drug, it is critical that
we overhaul our present laws, which are both crippling to otherwise non-criminal youth, and obstructionist to scientific research. Although some might deny it, our present laws once
had both purpose and effect. But the nearly four decades which
have passed since their writing have brought tremendous
change in our country. Tragically, too many legislators are forty
years behind, where cannabis laws are concerned.

Contemporary adults need to recognize that this drug may
not be as bad as they once believed, and youth critically needs
to recognize that it is neither as good nor as safe as they have
been led to believe. As Dr. Leo Hollister puts it, "The idea that
pot is completely innocuous is as assinine as the idea that it's a
devil drug driving people to heroin or insanity. The truth is
somewhere in between."[169]

BELOW OLYMPUS   By Interlandi

"Call the pigs — we've been robbed!"

the
law
and
mary jane

10

It seems to be logical that a man has a right to do
damn near anything he chooses until he interferes
with the rights of others to do damn near anything
they choose to do. The exceptions to this must of
course be where violence or coercion are [sic]
involved.
If doing your thing involves vegetating or becoming
so dependent on any stimulant (booze, drugs, religion) that you are unable to function as a human
being then it appears that someone, somehow, should
have a right to restrain you. We would not like to
have the job. We would not like to say when you
have gone too far.
Doing your thing should be considered as a contribution to the welfare of yourself and your fellowman.
If it does not do either of these it would appear to be
a bummer.
—EDITORIAL, *Haight Ashbury Freepress*, 1:2, 1968

I think we should have the freedom to do anything
we want, even if it does impinge on other people's
freedom.
—JACK MARGOLIS, *Los Angeles Free Press*, 5:21, 1971

*T*HOUGH IT MAY COME as a surprise to many,
most of those in the counterculture (with a few notable exceptions) do respect the law. But many individuals in the group
reserve the right to choose for themselves which laws are proper,
and which are of so little value that they should be ignored.
This is not unique. America has unenforceable and impractical
laws governing sexual behavior. The counterculture ignores
these as being unintelligent and inapplicable to them, as do most
other sexually active people. Members of the Establishment

follow a similar route, but are more subtle in their violations. The counterculture considers their attitude hypocritical, and openly flaunts its sexuality in the face of the older generation.

Where marijuana laws specifically are involved, the counterculture vigorously sponsors the idea that the laws are invalid because they are constitutionally in violation of the individual's right to "do his own thing" in ways that "don't hurt nobody." Unfortunately for those who run into conflict with cannabis laws, this flexibility of thinking is not permitted by legislation. And while some may agree with Dickens' Mr. Bumble that at times "the law is an ass," it is the law nevertheless, and those who run afoul of it often suffer severe consequences. That is what all the discussion is about where the law and cannabis is concerned.

Back in the days when a different category of individual was constantly involved with marijuana law infractions and the white middle-class American directed his interests elsewhere, no one paid much attention to either the laws or those who were severely punished when they broke them. Now that the scene has changed, however, and the "good kids" are using pot in increasing numbers, people are beginning to care. As the concern of "proper" people has mounted, three schools of thought have developed, with the various schools almost at swordpoints with each other. The first, usually those who have no children, or who have very poor relationships with youth, tend to be rigid supporters of the current restrictive laws; they insist that the way to handle all problems is through rigid law enforcement and the incarceration of those who flaunt these particular laws. (Their viewpoint is usually quite different, however, toward laws that intrude upon *their* special interests.)

A second school appears to feel that while the laws have purpose, restraint should be shown toward outright legalization. They reason that it is both dangerous and impractical to legalize a drug which, because of recurring scientific findings, we may have to try to make illegal again in a few short months. This school, however, also recognizes that the flaunting of the current restrictions has made the laws (a) dangerous in the amount of associated damage they can do to otherwise non-criminal citizens, and (b) impractical from the standpoint of rigid enforcement either by the police or the courts.

A third group seems to have decided to throw in the sponge,

saying in effect, "Go to it kids, and while you do we'll make a few bucks off your bodies and heads and then, later, if things get too hot, we'll try and take the stuff away from you again."

No matter what one thinks or feels about this situation, anti-pot laws still exist, and as we shall note in the next chapter, may continue to exist until some marked change in the chronological age of our citizenry occurs. It is well to look at the law in this section, then, from the standpoint of its effectiveness and the propriety of staying within its restrictions. This should not be a problem *if* indeed people can "take pot or leave it alone." If this logic is proper, then it follows that infractions of the current law are because of contempt for the law and only three courses of action are available.

1. We can leave the laws as they are and enforce them selectively, if at all. This, of course, is not practical or probable. At present the laws are being highly enforced, not because the "pigs" are overly eager to lock kids up, but because the Establishment is pressuring the police for a magic solution and in turn letting the police take the blame and receive the contempt which accrues from this action.

2. We can change the laws without casting social approval on this drug (a point that will be amplified later) so that the problem is handled as a public health challenge, or

3. We can eliminate the laws altogether and assume we have lost the battle and must live with the disaster that may result from abuse of the drug.

For the moment let us take the stand that the laws have merit, and that adults should spend their time in encouraging respect for the law rather than in attempts to eliminate restrictions on the drug's use. Here it is interesting to note that while many choose to assert that the marijuana laws have never worked, this assertion is totally false. The laws were highly effective until around 1965, when the total structure of law began suffering assault and a new group of highly influential individuals, young and old, decided to choose marijuana as their socio-recreational medium. Whether or not the law has merit is at this moment immaterial. The fact is that the laws are in effect and we must relate to them. What, if anything, then, do the laws have going for them?

Writers such as Rosevear never tire of telling us that the laws are at fault, not the people who choose to use the drug in defiance of the laws. The laws, states Rosevear, cause the user to become paranoid. "It appears," he says, "that the antimarijuana laws are solely responsible for his [the user's] paranoia, and not that the drug per se causes any such emotion."[1] Of course, the user has no driving need to take cannabis; it is instead a matter of his resenting the prohibition of his enjoyment. "He does not need the drug, it must be understood," Rosevear advises us, "but the pleasant prospect of having it when he wants it overcomes his fear of being caught."[2] The reason one smokes the weed in the face of severe legal opposition, says Rosevear, is that "the occasional smoker feels that if he quits smoking because of fear, he is somehow a liar, and a puppet of an unjust law."[3]

Further, Rosevear tells us that the users are "dangerous in that they are not obeying the doctrines of law that have been so carefully written to protect them. Their activity is deviant. Because of the law, their meetings must be kept secret. And because they experience a sensation that is relatively forbidden, they frequently act a little smug."[4] Smug or not, however, Rosevear assures us, the pot smoker really doesn't like to be an outcast from the rest of society. In fact he "has a great deal of difficulty in adjusting to the position of being on the 'other side' of the law. As his resentment grows," says Rosevear, "he develops the attitude that the police aren't really serving in the capacity as 'defenders of rights,' but that they are infringing on the smoker's rights to smoke. This change in attitude may, admittedly, be a cause for a criminal attitude, and then, after the feeling is developed, even a justification for a crime. After all, the smoker may think, what could be less criminal-like than quietly sitting in a room?"[5]

Rosevear likes to think there has been no change in the user picture since 1937 when the anti-marijuana laws were first passed. In fact, he says, the only thing that has changed in the drug picture since 1937 is the passage of these laws. "Perhaps, because of the Federal Marijuana Tax Act, marijuana users suddenly had no choice but to deal with those who knew the drug picture," he comments in a sort of off-the-cuff explanation as to why cannabis users tend to consort with some underworld elements. "In other words," he reasons, "it is possible that the association of marijuana and heroin was brought about because of the anti-marijuana law."[6]

Perhaps it's good to have something to blame for the current increase in cannabis use. Certainly no one person likes to think he is responsible, so, if nothing else, it's convenient to blame the laws. One could say the same for the man who violates the speed limit on an empty highway and is arrested: he was hurting no one, and the law has made him a criminal.

THE LAW AND ITS ENFORCEMENT

If indeed the law is at fault, it all began some thirty years ago, in 1937, when the Marijuana Tax Act was passed by Congress. It was passed because legislators were convinced that the use of cannabis was getting out of control in America just as it had so many times in the past in other nations where it had acquired at least a quasi-social acceptance. Inflamed by lurid stories in the press and appalled by testimony of men such as New Orleans District Attorney Eugene Stanley that many of the crimes of the South were committed by criminals who relied on the effects of the drug to give them a false courage and freedom from restraint, the law was passed in an attempt to prevent further contamination, particularly of American youth from the habit of smoking cannabis.

The Marijuana Tax Act, patterned after the Harrison Narcotic Act, attempted to curb the use of cannabis by employing federal police power and the imposition of penalties upon both buyers and sellers. These penalties were increased in 1951 and again in 1956 by the passage of the Federal Narcotic Control Act. In essence, the marijuana law provides that sales of cannabis must be accompanied by the payment of a transfer tax of $1.00 per ounce in legitimate sales and $100.00 per ounce if sold to unapproved purchasers, the latter transfer being considered illegal and prohibited. Punishment on the federal level for violation of the Act may result in maximum sentences of from ten to forty years, depending on the offense, if one possesses, sells, or gives away cannabis without filling in the prescribed federal form. The tax obviously is designed to make it extremely difficult to acquire cannabis for abusive use and to develop an adequate means of publicizing dealings in the drug in order to tax and control the traffic effectively.

In addition to federal control, each state has its own laws

that regulate and monitor traffic in all dangerous drugs, including cannabis. The specificity of the law and the penalties provided vary from state to state, but in general the state laws are patterned after the Uniform Narcotic Drug Act, which is similar to federal law in its controls. Interestingly, federal law, which places controls over cannabis in a manner similar to that imposed on narcotics by the Harrison Narcotic Act of 1914, does not consider cannabis to be a narcotic. State laws, however, tend to define it as such, a point of definition which has been declared fully legal by the Supreme Court of Colorado.[7]

Despite the presence on the books of federal and state laws, marijuana violations are on an alarming upswing. In many cases misinformation from adults has led young people to believe the penalties are less severe than they are, and of course publicity through some communications media has lent an air of glamor to the use of cannabis. The result has been, in the words of *Life*[8] magazine, "the greatest mass flouting of the law since Prohibition."

Just what conviction for violating marijuana laws can mean was made clear by Judge John H. Saunders[9] of the Santa Anita, California, Municipal Court in a recent address: "I am heartsick," he told a young audience, "over the number of young people who come into my court charged with narcotics violations. Many of them, I felt, really didn't know the consequences. These consequences," the Judge informed his audience, "can be severe and the time spent in prison is the least of it. When the convict is released from prison, he becomes a second-class citizen economically. . . . Persons convicted of a felony in narcotics cases will not be licensed by the state in a wide variety of fields ranging from accounting and medicine to engineering and funeral directing.

"You can't even be a barber," he warned, "and most school districts will not hire teachers with a conviction on their records and the government will not give them clearance to work in the defense industry."

"No amount of discussion about the appropriateness of the state narcotics law," warns Yale University Dean Georges May,[10] "can detract from the hard fact that at the present time possession, use or distribution of illegal drugs, including marijuana, makes anyone involved with narcotics, even in a single experiment carried out in the privacy of one's room, liable to arrest, conviction, fine and imprisonment.

"Regardless of the ultimate disposition of the case in courts," he continued, "the arrested student is immediately faced with the heavy financial burdens of bail money and legal fees, which often exceed $1,000. The long range expense to the student may be even greater. Moreover, a conviction for a narcotics law violation may preclude consideration for graduate or professional school acceptance, disqualify for graduate fellowships, jeopardize employment opportunities upon graduation and be a source of personal disadvantage for the convicted student for the rest of his life."

The Federal Bureau of Narcotics and Dangerous Drugs quite properly notes that in its jurisdiction students and other occasional users have not been prosecuted. But this is not true in states where young people have been arrested under state law. There, the rigidity of the laws has sometimes resulted in the imposition of penalties that were out of proportion to the seriousness of the crime. This has resulted in senseless prison time being imposed on casual users or juvenile offenders, a punishment that has been both cruel and ineffective. In some instances misguided jurists have sent users to jail to "cure" a non-existent "addiction." Jails being what they are, these individuals, registered as criminals with all this label implies, have been forced in some instances into a criminal existence by those very forces sworn to prevent crime.

On the other side of the coin, some juries have failed to convict drug abusers who were actually involved in criminal activity, but whose concomitant use of marijuana has involved such unreal sentences that the process of justice seemed distorted. Still, we must have laws to protect society from those who cannot control themselves, for in the area of cannabis abuse there seem to be many who are ready, willing, and able to become cannabis converts.

"It is well to realize," as Royal Canadian Mounted Police Commissioner George B. McClellan[11] has noted, "that for every freedom, right or privilege we enjoy in a democratic society there must be an equal and compensating sense of responsibility and an absolute requirement for self-discipline. When one exercises freedom without responsibility, without self-discipline, he is like an engine without a governor and runs wild. The system of law which we have today exists, or should exist, to maintain that balance between rights and responsibilities."

There is yet one further dimension to existing anti-marijuana laws, one that is almost entirely neglected by those who advocate the repeal of present restrictions on the possession and use of cannabis: the participation of the United States in an international agreement, The Single Conventions Treaty of 1961, signed by the President and ratified by the U.S. Senate on May 8, 1967. This treaty requires that the United States, along with some seventy-three nations of the World Health Organization, include cannabis among the dangerous drugs that should be prohibited. This treaty, as determined in a decision rendered by the U.S. Supreme Court in the case of *Missouri vs. Holland*,[12] is considered along with similar treaties to be the law of the land as is the United States Constitution.

The treaty[13] sets as its goal the elimination of the use of cannabis in member countries over the next twenty-five years. It hopes to do this by education and by legislation in countries where it has previously been legal to use the drug. The World Health Organization has strongly recommended that no country where marijuana is now illegal should change the status of the drug. To have entered into this treaty only to renege on its enforcement would place the United States in a most undesirable position. The treaty could be circumvented if the United States should decide, as India has, to eliminate low-potency cannabis from the list of prohibited drugs.

Such then is the broad picture of the law as it stands. But perhaps the most striking thing about anti-marijuana laws today is that they are under continued assault. An adequate understanding of the present legal situation requires some consideration of the fight to legalize cannabis. Here is what seems to be happening.

SOME RECENT LEGAL SKIRMISHES

For two decades or so the anti-marijuana laws created little stir in the nation, but in the last half-dozen years they have come under severe attack. No doubt many deep underlying causes have contributed to the change, but on the more identifiable level one can note simply a change in fashion. It is, circa 1971, "in" to be "for pot" and "square" to be against it. Given ten speakers at a symposium, nine against the use of the drug and one for it, the headlines will usually feature the remarks of the pro-cannabis speaker. Ostensibly this is because being anti-marijuana is no longer newsworthy. People now wish to read "good news" about pot. The situation in America has drastically changed where news releases are concerned. Twenty-five years ago the communications media spread horror stories about the dangers of cannabis. Now these same media, and some new ones, seem to be contributing to its popularity.

Some remarkable people have also joined the pro-cannabis forces. In Los Angeles, in late 1967, the presiding judge of the juvenile department of the Los Angeles Superior Court made headlines by stating he felt the use of marijuana should "be left to the good judgment of every adult."[14] The judge's statements were not wholly consistent throughout, for he admitted that, like alcohol, cannabis should be restricted for use by minors and that even for adults marijuana might become as serious a problem as alcohol. Still, he expressed an opinion in favor of individual adult choice in the matter of using marijuana.

For his efforts the jurist found himself transferred out of juvenile court by his presiding judge. "I am afraid," his superior said, "that his statements concerning the controversial drug have destroyed his value in the juvenile department."[15] Concern about remarks of this type has been voiced by many authorities in the field of drug abuse. "If we legalize marijuana [of the American type]," Dr. Donald Louria warns, "are we not taking the first steps to legitimize the widespread use of more potent hallucinogens with all their immense potential dangers? With legalization, inevitably there would develop in this country a substantial number of chronic, excessive users, thus encouraging the likelihood of chronic psychosis and criminality."[16]

Indeed, one of the concerns most frequently expressed by those who oppose legalization is the possible creation of a large body of drug-dependent persons who would become drains on society. Attorney Gene Haislip, advisor to the former Federal Bureau of Narcotics, says that we cannot know what kind of problems might result from legalization. "It would take a generation of permissiveness to discover how many millions would eventually become dependent, turn to narcotic addiction, fill the asylums, jails and hospitals. If we permit the legalization of marijuana on the basis of our inability to unequivocally prove how much worse legalized marijuana would be than legalized alcohol, then by the same standard we cannot continue to prohibit the abuse of narcotics, amphetamines, barbiturates, LSD, or any other drug. This would seem to be the absurd conclusion of an absurd logic."[17] Such authorities as Dr. Sidney Cohen and Yale psychologist Kenneth Keniston agree with this point and warn that the consequences to both the individual and the society as a whole are at this point incalculable.

While the authorities debate, the problem confronts more and more people. "When only the poor sought paradise by way of pot," says Ferdinand Mount,[18] "nobody cared about the enhancement and enrichment of perception. They just flung 'em in jail." Observing that today as their own children are being caught in the web of enforcement a new breed of marijuana supporter is arising from the middle-class and/or intellectual drug-taker group, Mount says,

> I note also a new snobbery emerging, namely that it is a mistake to enforce the laws against marijuana because this cultivates a disrespect for the law among students who are well able to distinguish between the dangers of pot and heroin.
>
> The opening of the drug world in all its glowing illusion to the children of the middle-class has revealed absolutely no superiority of moral intelligence. The distinction (as usual in matters of self-destructive indulgence) is not between income or IQ groups but between the morally and spiritually strong and the morally and spiritually weak. There is little evidence that the children of the college professor are necessarily better able to deal sensibly with drugs than the children of the poor. The only difference is that until recently the professor's children had little or no contact with drugs.

For the most part enforcement personnel have stood foursquare against the watering down of present narcotics laws as they pertain to cannabis. At the annual meeting of the California Narcotics Law Enforcement Officers Association in 1967, the convention adopted a resolution, which has yet to be fundamentally changed, that said:

> Recognizing that inadequate control of the illicit marijuana traffic breeds drug dependence, creates enforcement problems and injures the national welfare: therefore, be it resolved that the federal and state laws controlling marijuana be retained in a form which will insure that illicit traffickers will be severely dealt with, and that the possession of marijuana be restricted under criminal penalty to legitimate medical, scientific, research and industrial use.

In agreement, former Los Angeles Police Chief Thomas Reddin[19] said: "Until the truth of the problem is known law enforcement must cope with the current abuse problem." He was perfectly willing, the chief said, to "let the scientists and lawmakers take over, and when they find the total answers, we will do as they say. Until then, policemen must enforce the law as it's written now. Based on the findings of men I've spent most of my adult career working with," he said, "men who have worked with the marijuana problem, I have to conclude the drug should be outlawed. In the absence of scientific proof otherwise, I couldn't change my mind."

The issue turns again and again to learning the full truth about the effects of cannabis. The problem is that controlled trials, the few that have been made (including the clinical study of the La Guardia Report) have generally tended to disrupt the dreams of cannabis smokers by declaring that, at best, cannabis has nothing to offer its users but an unreal illusionary state or temporary euphoria and, later, possible significant emotional and mental harm. Pro-cannabis forces continue to push for more studies, presumably in the hope that a favorable one will emerge. Even more strongly, they push for legalization, even without the studies One such force[20] suggested that "a group of dedicated attorneys should prepare a 'marijuana test case' worthy of consideration before the highest court in the land." They may yet obtain their wish, but it may not win them their goal. Several attempts have been made to disenfranchise the current anti-marijuana laws. To date, the pro-cannabis forces have lost. One of the more significant of these tests was held in the city of Boston, Massachusetts in 1967.

THE BOSTON MARIJUANA CASE

The Boston case was fought by Joseph Oteri, a cheerful, disarming, pipesmoking defense attorney who also, interestingly, has served as a counsel for the National Association of Police Officers.[21] The marijuana law "gripes me," he recently said; "the hazards of marijuana are a myth." But Oteri appears to be intent, not on legalizing the drug or promoting its use, but instead, on eliminating the current laws, which he feels are poor, and starting over with proper drug legislation. So motivated, he undertook the defense of a marijuana violation in Boston.

The facts in the case were that Oteri's two clients were arrested at Logan International Airport in East Boston on March 11, 1967, when one of the defendants presented at the baggage counter a claim check for a trunk that contained fifty pounds of sand and five pounds of marijuana. They were tried and convicted of violations of the state's marijuana laws on two counts, and sentenced to jail. The defendants appealed the decision on the grounds that the laws relating to the possession, use, and sale of marijuana in the Commonwealth of Massachusetts were unconstitutional because they were arbitrary, irrational, and unsuited to the accomplishment of any valid legislative purpose. The defendants argued that their rights had been violated under the Ninth Amendment to the U.S. Constitution and the Due Process and Equal Protection Clauses of the Fourteenth Amendment. They claimed that the statutes imposed cruel and unusual punishment on users, possessors, and sellers of marijuana, in violation of the Eighth Amendment as applied to the states by the Fourteenth Amendment.

The defendants pled their case before the Chief Justice of the Superior Court, G. Joseph Tauro. Judge Tauro deliberated on the findings through a mountain of testimony equally divided between those who felt cannabis posed a social and individual threat, and those who felt it was basically an innocuous weed. After three months he returned the judgment that, "It is my opinion, based on the evidence presented at this hearing, that marijuana is a harmful and dangerous drug." The judge went on to give a thorough summary[22] of the effects of marijuana, and finally concluded with a lengthy statement on arguments about the use and sociology of marijuana and the desirability of its legalization, much of which is repeated here because it constitutes one of the most recent high-level legal judgments on cannabis in the United States.

> To my knowledge, this has been the most extensive judicial inquiry into the legal and factual aspects concerning the use of marijuana. At this hearing, many eminently well qualified experts on the subject from here and abroad have had their opinions subjected to searching cross-examination and careful analysis by learned and thoroughly prepared counsel. One of the principal factual issues presented for determination is whether marijuana is a harmful and dangerous drug. Several legal issues are raised by defendants' motion to dismiss, but basically this is the question which requires an answer.

I found the testimony of the experts in the various branches of science very illuminating and helpful—although often controversial. On the other hand, there were areas of agreement among them, which are delineated elsewhere in this decision.

Of grave and immediately apparent importance is the growing appeal marijuana has for young people of high school and college age and for those having underlying instabilities or personality disorders of varying degrees. In many instances, the ones least capable of coping with the mind altering effects of the drug are the ones most likely to be adversely affected by its use.

The serious effects of marijuana superimposed upon mental and personality disorders have been described at length and in great detail by competent experts. I find this testimony persuasive. Actually, there is little, if any, dispute in this area between the defendants' experts and the Commonwealth's experts. Furthermore, all of them testified that they do not advocate the use of marijuana.

In its application to youngsters of high school and college age, the problems presented by the use of this drug assume tremendous proportions. There is no persuasive evidence that its use produces any beneficial results. The defense asserts that the drug causes no direct physical harm. Neither do heroin and other "hard" drugs, but few youngsters dare to experiment with these. Unfortunately, many marijuana users do not have the same apprehension or fear concerning its use, as they do of the physically addictive drugs. This, I feel, is one of the real dangers which permeates the problem. Marijuana is likely to be used, at least initially, as a lark, as an adventure without fear of serious consequences. Thus, the first and apparently innocuous step may be taken in a succession of others possibly leading to drastic results.

This phase of the problem is further complicated by those who unwittingly and perhaps unintentionally create the impression that marijuana is harmless, because it is not physically addictive. The young seize such utterances to rationalize their conduct.

While it is generally agreed that marijuana does not cause *physical* addiction as do heroin and the other "hard" narcotics, there was ample and compelling testimony that its use causes psychological dependence. Its users may not be driven to its repeated use by a physical craving, but they may come to resort to it habitually in order to compensate for real or imagined inadequacies or to avoid real or imagined problems. This pernicious and insidious form of addiction is sometimes the first step in the direction of the more potent or physically addictive drugs.

It is a universally accepted fact that marijuana is a mind altering drug and is used for that specific purpose. It is also a generally accepted fact that the drug has no medically recognized therapeutic value. In addition to its adverse effect on ill-adjusted persons, at best, it provides an insubstantial crutch to its user, giving him a feeling of intoxication in varying degrees. It provides a false sense of capabilities, strength and courage. This is of great importance when the drug user is faced with a problem which demands exercise of judgment and where the drug substitutes a euphoric and unreal feeling of exhilaration for the calm and logical thinking required by the circumstance.

In place of positive thinking and positive action, the user's mind is altered and distorted causing serious interference with his powers of perception and coordination and his ability to judge the passage of time and space.

The defendants assert that marijuana provides a certain amount of happiness or relaxation without harmful results. I am not persuaded by the evidence that the resulting euphoria is, in fact, a pleasurable and rewarding experience. I remain unconvinced by the evidence that the average user is made happy or contented—even for a short period of time. The normal brain function is altered or suspended, making the user more susceptible to the influence of others. The use of the drug also tends to accentuate any tendency toward improper conduct. In addition, it induces an abnormally subjective concentration on trivia. In short, marijuana produces a state which is analogous to a temporary mental aberration. Its prolonged and excessive use may induce a psychotic state, especially in those individuals with pre-existing psychological problems.

In my opinion a proper inference may be drawn from the evidence that there is a relationship between the use of marijuana and the incidence of crime and anti-social behavior. Within the limitations of our present statistical information, we can only speculate as to the precise nature and scope of the relationship. This is, to a certain degree, the hidden aspect of the problem. We cannot, at present, ascertain to what extent marijuana is a contributing factor in motor vehicle and other accidents, school dropouts, criminal activity, cases of "hard" narcotics addiction, broken homes and ruined careers, irrational and deviate acts, or losses of ambition and of the desire to become productive members of society. Although the *extent* of such results may be speculative, it is my opinion that a strong inference may be drawn from the evidence presented at this hearing that a causal relationship does exist between the use of marijuana and those assorted social evils. In order to establish more firmly the nature and scope of this relationship, exhaustive and incisive studies must be undertaken.

In any event, there is no indication from the evidence that the user of marijuana becomes, through its use, a better student, a better worker, more dedicated to the public interest, or more efficient or productive in any undertaking. On the contrary, there is convincing evidence that the converse is true.

Many succumb to the drug as a handy means of withdrawing from the inevitable stresses and legitimate demands of society. The evasion of problems and escape from reality seem to be among the desired effects of the use of marijuana. Its use is not so much a symbol of dissent in order to effectuate changes in our social system, but rather a manifestation of a selfish withdrawal from society.

The lessons of history and the experiences of other nations teach us that such artificial alteration of the normal brain function by the use of drugs has been harmful both to the individual and to society in which he lives. The evidence clearly indicates that where a subculture has developed which tolerates the general use of marijuana or its derivatives, the harmful results have become clearly manifest. It is of great significance that the vast majority of nations have outlawed its use.

Although its relevancy is doubtful, there was the unavoidable comparison of marijuana with alcohol. Alcohol has some therapeutic value and its use is not limited solely to the achievement of a state of intoxication or the alteration of the mental processes. Furthermore, the use of alcohol is supported here and elsewhere by many centuries of cultural experience. Admittedly, its misuse has posed serious problems and continues to do so. But these problems, as they now exist, could be greatly expanded and compounded by the legalization of the use of marijuana. It is difficult to justify any law which would permit an expansion in the use of marijuana to the point where conceivably it would fall into the same category as alcohol and become a part of our national culture. That the use of marijuana may have results similar to those associated with the abuse of alcohol is hardly a persuasive argument for its legalization.

Marijuana users must, of necessity, consort with opportunistic pushers and other hardened members of the criminal element. In the case of youngsters, this is especially dangerous. It introduces them to and establishes a rapport with persons whose total influence is apt to be corruptive. As serious, if not more so, as the young user's association with pushers and the criminal element is the frequency, duration and intimacy of his contacts with other basically unstable users who not only involve him in their problems but compound his own.

The defendants argue that the statutes are also criminogenic in nature, as well as cruel and unusual, in that they prescribe serious criminal penalties for what may be relatively minor offenses. These arguments certainly do not apply to pushers. The legislation might profitably be reviewed with regard to the penalties provided for possessors as opposed to pushers or where the evidence indicates a first offense with the improbability of repetition. In such cases, the judge should be given wide discretionary powers so that the imposition of a criminal record may be avoided whenever warranted by the facts.

TRENDS IN THE LAW

Judge Tauro's final paragraph reminds us that more and more legislators are asking whether we ought to review and possibly rewrite state laws pertaining to the control of cannabis. More often than not the answer arrived at is, yes. The argument most often advanced from the legislative point of view for modifying cannabis laws is that existing laws have not been effective; violations have been on the increase and they have bred disrespect for law and order. On the other side many counter with the argument that total effectiveness is not the ultimate test of whether a law is good or not and that, in any case, much effective work has been done by existing laws, such as the prevention in the main of availability of the higher-potency hashish type of cannabis from the United States and the deterrence of persons who might have entered into the sale of marijuana for profit.

Ferdinand Mount[23] argues,

The fact that people evade a law does not mean that the law in question is unworkable, still less that it is undesirable. Many traffic violations go unpunished; many of the punishments go unpaid. There are hundreds of thousands of scoff-laws in New York State alone. This does not indicate that the majority of people oppose the laws, nor that the police do not attempt to enforce them, but merely that universal enforcement would be a task far exceeding the capacity of the police. The laws and their partial enforcement do have an effect on the behavior of motorists, nevertheless. Similarly with marijuana. It is not now sold in stores. Though access is now far from difficult, many young people who might fear not to try marijuana as a badge of manhood were its use legal, do not bother to under present restrictions—or not more than once or twice. Forbidden fruit may be sweeter but most of us are too lazy to climb over the wall after it.

In regard to whether restrictive laws work or not, it is interesting to note that Great Britain, which has recently instituted an anti-alcohol, safe-driving program utilizing a breathalyzer law, has experienced a marked drop in traffic accidents. That there is a direct correlation is suggested by the statistics that reveal nighttime pub sales have dropped off as much as 25 percent during the same period that nighttime road accidents declined 42 percent. No doubt there continue to be those in England who drink and have accidents. According to pro-cannabis logic the British law ought therefore to be repealed.

Meantime, legislators throughout the nation continue to wrestle with the problem of whether to modify, repeal, or let stand existing marijuana laws. As California Assemblyman Pete Wilson[24] says,

Except for narcotics agents, police officers, and bewildered and heartsick parents who have discovered their children to be drug users, California lawmakers suffer perhaps the most acute frustration of all those attempting to deal with the problem. The success of attempted legislative curbs on drug use is not accurately measurable. No one can say for certain what the juvenile drug arrest figures would be in the absence of present legislation but the hard fact is: it has not prevented the sharp rise in arrests that so alarms us.

We are compelled [Wilson admits] to re-examine the laws we have enacted, and to consider new approaches. Our efforts to date have been chiefly in the area of defining and proscribing the use of intoxicating substances thought to be harmful; on occasion of increasing penalties for violation; of attempting to remove juvenile users from schools so as to avoid "contamination" of non-user students; and finally of requiring instruction in our public schools in the hazards of drug use. Legislating against drug use is fraught with problems.

In October, 1967, California State Senator Anthony Beilenson held a meeting of the California Senate Public Health and Safety Committee for the purpose of acquiring up-to-date information and opinion in the field of marijuana because he felt it likely that various bills would be introduced into the state legislature in the forthcoming months which would attempt to effect changes in the state's marijuana laws. As usual, a considerable amount of conflicting testimony was introduced. And, as usual, the testimony reflected concern about the fate of the current crop of high school and college youngsters who have chosen to violate existing laws by trying or continuing to use the drug.

A series of pertinent observations was offered by Los Angeles County Deputy District Attorney Joe Reichman,[25] whose job it is to file all marijuana complaints in his area. Expressing his own opinions and not those of his office, Mr. Reichman said: "I thought if I were a legislator, and I had the task of attempting to revise the marijuana laws, I would want to know the answers to some of the questions. I would want to know what the cost of enforcing the marijuana law is, and how effective that enforcement is. I would want to know whether there is any relationship between the use of marijuana and the commission of subsequent crimes, and I would also want to know what effect the use of marijuana had upon the user."

Reciting current statistics concerning marijuana arrests (at the time of testimony they constituted 17½ percent of all felonies issued by the Los Angeles District Attorney's downtown office, excluding those arrests where no complaint was made), Reichman expressed the opinion that the cost of enforcing the laws was very high and suggested that consideration be given as to whether or not it is worth the cost to continue enforcing them. Reichman testified:

Every time an arrest takes place, it usually involves two police officers, and several hours are involved. There is the initial interrogation, the arrest, the transportation of the defendant to the police station, the booking, the preparation of the police report; two or three hours go by without any difficulty at all. A police officer on an eight-hour shift could normally not handle more than two or three arrests during this particular period. Add to it the cost of the police officer coming to court. They have to appear twice. They have to appear at a preliminary hearing. This involves easily a half day in our crowded courts.

Then, there is the matter of the trial. That would be another day. Add to the cost of the police officers the cost of the deputy district attorneys that had to prepare and process these . . . cases. Add the cost of the salaries of the Public Defender's office to defend them; the costs of the salaries of the judges and the juries to hear the cases, and the costs that also go along with running a court. The cost of the clerk and the reporter. There is no doubt in my mind that the cost is staggering.

I have spoken with numerous narcotics officers, and they have the same opinion that I have: that the effectiveness is almost nil. We are barely scratching the surface. For every arrest that takes place, there may be 1,000 or 2,000 other people that are using marijuana.

There is no way for me to prove this. The only instance that I can cite to you is the manner in which most of these arrests take place. These arrests take place, for the most part, by accident. They are not arrests where the police are going out looking for marijuana. That does happen. But the majority of arrests are by accident. A person is driving an automobile, and he goes through a red light. The police give him a ticket, and they notice a marijuana cigarette in an ashtray. Then, two hours of time are taken in processing the individual. Or, somebody is shot, and he is rushed to the hospital and prepared for surgery and a marijuana cigarette falls out of his shirt. There is no question in my mind that most of the arrests occur in this fashion.

While arguing that the cost of enforcement is high and the effect "minimal" Reichman does state he feels these factors should not be the guiding points that determine whether or not existing laws should be changed. In testimony, his primary interest was directed toward the question of whether or not the use of the drug had any relationship to subsequent crimes. Reflecting on the high cost of alcoholism and its relationship to crime, Mr. Reichman states that, on the basis of his experience, he sincerely doubts "that the use of marijuana plays a vital factor in the commission of other crimes."

Aiming his guns at the current laws, Reichman specifically criticized the manner in which most cases had to be handled in California (and in most other states) when an offender is brought to trial.

A man can go out and steal a car and receive a misdemeanor sentence, and a man can go out and commit an assault with a deadly weapon and receive a misdemeanor sentence, but a man that is smoking one marijuana cigarette, he is going to receive a felony. [Reichman notes that] there is a world of difference between someone that possesses three or four kilos of marijuana, and somebody that possesses one marijuana cigarette. I feel that the court should be given discretion to impose misdemeanor sentences in marijuana cases if they so desire [yet] a person convicted of possessing marijuana cannot receive a misdemeanor sentence. Ethically, I think such a change [i.e., giving the court misdemeanor discretion] will, somewhat, reduce the costs. I have no doubt that many of our marijuana cases go to trial because the defendant, who was caught with one or two marijuana cigarettes, doesn't want to have this stigma of a felony facing him for the rest of his life. And if there was this misdemeanor alternative, I think many of the cases would terminate in a plea.

In summary, Reichman suggested that if the legislature really wanted to handle the situation correctly, they "should give serious consideration to treating marijuana violations the same way that alcohol violations are concerned. It is my feeling," he said, "that the marijuana law is just like any other criminal law, whether it is marijuana, whether it is a traffic violation. It is a problem of balancing the interests. On the one hand, the interest of the individual to a freedom of choice and, on the other hand, the interests of society to protect itself."

And in conclusion the Deputy District Attorney had this to say: "I want to add one thing here. I don't smoke marijuana. I don't urge people to smoke it. On the contrary, I urge people not to smoke it. . . . I don't want my remarks to be misconstrued. Regardless of what is done, it should still be made a crime to furnish marijuana to juveniles. It should still be made a crime to drive an automobile under the influence of marijuana."

Wilbur F. Littlefield,[26] chief trial deputy of the Public Defender's Office in Los Angeles, had this to say in regard to Reichman's testimony:

I agree . . . that there should be an alternative sentence so far as the first offender on possession of marijuana is concerned. . . . I practised law when we did have an alternative sentence for possession of marijuana . . . and it was my experience during that period, that it was much more likely that a defendant would plead guilty. If he has a straight felony, as the law is at the present time, facing him, certainly he has nothing whatsoever to gain [in pleading guilty] even if he is given probation with proceedings suspended and no time whatsoever in jail. He is still a convicted felon.

And considering the youthfulness of many of our persons who are charged with possession of marijuana . . . many of them are between the ages of 18 and 21 and they don't realize what the seriousness of a felony conviction can mean ten or fifteen years after the conviction. . . . I think we have made a great mistake in California in taking the discretion completely away from the court as we have in marijuana offenses, so far as sentencing is concerned."

But Littlefield also saw fit to add this comment: "It is not the position of our office to say that marijuana should be legalized. We don't believe that it should be. But, we do believe that the penalties for possession of marijuana should be reduced."

If there are those among state legislators and law enforcement personnel who advocate modification of the marijuana laws, especially with an eye toward reducing the severity of sentences for youthful first offenders, there are those of the procannabis lobby who press for complete repeal. On July 24, 1967, for instance, the *London Times* carried a full-page advertisement apparently instigated by American psychologist Stephen Abrams, bearing the headline, "The law against marijuana is immoral in principle and unworkable in practice." The ad carried endorsement signatures of some sixty-five prominent Britishers, and introduced its arguments with a quotation by Spinoza:

All laws which can be violated without doing anyone any injury are laughed at. Nay, so far are they from doing anything to control the desires and passions of man that, on the contrary, they direct and incite men's thoughts toward those very objects: for we always strive toward what is forbidden and desire the things we are not allowed to have. And men of leisure are never deficient in the ingenuity needed to enable them to outwit laws framed to regulate things which cannot be entirely forbidden. . . . He who tries to determine everything by law will foment crime rather than lessen it.

It is, of course, extremely difficult to legislate moral conduct. Barry Goldwater emphasized this point during the 1964 presidential campaign, and he added: "I propose to extend freedom. My aim is not to pass laws, but to repeal them. It is not to inaugurate new programs but to cancel old ones that do violence to the Constitution, or that have failed in their purpose." Antoni Gollan[27] uses this Goldwater quotation to expand on his point that the marijuana laws have failed and should be repealed. But Ferdinand Mount replies:

Sweep away the prohibition and you sweep away the racketeering? Not so. Britain abolished most of her legal restraints on betting and gaming [the parallel with Prohibition and its repeal was made during the passage of this legislation too], and what happened?

The British embarked on an orgy of gambling such as was never seen before. Millionaires and workingmen ruined themselves, and the gangsters moved in, not out. Gangland killings erupted and the American Mafia even started hotfooting it across the Atlantic. Nor, to put it mildly, is racketeering less in evidence in states where gambling is legal and liquor easy to get than in those where they are not. It is obvious that if marijuana were legal more people would smoke it. More people would therefore be aware of the delights of taking leave of their senses. Anybody who claims that there would then be *fewer* people ready to go on to experiment with heroin is operating with an exiguous knowledge of human nature. Did the end of Prohibition bring a significant or lasting reduction in alcoholism?[28]

Perhaps current legislation against users is too strong. Yet, while recognizing this, prominent authorities who have to work with this problem urge caution in becoming too lax in permitting the use of the drug. Although the laws may be changed soon, at the time of this writing possession in many states demands a felony sentence. In such states, the judge has no discretion in the matter. Some judges are reluctant to give a young, first-time offender a felony record. But under the circumstances, even if the judge suspends sentence, the defendant's record still retains the felony conviction, with all its attendant detrimental effects.

In a preliminary position paper concerning the point,[29] California lawmen said: "That the narcotic marijuana is a harmful and destructive substance is not open to question or debate by reasonable individuals." On the other hand, the paper noted some judges may exhibit reluctance to convict defendants on a first-time charge of possession with the result that this has "led to a diminution of our ability to effectively enforce the law." The lawmen expressed the hope that giving judges discretion to fix the degree of the crime as that of a misdemeanor in certain deserving cases will cause them to give "more realistic" disposition of marijuana possession cases.

Where marijuana is concerned it is one thing to quote arguments against prior laws and quite another to ascertain for certain that the laws against marijuana are, indeed, bad. What must be determined is whether or not the problems produced by cannabis use are sufficiently dangerous to society that a stiff penalty deterrent is necessary to force and persuade people to give up enjoying the effects of cannabis.

Two relatively minor changes in federal law took place on May 19, 1969, when the United States Supreme Court overturned the conviction of Timothy Leary under two clauses of the Federal Marijuana Tax Law. Leary's comments on this occasion were less than accurate. "The facts of the matter," he said, "are that today there are no federal laws against marijuana."[30] This is not true. The laws which were held invalid were relatively narrow ones involving the presumption that a person carrying marijuana across a border was importing it illegally and knew that the importation was illegal. Federal laws concerned with possession and illegal importation itself still exist. More importantly, most marijuana arrests are made in accordance with state laws against use and possession. These laws are still in force and are the ones most frequently violated by American youth.

Some, then, strongly feel that our system of laws governing the use of marijuana are not only outmoded but are producing their own kind of "criminal." *Playboy* magazine, in late 1970, with an accompanying letter of sympathy to the parents of Robert F. Kennedy Jr. and R. Sargent Shriver III for the mishaps incurred by the boys in their alleged episodes with pot, noted the current status of cannabis legislation in this country. While many of these laws will slowly change as time progresses, they were in this condition in early 1971:[31]

PENALTY FOR SIMPLE POSSESSION OF MARIJUANA (FIRST OFFENSE)

ALABAMA 5–20 years and may be fined up to $20,000

ALASKA Up to 1 year and/or up to $1000

ARIZONA Up to 1 year in the county jail or up to $1000 or 1 to 10 years in the state prison, at the discretion of the court

ARKANSAS 2–5 years and up to $2000

CALIFORNIA 1–10 years in the state prison or up to 1 year in the county jail

COLORADO 2–15 years and up to $10,000

CONNECTICUT Up to 1 year and/or up to $1000 or up to 3 years in the house of correction, at the discretion of the court

DELAWARE Up to 2 years and up to $500

DISTRICT OF COLUMBIA Up to 1 year and/or $100–$1000

FLORIDA Up to 5 years and/or up to $5000

GEORGIA 2–5 years and up to $2000

HAWAII Up to 5 years

IDAHO Up to 10 years

ILLINOIS Up to 1 year and/or up to $1500 (for possession of less than 2.5 grams)

INDIANA 2–10 years and up to $1000

IOWA Up to 6 months and/or up to $1000

KANSAS Up to 1 year

KENTUCKY 2–10 years and up to $20,000

LOUISIANA   1 year and/or $500

MAINE   Up to 11 months and up to $1000

MARYLAND   2–5 years and up to $1000

MASSACHUSETTS   Up to 2½ years in jail or house of correction or up to 3½ years in the state prison or up to $1000

MICHIGAN   Up to 10 years and up to $5000

MINNESOTA   5–20 years and up to $10,000

MISSISSIPPI   2–5 years and up to $2000

MISSOURI   6 months to 1 year in the county jail or up to 20 years in the state correctional institution, at the discretion of the court

MONTANA   Up to 5 years in the state prison

NEBRASKA   7 days in jail and the offender must complete an educative course on drugs (for possession of less than 7 ounces or less than 25 marijuana cigarettes)

NEVADA   1–6 years and up to $2000

NEW HAMPSHIRE   Up to 1 year and/or up to $500 (for possession of less than 1 pound)

NEW JERSEY   2–15 years and up to $2000

NEW MEXICO   Up to 1 year and/or up to $1000 (for possession of 1 ounce or less)

NEW YORK   Up to 1 year (for possession of up to ¼ ounce)

NORTH CAROLINA   Up to 2 years and may be fined at the court's discretion (for possession of 1 gram or less)

NORTH DAKOTA   Up to 6 months in county jail or up to 2 years in the penitentiary and/or up to $2000

OHIO   2–15 years and up to $10,000 (the same penalty applies to having carnal knowledge of someone under the influence of marijuana)

OKLAHOMA   Up to 7 years and/or up to $5000

OREGON   Up to 1 year in the county jail or up to 10 years in the state penitentiary and/or up to $5000

PENNSYLVANIA   2–5 years and up to $2000

RHODE ISLAND   Up to 15 years and up to $10,000

SOUTH CAROLINA   Up to 2 years and/or up to $2000

SOUTH DAKOTA   Up to 1 year and/or up to $500 (for possession of 1 ounce or less)

TENNESSEE   2–5 years and up to $500

TEXAS   2 years to life

UTAH   Not less than 6 months

VERMONT   Up to 6 months and/or up to $500

VERMONT   Up to 12 months and/or up to $1000

WASHINGTON   Up to 6 months and/or up to $500

WEST VIRGINIA   2–5 years and up to $1000

WISCONSIN   Up to 1 year and/or up to $500

WYOMING   Up to 6 months in jail and up to $1000

While it is true that most youths who smoke pot do not end up in trouble, it is perhaps due more to luck than anything else that they escape. Surprisingly, a number of notables fall into the net, although, to no one's surprise, few if any of these ever land in jail. In just one week in February, 1970, notes Jean Strouse, the following crises occurred where marijuana legislation, being actively enforced, changed the lives of the individuals involved. Strouse has vividly catalogued a number of these, but the total list of arrests in that one week period is not given.

In that week, he said,[32] "John Cahill, the son of New Jersey's newly elected Governor, William T. Cahill, was arrested for possession; in Pasadena 20 persons, including 7 scientists, were busted for possession of marijuana and hashish at a party held for a group of space scientists for the Jet Propulsion Laboratory, a space agency run by Cal Tech; Harvey Fleetwood, son of a New York banker, was charged with trying to smuggle $200,000 worth of hashish from India into Puerto Rico inside a scuba tank and a stuffed horse—with the aid of a girl named Constance Ziambardi who said she lives in a tree house in California. . . . Howard Samuels, Jr. son of one of the leading candidates for the Democratic nomination of Governor of New York, was arraigned on charges of possession of hashish."*

A number of things can be noted from Strouse's list. One is the caliber of the "victims" of the enforcement of marijuana laws. Another is the infrequency in which "mild" American weed played a role in the drama. Numerous lists of daily events in the pot arrest world could be cited and each time it could be stressed that America is Neanderthal in its approach to the management of pot users. This type of argument gives rise to a dangerous myth—that everywhere but in cruel, out-of-fashion America it's cool to smoke weed since the rest of the world recognizes that "it can't hurt you." During 1969, this type of reasoning and mythmaking resulted in the arrest and/or conviction (in some countries conviction seems to be a minor point) of 556 Americans who were awaiting trial or serving sentences of up to eight years in foreign jails on drug charges. This was three times as many as were reported a year before, *Life* magazine noted in June, 1970,[33] and the number keeps swelling every week.

"I've just come back from a tour of the Hashish Trail—from Turkey and Lebanon to Morocco, Spain and France—and there are so many Americans locked up for hash and pot and LSD over there that it isn't even shocking anymore, just pathetic," *Life* magazine writer Rudolph Chelminski advises his readers. So, he said, if you are suffering from the idea that Europe and the Middle East are an overseas annex of the Woodstock Nation, "Take some friendly advice: don't be so dumb."

"All fool beatnik—very bad," the head of the Istanbul narcotics squad told Chelminski. In other words, anybody selling or carrying drugs is undesirable. If his comments sound funny, the writer notes, "go have a laugh with . . . a basketball player whom

---

* Charges were dismissed against John Cahill (10/6/70) and Howard Samuels, Jr. (8/6/70); the case against Harvey Fleetwood, III, *et al,* was pending at press time (8/71).

[the officers] caught in one of those quaint little hotels with two kilos of Afghan hash." The American is in the clink for five years and Chelminski notes that a Turkish prison is not the place to spend that amount of time.

The *Life* report noted that in November of 1969, a twenty-one-year-old Canadian actually fainted, and with good cause, at his trial in London on a possession of cannabis charge: the judge gave him ten years in jail. Another man in Spain was talked into selling a little bit of hashish to an undercover agent. His reward —six years. And that was a minimum sentence.

If one gets in trouble, then what? The answer seems to be, sweat it out. The U.S. State Department is allowed to visit prisoners, advise them, notify relatives, and help obtain a lawyer. That's it.

Down in Tangiers, it seems hash is easier to get than a camel ride. The shopkeepers peddle it. They are also police informers. One young couple, both twenty-one, bought some Tangiers goodies and got as far as the Spanish port of Algeciras. Here customs welcomed them with open arms and a bust. The judge gave them a minimum sentence: six years and a day.

"Transferred to Cadiz prison," the report said, "they are locked in two different wings, both of which share the full, rich sour smell of the garbage dump next door." Says the girl, "Tell the rest of the kids not to smuggle dope across borders. It's not worth it." This, oddly, is what it's all about. Penalties are instigated so that the alternative is so bad that the smuggling and use of pot isn't worth it. As we shall see, America has a long way to go before it matches the determination of much of the rest of the world in its attempts to stamp out the use of pot. Chelminski warns, for instance, that "Foreign jails are especially unpleasant, but that isn't the worst that can happen to you. In Iran they execute people for trafficking. Just shot four of them the other day. That'll teach 'em!"

The interesting thing is how much people will go through for this "nonaddicting" drug. In early 1967, a reader of *Playboy* wrote the editor complaining bitterly about American busts and sentences and the fact that he was caught because of an informer. At the time he wrote, he was in a Central American jail. The charge: possession of marijuana.[34]

In Japan, revulsion towards the use and possession of pot borders on the hysterical. One reason is that Japanese culture traditionally abhors drug abuse. They have good reason. They have had some severe epidemics of drug deaths. In 1969, teenage glue-sniffing took 161 lives. In the post World War II period, the country was beseiged by an epidemic of methamphetamine (speed) abuse. Soon after VJ day the Japanese increased their penalties for possession of pot from three years or an $80 fine to a flat seven years for possession with intent to sell and to five years for smoking even if the smoker only joins in a pot party and is not caught with cigarettes on his person.[35] They enforce these laws with ruthless energy. Out of a total of 265 marijuana arrests in the first six months of 1970, the Japanese police busted 126 Americans, mostly GI's on rest and recreation furloughs. On the strength of the word of a female informer, a young New York advertising man spent seventeen days in a local jail. She said she had "seen" pot in his suitcase.

As for America, Japanese officials shake their heads at recent congressional legislation softening penalties for users. They were shocked by a statement of the Director of the U.S. Narcotics and Dangerous Drugs Bureau when he announced that the U.S. is no longer "directing its enforcement efforts at the individual user," but instead at smugglers, processors, and middlemen. In contrast, Japan said it would put "increasing emphasis" on punishing the drug user himself, stating that he is as much of a threat to society as the rest. "We cannot achieve our results if we seek to control the supplier alone. We must strike at the source or the demand will grow."

So much for the land of the cherry blossoms. Let's look at Spain. In mid 1970 some fifty Americans were facing sentence, awaiting trial, or in jail on drug offenses. Says a young Berkeley youth, who sorts empty beer bottles to while away the six year sentence handed him for possessing pot, "Never carry more than a stick. Don't sell it. Don't carry it in bulk and never, never, never bring it in by the border."[36]

Crete is more rigid. In December, 1970, five Americans, four from California, were handed prison terms of up to ten years and fined up to $24,000 for trying to smuggle a load of cannabis into Greece.[37] Sweden, once sympathetic to young American deserters, has now decided to deport all convicted on drug charges after they are released from Swedish prisons.[38] Alarmed at the growing number of convictions, Michael Collins, Assistant Secretary for Public Affairs for the State Department, wrote

Playboy that most of the kids, 522 at that time (August 1970), seemed to think other countries were playing the same non-decisional games employed in America. "The penalties for drug violations in most countries are severe. The charge—whether for possession or, more serious, trafficking—is usually determined by the quantity involved. Possession of more than [one pound] results in a minimum of six years in jail plus a heavy fine in some countries or, in others, one to three years in a 'detoxification asylum'—usually a mental hospital."

"Trafficking in drugs," he warns, "carries a penalty of ten years to life. In some countries, prison conditions are primitive: damp underground locations; rats and vermin; insufficient light, heat and food; absence of sanitary facilities; abuse by other prisoners. Pretrial confinement can be prolonged—in some countries, up to one year without bail. Language difficulties compound the tragedy."

He notes that when an American is busted in another country he is held by the laws existing in that country. Many of these nations lack the finesse in law promoted by American attorneys and the system of utilizing technicalities and/or a change of venue to a more permissive judge seldom if ever exists. About the only thing the U.S. can do for these unfortunate kids, he notes, is to be certain they are not victims of discrimination, i.e., that they are treated the same way as the country treats its nationals.[39]

In early 1970, the *Los Angeles Times* reported the trials and sorrows of five American kids who were arrested in Beirut, Lebanon, and locked in the local "black hole" for possession of hashish. "Forty or fifty people sleep in an underground dungeon room about 50 x 15 feet—on cold, damp floors with only two blankets. There are rats all over the place. No lights, no air, only an hour of exercise a day, two meals of beans, no toilet facilities, and the overpowering odor of twenty years of decaying human waste which has never been removed. Said a young Californian who had won a scholarship to Stanford University and who had pled guilty to possession of hashish, 'This jail is absolutely blowing my mind—the wrong way. This is the worst scene I've ever made'."[40]

Lebanese law calls for mandatory sentences of one to five years for possession of hashish and a sentence of three to fifteen years for smuggling or trafficking. The laws here, as in Turkey, are in sharp contrast to Afghanistan or Nepal, where hashish is a legal crop and the country depends on its growth for economic reasons, as well as enjoying its pleasures. Sadly, young Americans often confuse the laws of one country with those of another and usually, where hashish or pot is concerned, they can't win.

Russia, too, has recently admitted problems with pot. There, a minimum eight-year jail sentence is imposed on citizens unlucky enough to get caught using cannabis. Even so, Russia shares a common problem with the United States: ". . . prison doesn't stop our teenagers," the Russian magazine *Krokodil* notes. "Many of the routes from Afghanistan and India have been eradicated, but the ever present demand for marijuana just gives birth to more supplies from somewhere else."[41]

Until 1967 and the Arab-Israeli war, Israel had little trouble with pot. Then came the American, Canadian, and European students to "help" the young nation with its problem. They began looking for pot and found hashish instead. It occurred to some that smuggling it to the U.S. could be lucrative. Additionally, the same group seemed determined to indoctrinate young Israelis on the techniques of modern revolt against the Establishment. Then came the axe.

In early 1970 officials caught two youngsters with several kilos of hashish and slapped them with six-year jail terms. Israel's Attorney General states he is now imposing even tougher penalties for drug traffic and for the possession and use of drugs for both Israelis and foreigners. As for hashish, the Health Ministry recently announced that in its opinion the drug could cause physical as well as emotional damage to anyone who smokes it.[42]

In Istanbul the penalty for possession and sale of pot is a long, long trip—straight to the local prison. Turkey's criminal code governing cannabis is a potsmoker's nightmare. Mere possession means a two and a half year sentence with a maximum of five depending on circumstances. Exporting slams the convicted into jail for ten years, importing up to thirty years. There are no suspended sentences for being involved with pot in Turkey. The country has decided it just won't tolerate the use of cannabis within its borders.[43]

The fascinating thing is that next to Afghanistan and India, Turkish hashish is the cheapest in the world—and among the best. An eighteen-year-old recently wrote friends from his miserable jail cell, "Man, Istanbul is on the hustle. There are countless ways to make money—or end your existence on this planet. You can sell your passport (maybe $150.00), you can sell your traveler's checks (twenty percent more than face value), you can sell hash, import cars that a Turk cannot legally bring into Turkey. . . ."

"Anyway," he said resignedly (and this is most interesting) "when we get back to the States, we will have several kilos of fine hash, one to sell and a couple to smoke for a year or two. . . ."

How about Mexico? *Stay away!* Mexico, source though it allegedly may be for much American grass, wants no part of the traffic in its own country as far as use by locals and tourists are concerned. "Tell the other college kids not to come to Mexico," a San Diego State College junior told the *Los Angeles Times.* "Tell them if they come here they lose all their rights." Among other things that can happen, the judge can take a year to make up his mind how he wants to try the case. It's a real bummer.

The thing that scared the Mexicans grass-green was the threat that a mass of hippies planned a rock festival in their country. No way, said the officials, and in early 1968 the busts began on long-hairs at the border. If you have long hair, they said frankly, don't come across. Next, Mexico started ridding itself of resident hippies that had managed to get in prior to the ban. The word was out. Hippies were dirty, immoral cats who smoked pot in the open. The pressure increased. Heads and beards were shaved by police "for hygienic purposes." Informers started turning in all drug buyers (except for regular accounts) making a dual profit, one from the victim and again from U.S. Customs.

How long is a jail term in Mexico? Who knows? *Mañana!* Maybe you'll get out tomorrow, maybe next year. One's cell, unless he has access to bread (money, that is) is nothing but a small hole with a cement floor. Beds (a rack of boards) cost $16.00 (American). You buy your own food. If you don't want to get (to put it mildly), "assaulted," you pay the guard $12.00 protection money. Compare this picture to American police who are allegedly such terrible "pigs." A twenty-year-old student from San Diego sums it up succinctly for kids that have the sense to heed him. "Tell Americans to stay out of Mexico," he said. "It's a bad place to get into trouble."[44]

France isn't much better for law violators. In an otherwise modern country, the rigorous workings of the old Napoleonic Code, with long periods of detention without trial for what might appear to be trivial or minute drug offenses, seem almost incomprehensible. The intent of Frenchmen to eliminate cannabis and other dangerous drugs from their country approximates the spirit of the inquisition. It is so bad that even the State Department is warning American youth what it means to be busted in France.

"In the United States, a kid probably figures that he can take a chance on a sympathetic hearing from a judge if he is picked up with a little pot in his pocket; if this doesn't work he's always got his father or a bail bondsman to put up bail and get him out pending a hearing or a fine," a consulate legal adviser recently said.[45] Not so in France. Here there is no sympathetic appeal for the self-styled "first offender," there is no bail, and the process of the law is inexorable and slow.

In the last three months of 1969, 6000 kids were stopped for identity checks by French police who were mainly looking for drugs. If you're a long hair with a guitar, a girlfriend and a Volkswagen, you've almost had it right there. Of the 6000, 1600 were taken in for questioning. This means being held incommunicado for up to 48 hours. In the end the police arraigned 300 of these youths for drug violations. Twenty of these were American, whom they treated with the same deference as they did French youths.

Once arrested, the trial (physical and emotional, not legal) begins. You can't phone. If the police are very humane, they may call for you or write a friend or relative a letter. In the meantime you sit. And sit . . . and sit. If you picked up a hitchhiker and he has pot on him, you've had it. If you hitchhike and a pot-holding driver picks you up . . . same thing. Sometime in mid-March of 1970 the French police picked up a twenty-four-old American and his twenty-two-year-old girlfriend as they crossed from Germany into France carrying a load of pot. They face customs fines of $90,000 and a four to five-year jail sentence. The girl tried to commit suicide at the police station. She failed.

What it all boils down to is this. There are a few places, (Afghanistan and Nepal, for instance) where one can go and blow grass and eat "Alice B. Toklas" brownies, and probably not be bothered. Except for these exceedingly few places however, the word is out. If you smoke pot, stay home. Terrible though this country may seem to some, one apparently has a better chance of beating a rap here than anywhere else on earth.

THE FUTURE OF CANNABIS

Where do we go now? Apparently time and circumstances will determine this. Laws per se are certainly not without serious complications. But neither are drugs. If it were possible to control the effects of dangerous drugs to the point where they could not alter the behavior or perception of the user, we would have no need for restrictive or punitive drug laws. Unfortunately, society has never been able to protect the individual or his neighbors from the results of the user's lack of interest in, or capability of limiting his intake of drugs, once he becomes dependent on them, and thus avoid the point where intoxication makes him a menace. As a result, we have resorted to a poor and not always effective method of control. We pass restrictive and punitive laws hoping we can maintain the balance between the individual's rights and his responsibilities. Where drug laws are concerned we try to protect the majority from adverse drug effects and drug abuse by a minority, particularly where such abuse can result in violence, death, and the acting out of anti-social impulses.

Moreover, through our laws, we hope to prevent drug-induced indolence, incompetence, unemployment, and the whole train of pathetic events secondary to drug abuse, which increase the burden on the majority to support an irresponsible, unproductive, drug-dependent minority. For it has been amply demonstrated that when drug-seeking behavior and drug abuse become the major goals of the individual, he becomes a drain on society.

The problem is that in our zeal we have in some areas permitted and promoted laws that are disproportionately severe to the crime involved. Once these laws were entered on the books and it became necessary for enforcement officials to arrest and for courts to condemn, the general public began to complain. This has been particularly true in recent years when the cannabis laws have begun to pinch the average middle- and upper-class American family. Now, along with complaints about the laws, recriminations of police and courts that are only carrying out the will of the voters (expressed through the action of their legislators) have begun to fill the air.

In effect, the problem today is, do we or don't we want individuals smoking cannabis? Can we or can't we afford economically, socially, and individually to repeat the expensive experiments performed inadvertently in other nations throughout history where drug use got out of control? With alcohol firmly entrenched in the American way of life and with all the sorrow it brings, can we afford to legalize another habit that has at least equal, if not greater, potential of causing national harm? The problem, says one sociologist, is that "since the smoking of marijuana will undoubtedly continue regardless of legislation against it, it can also be argued that it would be better to accept the inevitable than to wage war for a lost cause."[46] In offering this solution he again equates the drug with alcohol and suggests we treat the marijuana problem in the same manner. The problem, however, is that we have never really dealt with the alcohol problem. We have only contended with it. And we continue to contend with it despite the fact that alcohol abuse constitutes the major drug abuse problem in the United States today.

When we repealed the Volstead Act the 96 percent of Americans who wanted to enjoy alcohol socially decided their desires were more important than the abuse problems that continued to arise from the misadventures of the remaining four percent. The financial profit that the few have accumulated as a result of this decision, and the emotional satisfaction that has accrued to many, have not yet counterbalanced the economic and social toll this habit has placed upon the nation.

Certainly there is wisdom in the statement of the President's Ad Hoc Panel on Drug Abuse when in 1962[47] it stated: "It is the opinion of the panel that the hazards of marijuana per se have been exaggerated and that long criminal sentences imposed on an occasional user or possessor of the drug are in poor social perspective." Yet, the panel recognized the need for laws in controlling the abusive use of all dangerous drugs. If we are to have these laws and if they are to be effective, they must have sufficient teeth to make it feasible and reasonable for enforcement officers to risk their lives in an attempt to fulfill the intent of these laws. If the law has no negative alternative to offer the abuser, the law will have no effect. In such cases would it be better if the law had not been written.

It might be well, before we exceed the intent of the recommendation of the President's Ad Hoc Panel and throw open the floodgates of approval to all who might wish to use cannabis, to consider a comment made by our nation's sixteenth President. Noting that destruction of our nation could not come from abroad, President Lincoln commented:[48] "If destruction be our lot, we ourselves must be its author and finisher. As a nation of free men, we must live through all times, or die by suicide." Although Lincoln had no reference to drug abuse when he made this statement, he nonetheless painted a clear picture of how drug abuse can become a national menace—a menace that clouds men's minds and deludes their thoughts. To date, no more effective method for controlling men has been devised than the process by which they permit themselves to be smothered by the effects of dangerous drugs. The victor in the struggle against such loss of reason must be the one who can keep his mind clear. Today, then, the struggle for the moderate use of drugs is aimed at the control of people's minds.

The time in history has come to make the decision as to what we want to do with cannabis. As we do, it might be well to remember that, while drugs can offer us escape through illusion and give us pleasure through euphoria, there is only one way of life that can give us happiness: facing, living in, and coping with reality on our own without a pharmacologic crutch. If we come to the point where we cannot do this, the battle is done and drug abuse will be the winner. This point brings us to one of the most critical questions of our current discussion: shall we legalize the use of cannabis in the United States? The problem is complex and cannot be answered with a simple yes or no, as we shall discover in the following chapter.

"Ronnie, come and watch this program about
the dangers of marijuana."

the
non-drug
aspects
of pot

11

The center was not holding. It was a country of bank-
ruptcy notices and public-auction announcements and
commonplace reports of casual killings and misplaced
children and abandoned homes and vandals who
misspelled even the four-letter words they scrawled.
It was a country in which families routinely disappeared, trailing bad checks and repossession papers.
Adolescents drifted from city to torn city, sloughing
off both the past and the future as snakes shed their
skins. Children were missing. Parents were missing.
Those left behind filed desultory missing-persons reports, then moved on themselves.
It was not a century in open revolution. It was not a
country under enemy seige. It was the United States
of America . . . and the market was steady and the
G.N.P. high and a great many articulate people
seemed to have a sense of high social purpose and it
might have been a spring of brave hopes and national
promise, but it was not and more and more people
had the uneasy apprehension that it was not. All that
seemed clear was that at some point we had aborted
ourselves and butchered the job. . . .

—JOAN DIDION
Slouching Towards Bethlehem

*S*OMETHING HAS GONE seriously wrong with
out attempts to evaluate cannabis sativa. Basically, there is only
one real issue: Is pot safe for public consumption? If common
sense and pharmacology were the only factors involved in this
venture there would be little argument. In the history of America no drug which has been *thought* to have dangerous side
effects has been licensed for general use until the full picture
was developed. This has been particularly true if the drug involved had the potential of endangering youth.

Some exceptions, alcohol and tobacco for instance, have sneaked through because the full story of their use pattern was unknown when they were given general license. With alcohol we merely shrug and lamely sigh, "Well, we're stuck with it," and continue to sweep up the carnage associated with its use. With tobacco, it is a constant fight to educate youth concerning the potential for serious physical harm associated with smoking, because the tremendous pressure of the tobacco industry, hiding behind the onus of the legality of the drug, obscures the problem with humor, cynicism, deceit, and seduction.

Mention the word pot and the conversation immediately fires to a boiling point. But pot per se is seldom the issue. As tempers flare and emotions erupt, it becomes immediately obvious that a deep, critical series of social questions has pervaded the argument, taking over the original issue and turning it into a symbol which can be used as a whipping post for an almost universal anger and frustration that now seems to permeate our nation.

What could be so important, so critical that it could precipitate such controversy? Not the drug itself! True, pot provides fun and pleasure, but other than that it has little to offer society that cannot be better provided by another pharmaceutical. If not the drug, then what? Let's take a short glimpse of a few of the crises that lie hidden behind the weedy, green screen of Cannabis sativa L.

THE POSTURE ISSUE

Today as never before, each company and each person attempts to maintain an image. To achieve the proper image it is critical that a person or an organization stand for something approved of by society in general. Many of our former cherished icons have been torn asunder by the strife of social revolution. The family, motherhood, the flag, patriotism, sexuality—each of these seems to have lost its ability to precipitate an immediate emotional response because of the divergence of opinion and difference of symbolism it now elicits. Out of this semantic jungle has arisen an old/new word which, partly because of the times and partly because of the exquisite public relations of its proponents, has come to stand for something diametrically opposed to its true meaning. The word is marijuana.

Just as tobacco companies strive to imply that their disease-associated product is a part of fun, life, dating, sportsmanship, family unity, and health, so promoters of cannabis (not to be confused with those who are socially concerned with the problem) have given the weed a new image. To be for pot is to be for youth. To be for pot is to be "in," modern, suave, and sophisticated. To be for pot is to recognize the freedom of man, his right to choose his "own thing" and his own course of action.

To be conservative in one's opinion concerning pot immediately places the speaker in the position of being considered against all these "now"-associated values. Many interested in their public image have therefore learned not to say anything bad about pot if they hope to be popular. It follows that it is not "in" to do more than casually question the safety of using pot, if that. Better, one should be slightly whimsical and evade the issue.

Some highly responsible experts in the drug field have tended to follow the philosophy that one should not stress the negative aspects of pot when one talks to youth. *Time* quotes University of Rochester psychologist Helen Nowlis as saying that emphasis on extreme reactions to drugs "just doesn't correspond with the experience the kids are having. It's like trying to teach a two-year-old that radiators burn in the middle of the summertime. It's a crazy imbalance to stress marijuana hallucinations when 99 percent of the kids who try a marijuana cigarette don't get hallucinations, and it may do serious harm."[1]

Dr. Nowlis is certainly correct in advising against overreacting. On the other hand, when is the best time to educate a child that a radiator can burn? When it is cool and you have time to lay the groundwork, or when it is hot so that his education comes from third degree burns? As for its being a crazy imbalance to stress adverse reactions when most kids *currently* see little problem with smoking pot, why then should we advise people concerning the hazards of either tobacco or alcohol when statistically so few are actually harmed?

Dr. Nowlis, taken in full context, has some weighty and practical advice for those concerned with drug education. "We should concentrate on why some people go from use to abuse," she says, "what the danger signals are and how to get help. We need to teach kids from the time they learn to talk that they need to respect drugs, that all drugs have risks, and that the human body is not just a car that can be given Bardahl when something goes wrong."[2]

The problem with cannabis education is the stringent polarization that has occurred: youth is either reassured that pot is absolutely harmless, or warned that with one puff, you're off to the booby hatch. Since young people know from experience that the latter is false, they give credence to the side that seems to have the most logic. Tragically, the permissive side tends to minimize the potential for harm to the point where the user may lower his guard.

Time quotes Dr. Nowlis as arguing against total abstinence because this "goal is doomed to failure." She draws this analogy: "Eighty million people use alcohol and only 8-10 percent of them abuse it and become problem drinkers or alcoholics. Only about 10 percent of marijuana smokers are more than occasional users."[3] In this, too, Dr. Nowlis is correct. But now we come to the critical question. Why should we be so concerned about the fact that most people do not get hurt and so unconcerned that "only 10 percent" will most probably suffer some disability. "Only 10 percent" where alcoholism is involved means nine million people, and that doesn't begin to count those who are indirectly influenced by alcoholics' plight. If the use of pot grows to comparable dimensions, the same catastrophic percentage applies here, too. In addition, an unknown number of casual users may have to endure the adverse reactions which have been shown to occur from occasional use.

In repeating her comments, this author in no way intends to denigrate Dr. Nowlis. The quotation is presented as source material almost verbatim as it was published in a national newsmagazine from which many, less knowledgeable than Dr. Nowlis, may obtain and misinterpret an isolated statement to enhance their "proper" posture in the pot field. Once we would have worried that one out of ten users is hurt by a drug. Now we seem happy to console ourselves that this percentage is so "low."

In the same issue of *Time,* which in the past five years has seemed less than conservative in its attitude towards pot, the editors review the January 31, 1971 report of the Secretary of the Department of Health, Education and Welfare to Congress. Admitting that the report "cautioned that information about marijuana—especially about its long-term effects—is still fragmentary and that final judgments await more research," *Time* nevertheless concludes that "the heads appeared . . . [in this report] . . . to have gained a slight edge over the straights."[4]

According to *Time,* HEW stated, "There is no evidence that marijuana affects unborn children." This author's copy of the HEW report states on page 16 that "There is no evidence to suggest that marijuana use in humans affects fetal development. Despite the present absence of such evidence, it is obviously unwise for anyone to use any drug of unknown teratogenic or mutagenic properties during the child bearing years. *Use during pregnancy is particularly unwise.*" (Italics added.)

Time also reported, "Although heavy use sometimes is associated with an 'amotivational syndrome'—loss of interest in conventional goals—there is no present evidence that the drug causes the syndrome. Indeed," *Time* continues, "there is the possibility that the syndrome causes the drug use; those without conventional motivation may find drugs especially attractive." Although they are quoted elsewhere in this book, HEW's comments on page 15 of its report are repeated here for comparison. "The fact that there are many worldwide reports of heavy, chronic cannabis use resulting in loss of conventional motivation and in social indifference," HEW says, "is of particular interest in that there are now some reports of somewhat similar findings among American heavy users of marijuana. Unfortunately, American use patterns are frequently contaminated by the use of other drug substances, making interpretation difficult. It is not certain to what degree this 'amotivational syndrome' is the result of marijuana use per se or of a tendency for those who lack conventional motivation to find drugs unusually attractive. If one confines his use of the term to a description of the present American scene one must conclude that present evidence does not permit the establishment of causal relationship between marijuana use and the amotivational syndrome. There is, however, increasing evidence that frequent, heavy marijuana use is correlated with a loss of interest in conventional goals and the development of a kind of lethargy. Research in humans is being conducted in an attempt to determine to what extent this observed correlation is due to alteration in brain functioning."

Time also quotes the report as saying, "Use may precipitate psychosis in perhaps one out of 300 cases, but only in 'those who were about to crack anyway.' Attacks of anxiety occur in a small percentage of cases, but the panic is transitory; it disappears when the victim is assured that nothing is seriously wrong with him." Not reported by *Time* is this comment on page 10 of the HEW publication: "Acute psychotic episodes precipitated by marijuana intoxication have been reported by a number of investigators. These appear to occur infrequently, usually at high dosages, but may occur, even at levels of social usage, in particularly susceptible individuals. Heightened susceptibility appears to be more likely in those who have previously had a marginal psychological adjustment especially in the presence of excessive stress."

The HEW report also notes on page 8 that, "As doses higher than the typical social dose are consumed more pronounced thought distortions may occur including a disrupted sense of one's own body, a sense of personal unreality—of being unreal, visual distortions, sometimes hallucinations and paranoid thinking. The more marked distortions of reality or psychotic-like symptoms become increasingly common if the dosage used becomes extremely high. Most users smoke to the point of 'high' which they find pleasurable and at which they are able to control the effect. It is, however, difficult to predict individual reactions. Rarely, individuals may become quite anxious or panicky on even low doses. When eaten, effects are less predictable and more difficult for the user to control."

Time's report of two other features, progression to hard drugs (little evidence) or association with major crime (none) agree in context with the HEW report. It is interesting, however, since this 176-page report is filled with concern about unknown effects and apprehension about premature use, that *Time* would conclude that HEW's summary gives the heads "a slight edge over the straights." In essence the magazine's report seems to remain in context with the posture issue, which appears to be dedicated to the concept that it is unpopular and thus unwise to urge caution in the use of pot. Inherent in this concept is the view that if one wishes to be "in" and "mod" and "accepted," he must follow the line of least resistance and agree that we can't positively "prove" that pot can hurt you, rather than acknowledging, as did the HEW report, that we are by no means certain that it is safe.

THE VALUE JUDGMENT ISSUE

Society is critically divided today as to what is proper in life styles, in goal direction, in achievement and in success. For many older Americans, the thought their children might "drop out and become pot-smoking hippies" precipitates near-hysteria. Kaplan quotes Glen Schofield's study of police views on the connection between marijuana and aggression which found that rather than fearing violence, the thing that bugged the officers most was the change in life-style they associated with the use of pot.

"The main evil and danger which these officers felt was presented by widespread use of marijuana was the creation and perpetuation of a life-style and set of attitudes and actions which was contrary to the values of the society as a whole," Schofield noted. The men tended to view marijuana as a central tenet and foundation and, perhaps, even the cause of youth's developing a way of life that is not only foreign to adult acceptance, but contrary to their sense of approval. "They get a new set of values," the officers said, "they're generally against everything and not for anything."[5]

The irony here is that those who view this change of style as not only appropriate but desirable will applaud it with vigor. This point demonstrates again that the critical gap in our society is not necessarily between young and old but between conservative and liberal youth. That which appalls one segment of the youth group often delights and provides cohesion for the other.

The value judgment issue is devoted to the determined preservation of the status quo by conservatives and its dissolution by the liberals. Pot is tightly associated either by cause or by effect with the latter group. Thus when cannabis is mentioned the question may become one of whose values shall prevail in our forthcoming society. It is an emotionally laden sub rosa issue in the controversy.

THE PLEASURE ISSUE

Contemporary older America grew up not only under adverse conditions but also under the philosophy that a man should earn his pleasure by the sweat of his brow or he was not entitled to fun. Further, usually on religious principles, man was not thought to be on this earth to enjoy himself excessively but, instead, to prepare himself for the Hereafter. Some older theologians taught or implied that God was not pleased with frivolity and thus it was to be minimized.

The post war group of Americans now in their teens and twenties often abreact to this philosophy. Faced with an immediate "pushbutton doom" that is made all too real by our involvement in a war most youth feel is unjustifiable, many feel they should live life to the utmost for the present because the future may never arrive. One of their media for achieving this is pot, whose prime if not only current contribution to society is providing pleasure for pleasure's sake.

"Marijuana should be legalized because it's fun," states Michael Aldrich, a young Ph.D. who as a Fulbright tutor in English spent eight months in India, where by his own admission he "turned on at least once a day with ganja, bhang or charas." "Social use of any preparation of cannabis depends primarily on the fact that altering one's perception is pleasurable," he states; "if the mental changes produced by smoking, eating or drinking marijuana are not pleasurable, use will not normally be continued."[6]

Aldrich's assertion that drug use will not continue if the user's mental changes are not pleasurable may be a wishful value judgment; the literature tends to negate this concept where other drugs are concerned. For example, Mello has demonstrated that alcoholics may continue to drink despite the fact that to do so usually induces dysphoria (the opposite of euphoria).[7]

Older America, give or take those few who have joined the counterculture, instinctively revolts against such a statement. These citizens grew up under a rigid puritan ethic which, said one wit, is "an unbearable state of discomfort brought on by the vague awareness that somewhere someone is enjoying himself without working for the pleasure." Such resentment is amplified by the realization that once one has adhered to this "sweat of the brow" philosophy, the years have gone by and there is no way of recouping the loss. "When I was a kid . . ." they mutter, and imply that because they had it hard, it is wrong for today's kids to have fun without experiencing a similar purgatory. Simultaneously, with a rationalization unique to the human mind, they provide youth with too many material goods, reasoning, "My kid is never going to have to go through what I did."

The Pleasure Issue can be defined as the pitting of the "fun must be earned" group's attitude against that of the "fun for fun's sake" group. The polarization is complicated by the religious overtones implying God's abhorrence of too much enjoyment. This attitude gives rise to resentment, and to a sense of guilt and remorse which must have some medium of expression. It is much easier to condemn pot than to face reality. Pot is an easy symbol, since it is currently a totally pleasure-giving item. This symbol can be discussed with invective without having to face the real issue troubling the mind of the speaker.

THE ANTISOCIAL ISSUE

As studies of committed pot users have progressed, it has been noted that they share the common denominator of being avant garde in their thinking, less conformist than many, and basically anti-Establishment in attitude. This may not apply to the casual user, but it seems to be recurrent in the personality of the chronic user or abuser.

It follows that two things may occur in this association. First, cannabis may be used as a cohesive element in a segment of society that strongly opposes the status quo. It has the potential of being a conditioning agent in promoting value judgments and anti-establishmentarian attitudes. Rebels who recognize this potential have the good sense to keep quiet and employ their knowledge, while those who love debates loudly acknowledge that this sort of mechanism is antisocially advantageous.

The point, of course, is that the Antisocial Issue is but a small part of the cannabis scene and its influence is most difficult to prove. Those who are most aware of such tendencies are those involved in law enforcement. Like the medical student who, having spent three months in brain tumor service, emerges with the conviction that the world is dying of cerebral neoplasms, so those who persistently see a recurrent negative factor in our society may assume it exists in larger proportion than is real. Conservatives tend to attribute antisocial attitudes to all those who smoke pot, because one group uses it for radical purposes. An analagous generalization is made at the liberal end of the spectrum, where radical attitudes in pot smokers are infrequently seen, and are assumed to be non-existent.

The Antisocial Issue can be defined as the uncomfortable

feeling on the part of those who have to deal with radical elements that the cause (pot) and effect (radical behavior), which seems to exist and which may well apply to a few, is a universal phenomenon. This feeling may be applied to pot users in general, particularly when, as a group, chronic abusers share antisocial tendencies which may or may not be catalyzed by the use of pot. Conversely, the suggestion strikes the casual pot users, who never see this scene, as being stupid, and they may react with disbelief and anger. Thus the battle goes on.

THE GENDER ISSUE

Authoritarian activities tend to attract certain types of individuals as do other professions. It would be as unlikely to find a traffic policeman moonlighting as a hair dresser as it would be to find a hippie voluntarily acting as a "nark." Authoritarian figures in general develop and sustain an intense masculine gender image. Gender may be defined not only as the attitude society has toward an individual as far as his "maleness" or her "femaleness" is concerned, it is also critically bound up with the attitude one has towards himself. The authoritarian figure—and the policeman is the epitomy of this—tends to have a distinct idea of what manhood is all about, and tends to detest those who do not measure up to this image. He abhors even more the individual who, by any device or influence, threatens the authoritarian's concept of his own masculinity.

Pot has been associated in the Establishment mind with hippies. Thus, "hippie attitudes" are attributed to all pot users. Male hippies do things which strike many authoritarian figures as highly unmasculine. They wear long (girlish) hair and flowered, colorful (feminine) clothing; they engage in activities traditionally associated with females—promoting peace and loving brotherhood, singing songs, and so on. All in all, the appearance and behavior of "average" male hippies do not strike the short haired, neatly dressed, socially compliant enforcement officer as being properly masculine. Their presence, therefore, may evoke the same hostility, anxiety, hatred, and fear often precipitated in the officer by the presence of an obvious homosexual. This point becomes particularly critical when one realizes that in many police departments vice and narcotics operations are conducted by the same officers working in the same division.

The irony here is that hippies, with rare exceptions, are aggressive, earnest, committed, practicing heterosexuals, their exteriors to the contrary. The gender threat they entail, of course, is not limited to sex per se. The hippie movement is basically anti-authoritarian and it is not uncommon for a dedicated member to flip a one fingered peace symbol at policemen. None of this goes over too well and the officers on the receiving end may thereafter often react adversely to the "pot smoking hippie" image.

The Gender Issue is a very complex, usually unrecognized threat to the power and masculinity of authoritarian figures, by individuals who among other things highly espouse the use of pot. Since hatred, anxiety and fear toward such individuals are not easily faced, it is much preferable to direct one's hostility toward a symbol, though it may not be recognized as such. In this instance, pot is a perfect ploy.

THE GENERATION GAP ISSUE

One of the more poorly-understood elements of the current "struggle" between young and old is the substitution of pot as the center of debate on issues relating to youth's maturation. There comes a period (usually coinciding with the pot-smoking age) when a young person must question the veracity and ability of his parents or he would probably not develop the impetus to acquire a self-identity independent of his parents. If this break-away does not occur, the child may never develop into a man. The break is made most difficult if the parents make the child feel that he should stay by the hearth. It is convenient for the youth to have a symbol to attack in lieu of his parents— in which he can, in effect, say, "Dad, you're not with it." Attacking a parent-substitute symbol is particularly effective when, as in the case of pot, the youth is quite right.

The parent hoping that someone else can assure his child that change is not good, that the new is undesirable, or that the vices of the past are preferable to those chosen by youth, is in for a serious disappointment. It is foolish to lecture a youth on the "evils" of pot when he is enjoying its effects, or is committed to its use. The prime time to approach him is before he has been involved with use of the drug at all.

The Generation Gap Issue is best recognized as the substitution of a symbol which can be vigorously attacked instead of facing the painful reality of the youth-parent separation period. Pot is ideal, since it is primarily a youth drug, with alcohol running second best as the bête noir of the over-thirty escapees. The argument is even more fun if one can confuse the issue by forcing a comparison of the two drugs.

THE RELIGIOUS-MORAL ISSUE

The problem with trying to define religious and moral issues is that once they have been identified as such, social taboos and religious doctrine enter the scene and screen out rational discussion. If one can outdebate his opponent through the simple expedient of announcing that a given thing is "immoral" or "against the will of God," he seems to win the argument—unless his opponent demands some concrete evidence that this statement is not merely a personal and highly-biased opinion.

Much of the Religious-Moral Issue is deeply bound up with the Sexual Issue and the Pleasure Issue. In part, these can be understood as an extension of the conflict between the Judeo-Christian heritage common to most Americans, and the Eastern-oriented philosophies associated with the use of cannabis.

The Judeo-Christian tradition places high value on a life of hard work, self-sacrifice, and perseverance. The concept of pure pleasure or hedonistic sex is anathema to its philosophy. Although many of its prophets preach peace, its adherants tend to be highly aggressive toward non-believers and "outsiders." Central is the idea that man is a created being—a child of, and responsible to God.

Sects using cannabis as a sacrament, in common with many Eastern religions that may use no drugs at all, have a much different outlook on life and the nature of man and God. In general, they seem passive, introspective, and peaceful. Some are highly hedonistic. They tend to teach that man is part of God, and may in time reunite with and "become" God. (This lack of boundaries between oneself and God is related to the kind of transcendent experience many pot users feel characterizes their "highs.")

The importance of the Religious-Moral Issue is highly dependent on the debater's knowledge of and involvement with the spiritual scene. This scene (not religious per se, but spiritual) is of intense interest to many youths who seek a new way of worshipping God. They often feel that organized Judeo-Christian religions no longer offer them the guidance they seek, or the support they need. For some, Eastern-based religions (with or without pot) seem a satisfying alternative.

THE SEXUAL ISSUE

The influence of marijuana on human sexuality is discussed in the Appendix. As far as the drug's use by most youth is concerned, that description is quite adequate. The situation does not end there, however. Far from it. In recent months, many adults have discovered that pot may act as a disinhibiting agent and reliever of guilt where their own sex lives are concerned.

Youth's attitude toward sexuality today is often quite different from that of their parents. Many adults, hung up on centuries of Judeo-Christian-puritan-victorian sexual suppression, have looked with horror at the attitudes expressed by a growing number of youth: that sex is enjoyable, decent, and desirable. Older adults have no doubt entertained this idea, too, but it has taken the younger generation with its fantastic resources of transportation and communication to finally throw off the yoke of impotence-producing fear and anxiety forced upon previous generations by a rigid religious-legal alliance.

For some older people the mere suggestion that a sex-grass connection exists is enough to make them anti-cannabis. Much of the opposition of the Establishment toward hippies or to drug self-help organizations such as Synanon has arisen from the justified suspicion that these groups possess a highly liberal attitude toward sexuality.

Some adults are openly envious of the freedom and enjoyment youth obtains today from sex, and in this envy develop guilt. As this guilt mounts they tend to rationalize their feelings and redirect the resulting hostility towards any available satisfactory symbol. Once again pot obliquely enters the scene. Too, another factor is involved in the sex-cannabis link.

Long before the heterosexual world discovered that cannabis could release inhibitions and allay guilt, the homosexual subculture was using pot with avid admiration. Being highly experimental, homosexuals reasoned, then proved through experience, that a drug that could alter perception, redirect one's sense of time, enhance sensory input and interpretation, and minimize guilt should have a highly-prized place in their subculture.

Recently the homosexual magazine *Queens' Quarterly* made the relationship of the use of cannabis and the gay sexual scene quite clear. "It is for those who have never tried marijuana in connection with sex," a writer noted in his story "Love Tripping on Grass," "that this article is written. Accordingly QQ readers in San Francisco, New York or New Orleans are advised to turn the page to the next article because it is unlikely that any homosexual who lives in a swinging city has not grooved on 'grass' long ago."[8]

The straight world has been more sluggish in discovering this association but when it once got the message it came through loud and clear. Recently Barbara Lewis interviewed 208 middle-class adult users to see what effects pot had had on their sex lives. "It became clear to me during the course of our conversation," she said, "that the pot phenomenon, while as yet only a minority taste, is closely tied to the winds of change that are swirling over the American landscape. Marijuana, to many of its satisfied users, is a means to an end, a way to fuller self expression—emotionally, sexually and even professionally; a way toward freedom from the constraints of the past imposed by the family or the customs dictated by society."[9]

The promise of this sudden freedom in sexual behavior and enjoyment may produce a relatively dramatic change in the attitude of many now conservative Americans toward constrictive laws against pot. This speaker has noted with interest the obvious restless change affecting an older audience when the subject of sexual enhancement through the use of pot enters the program. Almost literally a light snaps on over their heads as they begin to understand what the kids have been talking about. And one can almost hear their thoughts. "Uh . . . man . . . wait a minute . . . This casts a different light on this pot thing."

The Sexual Issue has only begun to make itself known. A growing number of adults, crippled by the teachings that sex is evil and not to be indulged in for pleasure, are beginning to take a difference stance. Sadly, many are psychologically incapable of making an adjustment to a more satisfying life with their spouses without intervening help. If it becomes verified that cannabis has a significant effect on impotence, not as an aphrodisiac but as a disinhibitor, it is difficult to guess which direction legislation may take.

There is, however, a disquieting factor here, too, for cannabis is as unpredictable in its effects on sexuality as it is in other aspects of altered perception. Some may find themselves less capable of physical activity, in contrast to others who find their abilities enhanced. Another problem is that once one becomes used to sexuality under the influence of pot, he may find it difficult if not impossible to perform without its assistance.

Significantly, the chronic use of virtually any psychoactive drug produces variable numbers of sexual cripples suffering primarily from decreased "libido" and varying degrees of impotence. If the pot scene spreads, the plaintive complaint, "He used to smoke pot and make love to me; now he just smokes pot" may be heard more frequently than it is now.

The Sexual Issue involves a complex, highly individual reaction on the part of each person. Some may hate pot because they fear the drug may destroy valued beliefs. Others may feel an intense guilt at having disrupted prior teachings, and react accordingly. More may feel the urge to employ any weapon at their command to rejuvenate their sexuality. Obviously, these reactions will vary immensely; the results will only add to the arguments over pot.

THE LEGALIZATION ISSUE

One fascinating aspect of the cannabis controversy is the continuing, noisy effort on the part of certain individuals and groups to make the use of cannabis legal in the United States, at a time when other countries, with few exceptions, are doing their best to outlaw it. Numerous emotional interreactions are involved here—from social scientists and attorneys to physicians and specialists in mental health.

In early 1970 a new voice joined the group advocating the legalization of cannabis. It belongs to John Kaplan, a respected professor of law at Stanford University. Kaplan expresses proper concern with the current system of laws, which he has declared unworkable. "When a law is unworkable," he recently told a physician audience, "you've got to change it."[10]

Kaplan seems to hold no brief for marijuana use. "The dangers of marijuana may have been grossly exaggerated," he notes, but "they are far from negligible—especially for the very young. And although the total number affected seriously may still not be very impressive compared to the magnitude of other public-health problems, there is no reason why we should not strive to keep it as low as practicable."

"There is in addition a unique social reason for the control of this drug," he says. "Marijuana today not only appeals powerfully to the young but seems to appeal especially to more educated, intelligent, and highly motivated members of that group. These users, including a large and growing number who are no longer minors, are often in varying degrees dissatisfied with aspects of society; in some sense, indeed, they use the drug as a protest against societal conditions. The fact is, however, that the use of any kind of psychoactive drug, including marijuana, can turn its user away from solving the societal problems responsible for his dissatisfaction. Even though this type of user by no means becomes a public charge, he may fail to realize his full value to society or to himself."[11]

Kaplan's entry into the scene is somewhat parallel to the story of Saul of Tarsus,[12] who was converted to join the religion of those he had persecuted. Kaplan spent a great deal of time successfully prosecuting individuals who violated the marijuana laws. But later, faced with the fact that seventy percent of his own law students were using the drug,[13] Kaplan began to see things in a different light. He voices his concern in his book, *Marijuana, the New Prohibition.*

Kaplan as a lawyer is one thing. Kaplan as an interpreter of medical findings and clinical observation is quite another. Since Kaplan has become the major voice in the pro-legalization field at this moment, some time will be spent here in comment on his observations. His remarks concerning the problems involved in prosecuting under current marijuana laws are vital and pertinent. His attempts to prove his point by using the adversary approach of seemingly nullifying previous medical observations to fortify his case, or using isolated and sometimes highly controversial investigative reports leave something to be desired.

He is correct in concluding, after examining one justification after another for the criminalization of marijuana users, that many of these arguments are weak. The problem is that, as he applies the adversary approach, he may leave the impression that all work to date, with the exception of a few articles he has chosen to accept, is irrelevant.

It is a risky thing for an attorney and a physician to attempt to apply the same sort of reasoning to one discipline that is highly successful to the other. This is particularly true where public health is concerned. A physician may completely upset the functioning of the law because he is clinically involved in and emotionally concerned with a given patient. In turn, an attorney may become so preoccupied with the letter of the law that he may fail to discern that the law tends to be impersonal in its overall concern with the populace as a whole. He may thus tend to be insensitive to a group's being critically harmed by the law's aloofness. Attorneys may practice law with justice blindfolded for impartiality. Physicians may not.

When an attorney faces a legal situation, he is concerned with a different set of circumstances than is a physician who attempts to treat an illness. A physician sees the recurrence of a given set of circumstances; his clinical intuition and experience warn him that even if he lacks laboratory evidence he should use caution before proceeding. To a physician, proof may be the intuitive awareness that things do not "compute." With his patient's life at stake, he reacts differently than, say, a research scientist, who may scoff at a family doctor's approach because it lacks the ivory tower elements so critical to the isolated researcher who seldom sees and is rarely responsible for patient care.

If clinicians differ within their own peer groups—i.e., the family doctor vs. the researcher—their collective perspective may be at total odds with an attorney practicing law within the limitations of his discipline. For instance, a defense attorney does not have to "prove" his client is innocent. He has merely to cast reasonable doubt and leave the decision as to guilt or innocence to the jury and/or judge. For an attorney, doubt that a man is guilty is enough to free him. For a clinician, concern that a man may be in danger is reason for restraint and caution. Proof to an attorney, therefore, means something quite different from proof to a physician.

Doctors are again divided when it comes to therapeutic approach. The division arises between those who practice clinical medicine and surgery, where time and intuitive experience necessitate immediate life saving (or destroying) decisions, and a discipline such as psychiatry, where time can usually be spent in study, debate and theory. If internists and surgeons practiced medicine and/or surgery with the same approach psychiatrists or attorneys properly use in their discipline, many patients could conceivably die during the debate process.

Where law is concerned the question to be decided by the court is whether the man is guilty or innocent and if guilty, whether or not extenuating circumstances should influence the verdict and sentencing. Attorneys are divided into antagonist and protanogist, and the goal is to win using any technique allowable within the wide framework of ethics surrounding the legal profession. Information detrimental to one side is suppressed, if possible, by those whose cause might be hurt by it and exposed where possible by the opposition. Witnesses are challenged, not so much because what they may say is relevant, but because the evidence may upset the prosecution or defense. If a witness' evidence is too detrimental and cannot be disrupted, then the witness himself is attacked, in an attempt to disqualify him or cast doubt on his testimony.

Thus in law, sides are divided. In medicine, they are not. In law, one attorney is for the defendant; the other is against him. If doctors practiced medicine as attorneys practice law, half the clinicians would have to line up on the side of the disease. To approach a problem that is primarily medical in nature with a legal type of reasoning, therefore, is fraught with many hazards. Yet, in the cannabis issue, law and medicine cannot be separated. They must work together, or total chaos will result. The problem is that bringing law into a medical issue (and in this instance it can not be avoided because drug abuse entails problems specifically related to enforcement) causes new problems. As Kaplan properly notes, the costs of enforcing the law have now become so prohibitive that one must ask whether the law may be as bad or worse than the crime.

Over and above this, however, is the critical issue of whether or not people are being harmed. In the pot scene they are, both through law and through inadequate medical treatment. Kaplan admits that "although the costs of using the criminal law to outlaw these 'socially approved' drugs obviously outweigh the benefits of criminalizing them, this does not mean that society has no strong interest in minimizing the abuse of these drugs."[14]

The common cry today is that the law is failing *us*. In fact, *we* have failed the law, for in effect, with some classic exceptions, *we* are the law, through our legislatures. The problem, where cannabis laws are concerned, is that the Establishment is engaging in the highly immoral game of trying to make the victims pay for the mistakes of older but not necessarily more mature citizens who have directly or indirectly promoted the abuse of drugs in general and pot in particular.

How have we failed the law? We have emasculated it by retaining on the books laws which long ago lost their meaning and which, if enforced today could work unnecessary hardship on the victim. Too often repressive laws are left on the books "just in case" police (i.e., the community) wants to control a minority group.

How have we failed the law? By exhibiting an unusual disrespect for it on the adult level when a given law becomes inconvenient or when it is in conflict with a given person's ideology. In California, for instance, a high court officer refused to obey a judge's direct order and arbitrarily violated it. He did this, he reasoned, to "test the law." If youths test the law where marijuana use is concerned they may land in jail for ten years. In the case of the attorney the court imposed a fine of $50.00.[15]

Recently, a judge lauded a woman physician who, because it was against her personal beliefs, violated her state's abortion laws. This woman, the judge said, should be admired and encouraged for her stand.[16] It's a matter for debate what the same judge might do to a youth who earnestly pursued the same course of action because of his beliefs where marijuana is concerned.

It is ironic that adults expect youths to respect a system that permits various individuals in the media, and the entertainment, and political, theological, and scientific worlds, to urge kids to believe that pot is "cool," but also punishes a young person for acting on the "propaganda."

This brings us to the cry that the marijuana laws are unworkable and bad. Perhaps, today, they are because things have changed. But is was not always so. Until about 1965, they were quite effective. Then people lost respect not only for marijuana laws, but for law in general. Much of this is evidenced by the over-thirty group. Is there an answer? Well, we legalized alcohol; why not pot? Adults don't respect the law. Why should youth? Reasonably, we should control alcohol, not legalize another problem drug. Reasonably we should work to increase reasons for adults to respect the law, rather than condemning the son for mimicking the father. . . . Reasonably!

Kaplan outlines three major models of law which he applies to drug control: the "vice" model, the "medical" model, and the "licensing" model. He discusses these from one attorney's point of view and comes up with some conclusions that are sharply divergent from those that might be expected to occur to a clinician.

The first concept assumes that the use of pot is a vice which society strongly wishes to suppress, but in suppressing it, does not want to harm the user. The most common rationalization employed here is that the consumer of the vice is merely a victim. As such he needs help, not punishment, whereas the seller is guilty of an aggravated evil because he makes a profit from the weakness of others.

Kaplan observes that adoption of the vice model would sharply cut the cost of the marijuana laws: He notes that two thirds of the arrests are for possession of small quantities of the drug and that elimination of such arrests would preclude many of the tragedies which now occur because of enforcement. Kaplan properly asserts that if we did not imprison marijuana users with others more criminally inclined, the Establishment would save itself a significant number of sociotogenically produced criminals. This latter point is critical to any solution to the present cannabis problem, and will be discussed later. The rest of Kaplan's presentation tends to minimize a number of vital considerations which seem to make the "vice model" relatively impractical where cannabis is concerned.

The first is that there is rarely such a thing as a user who does not deal. This is true with all drugs, but it is pathognomonic with pot fans. Pot users deal for profit, for fun, and to perpetuate an ideal. When one wants to score a joint, he doesn't duck down an alley and whisper, "Hey man, where's da nearest pusher?"; the modern youth goes to a buddy and says, "Hey pal, lay one on me will ya? I'm short this week."

More than eighty percent (and that may be an underestimate) of the grass that is sold passes from one user to another as a favor, for a few bucks, or because the user wants to share a "cool" experience with a buddy. The ideology of the pot world is almost universally misunderstood by its straight counterpart.

One does not usually pass a joint along to a friend just to make money. He does it because he believes the high to be a very great experience and, much like a religious convert, he wants to share his experience with those he likes and/or loves.

This philosophy of the pot-oriented counterculture is completely beyond the comprehension of the straight world. A few months ago this author was asked by a state government to testify in a preliminary hearing concerning the constitutionality of the state's laws governing the use of pot. On trial (the actual trial was held later when the constitutionality of the state's cannabis laws was assured) was a youth who had inadvertently sold some grass to an undercover agent. He was not a novice. In fact, he had been dealing for some time, an enterprise he made quite clear to the court he would continue if he were released.

In contrast to some anti-pot forces, the court and the prosecuting attorney had no wish to send this youth to a long term in jail. In the interests of justice, the prosecutor offered the boy a chance to cop a lesser plea if he chose to do so, rather than face a felony charge. The boy allegedly replied that the rap was bad, that the laws were immoral, that pot was good, and that he would continue to sell and share with whomever he chose when he got out. He also allegedly advised the prosecutor he could roll his case up in a snug cylinder and attempt to perform what was basically an impossible anatomical feat. Unlike the attorney who defied the law at an ideological level, and who was fined fifty dollars, this boy is now doing ten years of hard time.

A second point: how much can we demand from our police and still expect their cooperation? Attorneys base their efficiency on the number of cases they win in court or in out of court settlements. Teachers look to the educational achievements of their pupils as an index of efficiency; doctors measure their success by the number of individuals whom they restored to health, assist when cure is impossible, or prevent from contacting disease. Police measure their efficiency not so much on arrest rate, (although this looks good if an internecine tournament is going on between department heads), but on convictions that hold up in court.

If an officer spends months of hard work building a case, endangering his life and wearing himself out physically and emotionally, only to find that time after time the case is dismissed, he may in time only minimally enforce the law which the courts will not sustain. He will not often openly do so, since this is not politic, but it will soon be noticed that his efforts are being directed elsewhere. Suppose police are forced to accept the concept that only the "big" marijuana pushers are to be punished, when they know that (a) eighty percent of the "pushers" are casual users who deal, and (b) the "big" pushers make so much bread they can hire the best attorneys and thus often evade the law. Marijuana enforcement might come to a screeching halt. Pro-marijuana forces know this; thus their efforts are to destroy the current system of hitting the user-dealer. Other societies, Japan for instance, seem to go along with the philosophy that "it's the little foxes that eat the vines." It is not the big boy but the user-dealers who promote the spread, conversion to, and sale of cannabis.

Kaplan, though apparently not versed in the conversion phenomenon, is not oblivious to the exchange of grass on a friendship basis, nor is he unaware of the "little fox" theory. To avoid facing this he suddenly advocates the very thing his book is against—instituting penalties for sale. He suggests that sale of an ounce be a petty misdemeanor punishable by a sentence of up to three months, the sale of three pounds a misdemeanor carrying a maximum sentence of one year, and sale of more than three pounds a felony with a five-year prison sentence.[17]

Now confusion reigns. How do you enforce such a law without "making criminals out of users"? How do you do so without involving police and entailing the fantastic "too expensive" system of law enforcement now in practice? Further, if such a law were in effect, who in his right mind would be caught with more than three pounds of grass. And if sellers are that astute how can any control be attained? The "new" method will be merely to sell as much or more, but in smaller quantities.

Kaplan now enters into a realm of ideology: the age at which one should smoke pot. Twenty-one, he says, is a most unrealistic age to use as a dividing line for adulthood. As a matter of fact, it is. We are stuck with this phenomenon because in ancient England nutrition was so poor a youth had to be twenty-one before he could stagger around in a heavy suit of armor; the tradition has persisted.

Kaplan suggests that eighteen is a good age, then notes that in some states sixteen is the age when one can drive. He also observes most authorities feel that alcohol could be better regulated and alcohol misuse better controlled if the realistic level of age eighteen were employed as the legal drinking age.[18]

Inasmuch as alcohol currently is one of the major problems among teenagers in this country it could be successfully debated that "better regulated" is a euphemism. Aside from that, why age eighteen? Why not age sixteen? The answer most young users will give you if you ask them this about their own younger brothers and sisters is that "they're not ready for it?" Just why the older teens think this is so will vary from one youth to another but it seems that older teenagers, in contrast with many "mature" adults, recognize that the goal forming, decision making period of life is not the time to play around with a mind altering, sensory changing, ideology redirecting, inhibition releasing, concept fragmenting drug. But casual use doesn't do this, one may argue. Quite true. But in early and mid and perhaps late adolescence, how wide is the DMZ between use and abuse?

Suppose we legalize the drug for age eighteen and above. How legal is legal? Should we advertise the stuff? Imagine what Madison Avenue could do with television commercials as they talk about the ecstasies of Brand X over those offered by Brand Y. "There should be no advertising of any kind," Kaplan recently said. "Marijuana should be sold in alcohol stores."[19] This thought is a trip in itself. Packaged by tobacco companies, who have no conscience in peddling destructive drugs for profit, and retailed by alcohol outlets where a similar philosophy applies? It boggles the imagination!

Let's take a look at one of society's most hypocritical games. It's called, "Keep booze and tobacco away from Junior." How successful is this farce? The odds are almost one hundred percent *against* enforcement. Where tobacco is concerned, observe the lucrative selfservice device. Note the amusing notation, "Minors are forbidden to use this machine." See how kids from the age of ten or so deposit their fifty cents into the gadget and walk off smoking. Count the times the kid is discouraged from doing this, much less arrested, even though his smoking is against the law. Observe Junior's lack of respect for the law, its legislators, and its enforcers.

How about alcohol? It happens that many retail outlets are extremely concerned about giving booze to minors. One reason is that they can lose their license for doing so. How does one avoid getting caught and still sell to the under-aged? Usually inadvertently by selling to older youths and adults, who in turn give the booze to minors. This is not so? Then why is alcohol a prime problem, for instance where driving and youth are concerned?

In discussing the "vice" model, Kaplan also notes that an aspect of "public decency" may enter the picture since many older citizens may object to the use of marijuana. Thus growing the stuff could present a problem since the sight of the leafy green plant waving in the breeze might disrupt the emotional balance of conservatives. He also notes that some provision should be made covering driving while under the influence of marijuana,[20] although he has tended to dilute his concern not only by reliance on the Crancer report but also by his debate as to whether or not driving is a complex activity. But nowhere does he discuss how society could keep from criminalizing youths caught in this situation, or determine how we can keep the "excessive costs" of enforcing marijuana laws down when repeatedly exceptions are made which entail the employment of large numbers of enforcement officers.

Kaplan then discusses the "fallacy" entertained by some that legalizing the drug is the same as condoning it. Properly he notes that it is not necessary to compound a problem by labeling a person a criminal merely because we do not approve of his activities even though they are not socially detrimental to a significant extent. In contrast to previous suggestions for penalties for sale, Kaplan then suggests that we treat marijuana use like a parking or minor traffic offense. He says this would not increase the costs of marijuana control over those under a pure vice model but such an approach would nevertheless express society's disapproval of the use of the drug.

It is interesting that this suggestion comes from a seasoned prosecutor used to working with police. He is correct that this approach would not increase the costs of enforcement. What officer would be willing to go through the necessary maneuvers to make a narcotics (or cannabis) arrest if he knew the end result would be a two dollar fine? More and more cities are finding that a two dollar parking fine is ridiculous; it is cheaper to park on the street and pay the fine than submit to the extortion of the modern parking lot. What's the answer to this? Raise the fines? So one makes the fine really hurt. What then? More enforcement? What then? Criminalization of youths by police? Higher costs of enforcement? Seems we've heard that song before.

Kaplan, however, is not enamored with the "vice" model. He says it's too expensive, cannot restrict the supply of marijuana, encourages selling in larger amounts by those who feel if they're going to be "hung for selling a lamb they might as well sell a sheep," and drives sellers underground so, society loses control over the quality of the drugs they sell.[21] Further, he notes, the glaring discrepancy between the way we handle alcohol versus the way we handle pot enhances the credibility gap between youth and the Establishment. In short, he says, the "vice" model is too expensive. Thus he turns to a discussion of the "medical" model.[22]

The "medical model" works under the assumption that a drug, marijuana in this case, is a mild sedative and tranquilizer and should be sold by prescription. Kaplan laudably states that this whole idea is a bummer. First, most people use cannabis not as a drug, but as an enjoyable socio-relaxant. The demand, therefore, would quickly exceed the supply, and physicians would begin suffering acute cases of writer's cramp.

Further, it is noted that two of our most frequently used and most dangerous drugs, the barbiturates and amphetamines, are prescription items, and yet the large majority of users and abusers of these items outside the medical sphere obtain them from illegal sources. The medical model, then, would be too expensive and impractical to administer, and would criminalize the abuser who obtained supplies from the black market. This brings us to the system that seems to get Kaplan's nod of approval: the "licensing" model.

Under the "licensing model," states Kaplan, "we would treat the drug essentially as we do alcohol, licensing sellers who meet certain conditions *and of course, making sales by those who are unlicensed seriously criminal.*"[23] (Italics added). Kaplan's use of the almost parenthetical phrase here reminds one of the humorous rationalization of certain British representatives who used to loudly deny they had a drug problem in Great Britain. "Of course," they would add, "this doesn't include the Indians, the Chinese or the Blacks."

The main thrust of Kaplan's argument is that by licensing the material and distributing it through retail outlets, he could control both quality and content. This is quite true. He also suggests he'd "tax the hell out of it."[24]

How mild should a groovy joint be? Kaplan has an answer that surely must go down in history with Murphy's law. Commercial joints, he said, should be "just potent enough not to drive people to the drug culture in search of more powerful drugs and hard enough to get to discourage its use by youth."[25] Kaplan is cautious enough to see that many go on to hashish, but he seems unaware of the reason. Noting that federal authorities confiscated more hashish in one fiscal year (1967/68) than they had in the previous twenty years combined, he states that merely because people can get "weak" grass does not mean they will not go on to stronger grades of grass.[26]

At this point he seems to employ the old "well, they would have gotten hurt, anyway" argument by stating, "If people want the more powerful drugs, then licensing less powerful ones may not be sufficient to dissuade them; but the availability of a legal and convenient, though less potent, alternative, it would seem, could only shrink the market for more potent grades—as well as free large amounts of law-enforcement resources for the task of suppressing the illegal traffic in these drugs."[27]

Why do people smoke grass? Professor Kaplan says it's because "they like its effects."[28] Why do people attempt to get stronger and stronger types of grass? Because if they like the weaker grades they will probably enjoy the stronger grades even more. After all, who goes into a bar and says, "Hey, give me a watered-down drink?"

Kaplan now grows a bit reserved. "The dangers of hashish may be an argument for criminalizing that form of the drug," he says, "but a little thought reveals that criminalizing the weaker marijuana, if anything, will increase the use of the stronger drug."[29] This is a change of pace in thinking for Professor Kaplan, who seventeen pages earlier said, "It may well be that hashish should be treated no differently from marijuana, or indeed that criminal penalties for the drug user are not a sensible social policy for the control of any drug. . . ."[30]

"A licensing system, however," notes Kaplan, "can exert pressure away from stronger drugs. So long as marijuana of sufficient potency is available, even though it is not perhaps so strong as desired, the preference for legal and convenient drug purchasing will incline users toward the use of the more available rather than the stronger drug."[31]

How? The fact is that those who use the giggle-weed as a source of casual relaxation will indeed welcome this approach, and it may have little significance to much of society. However, clinicians are concerned not with the casual user, unless he sustains adverse reactions, but with the abusive user—and the abusive user, in the opinion of most experts, is not satisfied with mild grass.

Here is the most pertinent place for the argument that "if we make the drug legal it will kill the fun of doing something illegal." If we make mild grass legal, then indeed we will have helped those whose only problem has ever been being busted and marked as a felon for simple use and/or possession. This is a serious legal issue. It has to be dealt with. But the solution to that problem does not tell us what to do with the abuser. We are brought once again to the criminalization factor. If we follow Kaplan's advice we may find that we fail to properly assist the group which most needs understanding and medical care. This group differs from those who thumb their nose at the law just because they wish to enjoy the effects of pot and not because they critically need a pharmacologic crutch. Abusers often turn to the drug and become dependent on it because they desperately need to escape reality. In contrast to the casual user who can choose to smoke or not to smoke, *these individuals often cannot help themselves.*

Returning to the cost of enforcement, who is going to make the determination as to which users are on mild legal grass and which are on "potent" hashish? At the scene of an accident does one look for a legal package wrapper, or for signs of illicit possession of stronger grass? Additionally, with the more sophisticated means of making one's own rolled cigarettes, who can determine, without expensive laboratory systems and highly-developed enforcement techniques, whether the joint is one returning a profit to the government and the tobacco companies, or an illicit one that resembles the socially-approved type?

Kaplan notes another important feature of the licensing system: it allows us, he says, "to control price."[32] When a pleasure giving substance is taxed, there is always a black market substitute. In 1969, according to *U.S. News & World Report,* the illicit alcohol market in this country involved seven hundred million dollars worth of illicit booze.[33] Why? Because some people, usually those who can least afford it, will buy black market goodies regardless of purity and quality because they are cheaper. Once again, the cost of enforcement, not to mention the threat to public health, becomes a critical factor.

Kaplan notes that the main pragmatic argument against the licensing system is that by making the drug legally available, we will increase its use. "This," he admits, "is almost certainly true, though to what extent is not so clear."[34]

"In all probability then," Kaplan concludes without substantiation, "under a licensing system a much larger number of people will have tried the drug once or twice and then given it up because they did not like its effects; a somewhat larger number will use the drug regularly; and, in most of the nation, the number of marijuana abusers will not increase significantly."[35]

The last statement might be labeled "Kaplan's Dream" and he recognizes its importance. "While difficult to prove conclusively," he states, having spent over 300 pages thus far ripping apart the arguments of people who have theorized on the basis of clinical observations, rather than on ideology, "it nonetheless is probably true." Temperance and prohibition are two very different concepts, he notes, in that they are often at war with each other. "It is far easier to educate people to use liquor 'like gentlemen' than to convince them not to use it at all."[36] This is true . . . for the majority. But what about the destructive minority? And if this philosophy has pertinent social application, why is such a large share of our eight and a half billion dollar crime expense budget involved with alcohol-related events?

Kaplan's greatest problem in promoting the licensing model becomes glaringly apparent in four brief paragraphs dealing with the use of the drug by minors. Recognizing that leakage from the system to minors is a cause for concern *"since abuse of marijuana among the very young is a serious problem"*[37] (italics added), Kaplan offers some counterbalancing arguments as to why legalization of pot is still a preferable approach.

Under the legalization system, the cost would be higher than for the average joint now, he says. Cost has been a minimal problem for most kids to date. Why should it suddenly become a deterrent under the legalized system? The leakage can also be decreased, Kaplan says, by channeling the activities of law enforcement in this direction. How? Do we stop a youth when we see him smoking pot or under its influence, and ask for his ID? Further, if only socially-approved brands and potencies of pot are permissible, are police supposed to examine every package and make sure it's not contraband? Aren't we rapidly approaching a system which Kaplan might later complain is "too expensive?" Kaplan goes further. He suggests that the "forbidden fruit" aspect of using pot will be abated by legalization, then says, "Even if the licensing of marijuana did increase the abuse of that drug by the very young, this would be more than counterbalanced by the reduction in abuse of more dangerous drugs such as amphetamines, (etc.)."[38] How does this follow? If pot isn't fun any more because it's legal, what would deter kids from applying the "forbidden fruit" philosophy to more dangerous drugs? If pot is so cool and the other drugs are so bad, will we now precipitate a rush to more dangerous drugs by legalizing the less dangerous intermediate?

Probably not. Today's kids under age fourteen seem to be turning away from drugs, including marijuana.[39] Some of this shift is due to education. It also comes from the kids' observing the results of drug abuse (including pot abuse) in older youths. Further, the "forbidden fruit" philosophy is applicable to only a segment of the drug-using population. In heavily Mormon-populated Salt Lake City, this author once expressed the view that the "forbidden fruit" concept had significant meaning for American youth. Later, surrounded by a group of grinning Mormon kids he was told, "You got a lot to learn about pot, man. If we wanted to bug our parents or indulge in 'forbidden fruit,' we'd get drunk or walk into the house smoking a cigarette. We smoke pot because it's fun and because our friends smoke it, man, and that's the deepest, darkest, most subversive reason we can give ya for doin' it."

Kaplan implies another idea that is not particularly likely to win him friends among his own peer group: "the family that gets high together will fly together." Of course, he didn't phrase it just that way. What he said was, "One would think then, that insofar as some 'leakage' from a licensing system might be merely parents teaching children to use a drug moderately, marijuana abuse might be even less likely than as at present, where the typical introduction is made within the peer group under conditions that tend to increase the thrill of doing what their parents are afraid to do."[40]

This sentence assumes a number of things: first, that adults will turn on, and having adjusted themselves to the casual use of pot, can or will educate their kids to use it properly. How, for instance does one *use* tobacco properly? One can only *abuse* tobacco, since it offers pleasure counterbalanced with the threat of severe physical harm. Where alcohol is concerned, Kaplan is correct that families who use the drug in moderation are less likely to have alcoholic children than are those who rigidly abstain or those who abuse it. This point will raise the hackles of many who are totally anti-alcohol, but statistically it has seemed to be so. Kaplan also notes that if the drug is socially approved the kids will no longer feel "guilty" about using it.[41] This author has not encountered much "guilt" in the youth with whom he has discussed marijuana. Resentment against the law, yes. Hostility toward the Establishment, of course. Curiosity, naturally. But guilt . . . seldom.

Shall we legalize pot, tax it, and put it on the market as Kaplan has suggested? He feels the advantages of the licensing system greatly outweigh the disadvantages. The plan, Kaplan asserts, "would, in essence, do away with virtually all of the costs of the criminalization of marijuana."[42] Having given the government a new source of revenue Kaplan now computes the costs.

The first cost he sets out is that of administration of the project. Those administering the program must determine the potency of the product to be sold, the proper tax to be levied, the proper number and location of licenses. (Although the aim of the plan is purported to be to make pot available, so that one does not have to go to less desirable sources to obtain it, Kaplan asserts no purpose is served by making access to the drug *too* convenient.) Administration must also decide among applicants for licenses, and (this should be good for several hundred thousand dollars a month) checking on the compliance of the licensees.[43] The second major point in this cost-conscious program centers around the social expense of the enforcement of criminal law. This involves the enforcement and correctional resources devoted to apprehension and punishment of those who sell outside the licensing system.

Now, states Kaplan, by adopting a licensing system, "we will have asserted explicitly that both alcohol and marijuana are of approximately equal dangerousness."[44] Society is not yet justified in making this conclusion. Yet on the basis of Kaplan's adversary approach, which for the most part has dissected and denegated the majority of clinical observations made to date (which have urged caution in the legalization of cannabis), we are asked to accept as fact what is in reality an attorney's wishful thinking.

No longer, Kaplan says, can "the young point to the difference between our treatment of alcohol and marijuana as an example of the older generation's hypocrisy or as an example of the unresponsiveness of the political process to the needs of at least their segment of the population."[45] That sounds great. But what if, in the future, trends in today's research continue, and we obtain adequate proof that pot produces adverse reactions from short-term use, and gives rise to serious reactions from long-term use? Will youth be grateful for our jumping the gun, when it is their generation, not Kaplan's, that will foot the bill for the cripples that may be produced by a premature acceptance of a drug we are not sure is safe?

What are we actually doing? Showing how avant garde we are by saying alcohol is bad and pot is no worse, so we'll legalize them both? Or are we demonstrating that no matter how chronologically advanced the current Establishment is, it leaves much to be desired in intellectual maturity?

In this writer's opinion, we would be acting prematurely to legalize marijuana today. In a short time, we should have definitive information as to the effects of pot use. If we wait until then to act, the incorrect side must stand aside and say, in effect, "We were wrong." If pot is not harmful, the only disadvantage in waiting to legalize it is the inconvenience to users (assuming that we meanwhile correct the undesirable aspects of our present laws). If we legalize it now, and the anti-marijuana side turns out to be right, we could have a huge group of seriously crippled users. Professor Kaplan must be praised for his concern for youth, and his attempt to solve a knotty problem. But less positively motivated persons may have access to information about which society is unaware: that if we don't immediately legalize marijuana, we may soon be so concerned about its negative effects that we would never think of legalizing it. And, if we jump the gun, we may be stuck with the consequences. Perhaps it is true that "the Lord giveth and the Lord taketh away," but society is not so omnipotent. Once a pleasure-providing, habituating drug is introduced into general consumption, it is nearly impossible to remove it from circulation.

Another point is that the pro-drug people, especially those who request immediate legislation as a "solution" to the cannabis problem, fail to recognize that for the first time in American history, society is being asked to accept a drug about which a significant number of scientists express serious concern. At a time when the government is assuming increasing responsibility in the area of consumer protection, it is simultaneously being asked to abrogate this responsibility in the area of marijuana legislation.

Kaplan argues that legalization does not mean acceptance, but others with equal reasoning capacity and with more clinical experience disagree. "To legalize marijuana today," argues Harvard psychobiologist Peter Dews, "would not be merely to make it no longer illegal to possess and use the drug; it would be tantamount to an endorsement of its use . . . if the government legalizes marijuana it is not merely saying, 'We will no longer arrest you for having marijuana'; it is in effect saying, 'We believe marijuana to be safe for general and regular use; safer for example than cyclamate [which was pulled off the shelves on the basis of adverse reactions in animals and without a single reported case of human difficulty]; so go ahead all you young people and indulge without fear'."[46]

Even the most warped Establishment rationalization could hardly justify urging youth not to use a drug if the substance were not only legalized, but (if Kaplan's suggestions were followed) taxed as a source of income. The hypocrisy connected with today's tobacco industry is bad enough, but at least it can be partially excused on the grounds that nicotine use was legalized in an age when scientific investigative techniques were primitive.

Let's assume the warning signs are correct. (Frankly, this author hopes they are not, considering the number of American young people now involved with cannabis use.) In a few years, the American public may show a rather unique emotion when it faces an overwhelming rehabilitation bill for legalized pot users, and asks its legislators, "How could you have been so stupid?"

The alcohol argument has always been a red herring where cannabis is concerned. "Why talk about pot when we should be talking about booze?" is the inevitable question. The answer is that when one discusses oranges he does not divert his attention to problems involved with the cultivation of bananas. "Mere suspicions of marijuana contrast with known evils of alcohol," Dews notes. "It does not follow from this that marijuana should be legalized but rather that alcohol should be regulated. It is easier to prevent the legalization of a new drug than to get rid of a drug that is already legal and widespread."[47]

"We may be inclined to believe that marijuana is harmless,' Dews argues, "but we should recognize frankly that our scientific evidence for doing so is poor. Furthermore we should not forget that marijuana affects the behavior of people who take it. This is what taking it is all about. It changes what people say and do in particular circumstances and, more remotely, it affects the circumstances into which people get themselves and what they say and do after the drug experience. All these changes may lead to harm to the subject, indirectly due to the drug."[48]

Not all researchers believe the present marijuana laws are having no effect on pot use. "The seventy percent incidence of law breaking by Stanford undergraduates does not mean the law is having no effect," Dews notes. "Most people in Boston if not elsewhere break at least one or another of the laws relating to automobile deportment or stationing most of the driving days of their life, but their driving habits would be even worse were there no laws."[49]

"The analogy between driving regulations may be taken one step further," he continues. "There is statistically a positive relationship between speed and accidents, justifying speed limits; there is equally statistically a positive relationship between gratuitous drug taking and deleterious consequences, justifying drug controls. High speed is more dangerous on some sections of the highway than others, and some drugs are more dangerous than others. The law does not attempt to make every speeder a felon and should not attempt to make every user of self administered drugs for non therapeutic purposes a felon. The law clearly signifies its disapproval of speeding by roadside signs and by more or less expensive traffic court actions. The law could do the same for drug usage."

We need to take a close look at marijuana legislation, realizing that there is a marked difference between the youth who plays with a drug or experiments casually with it and the one who becomes dependent on it. This is so, just as there is a difference between the person who violates a law against discharging firearms within the city limits by shooting at a skunk and one who chooses to take a potshot at a passing motorist.

The simile may strike some as nonrelevant but the two situations are not that dissimilar. Simple use of low grade pot by reasonably stable kids for socio-recreational purposes under salutary conditions really isn't that big a thing. It's the potential of deciding to (or more important, needing to) progress to the use of more potent drugs, including more potent cannabis, that is critical. Some ideologists argue this doesn't happen, but clinicians and police know from experience that it does—not because of the steppingstone theory, but because the drug-prone person, whatever that is, once having tasted the euphoria and release of the drug experience through the seductive, apparently innocuous cannabis experience, is encouraged to go on to a seemingly more exciting venture.

Aligned with this is the drug milieu and the encouragement of other users to "try a new trip." Kaplan suggests that legalizing the drug would eliminate these undesirable associations. To the contrary, it may increase their number and augment their efficiency. Elsewhere we have noted the tendency of pot users to blame their paranoia on the law and the police and the rebuttal of this concept by a trained observant clinician. The same may be said of the argument that if we legalize pot, suddenly the magic moment will arrive when those who *abuse* the drug will no longer associate with the rest of the subculture. If this is so, why does it not apply to barbiturates and amphetamines, which are legal and too easily available by prescription?

We are aiming our guns at a problem and complicating it by assuming that the segment of our society most susceptible to the effects, pleasant and adverse, of cannabis will be excluded and controlled by law. This is the height of idealistic naïveté. We have noted before and will note again that it is one thing for a reasonably mature individual with goals in sight or accomplished to use a substance that can change the direction of his thinking. Such an individual may withstand assaults on his motivation and ideology because hopefully he has developed defensive mechanisms against such an experience. Not so the growing, deciding, goal-seeking, idealistic youth who has yet to establish solid methods of meeting emotional and mental crises.

In other cultures a forty-year-old would be reticent to turn a youth on to adult habits with their associated problems if the youth was not already involved. Not so the post-Neanderthal-American who, if he can make a fast buck, is often too willing to encourage youth to indulge in habits the adult inherently knows may be harmful—the most classic modern example being tobacco, which is primarily aimed at the youth market, while an older, wiser, singed generation is trying to quit the drug.

While pro-cannabis forces encourage legalization, a more conservative group urges caution. A wait of a year or so will not be that critical, provided we eliminate the current problem of legislation that treats youths as felons, and indeed may turn them into criminals.

If we decide to play it cool and wait, what can we do in the interim, until the issue is decided? If legalization is not the answer, is there another available? This author feels there is. This alternative will be the subject of our next chapter.

"*...Son!*" "*...Dad...!*"

first person singular: is there a rational approach?

12

When, in the course of human events it becomes necessary for one people to dissolve the political bands which have connected them with another, and to assume among the powers of the earth the separate and equal station to which the laws of nature and of Nature's God entitle them, a decent respect to the opinions of mankind requires that they should declare the causes which impel them to the separation.

—THE DECLARATION OF INDEPENDENCE, July 4, 1776

*F*OR ELEVEN CHAPTERS I have tried to remain in the middle of the road and to write in the third person. It is with some relief that I now shed this role to express some personal opinions.

There should no longer be any question in the reader's mind about my concern for those who may be hurt by the gameplaying which currently dominates the marijuana controversy. It should be obvious, too, that I recognize that the individual himself must make the decision as to whether or not he will experiment with marijuana, using it as a socio-recreational outlet or as an escape from reality. I have placed stress, honestly I hope, on the accumulating evidence which signals a warning against the headlong dash to legalize the drug, when the answers to a centuries-old dilemma may be only a short time away.

I do not apologize for making available to the reader a large source of material which is negative to pot, because this book is one of the few places where a reader can evaluate these articles. The current tendency for writers discussing cannabis use is to eclectically select material favorable to a given cause and deny that opposing evidence exists—or, if it does exist, that it is pertinent. I have tried to present material from both sides. More information is available *against* pot than *for* it because this is the way the observation and research pendulum has swung ever since man began making written observations concerning this remarkable plant and the drugs contained in its resin.

My concern is totally toward the discipline of public health. If, as additional evidence accumulates, it becomes clear that my conservative approach has been unwarranted I shall be not only glad, but relieved to admit I was wrong. Until then, the hundreds of youthful contacts with marijuana which I have observed in over twenty years of study cause me to urge caution where continued use of marijuana is concerned, and to express some degree of apprehension for casual use by certain types of individuals.

Law is not my profession. Yet I am affected by the law and thus have some definite opinions. These opinions may have had some far-reaching influence in that I have had the privilege of testifying before several state legislatures or their committees. I hope I have influenced their decisions toward looking carefully at the problem of cannabis use as a whole.

I feel we have gone past the point of no return where the management of the use of pot through harsh legislation is concerned. Once, it had value. Now, for reasons we have extensively discussed, I feel the time has come to critically review and revise the legal structure which attempts to control use and abuse of this drug.

In medicine, we have an adage: first do the patient no harm. I do not know if the profession of law has an analogous dictum. If it does, it is not always apparent today where the management of cannabis users is concerned. I feel with the same vigor expressed by John Kaplan and others that the harsh laws which facilitate categorizing young Americans as felons because they have expressed curiosity and/or delight over marijuana are unjustified and should be repealed. I do not feel, however, that for society in general the legally-regulated distribution of marijuana is a valid solution at this time. If, at a later date, (within the next two or three years) we find that our fears about pot are unjustified, I shall be the first to admit being overly conservative. But I will have no regrets about my present assessment of the situation.

I have witnessed some great "scenes" where pot has been the catalyst for social communication. On the other hand I have observed some very real and unnecessary tragedies resulting from marijuana use. I have a deep respect for marijuana. Let me explain: I suspect that as the hysteria surrounding the evaluation and investigation of marijuana subsides, and we obtain a reasonably unemotional evaluation of this unique plant, we may find pharmaceuticals in cannabis that will be highly useful to the medical profession. However, I do not trust cannabis, for it is too often the master rather than the servant of those who use it. In this respect marijuana is no different from alcohol, which I also respect and distrust for similar reasons.

Will America legalize marijuana? We may, but probably not before fairly large numbers of older citizens in the current Establishment are "laid to rest" or become too senile to fight the battle against pot. I assume that the legalization of marijuana, should it ever take place, is at least three or four years away.

However, deferring legalization has little to do with the pharmacological aspects of marijuana—pro or con. In fact, if the pharmacology of the drug were the focal point of the issue, the pro-cannabis forces would quickly lose their ground, since most of the available material (at this time) *suggests* that extreme caution be employed in releasing it to the general public.

We must defer a decision on legalizing marijuana, partly because of our emotionally-charged society, which cannot or will not face the issue objectively, but instead veils it in rationalization and myth. There is a vast polarization where cannabis is concerned, wherein neither side wishes or really attempts to communicate with the other. I hope that this book, as I have conceived it, will be meaningful and acceptable to the moderately polarized sides. I would like, but cannot expect, to reach the extremely polarized. I can only hope to assist those still on the fence to make a decision as to whether or not they should get involved with the use of pot. If, knowing the potential price as well as the anticipated pleasure, they decide to turn on, I can then only wish them a safe and enjoyable experience.

While respecting the law and recognizing the propriety of ethics and morality, my concern towards the pot issue is primarily that of a clinician. *In this role,* I am indifferent to what others do if they do not experience harm or create problems for those around them. For the most part, the casual user of pot, like the casual user of alcohol, does not worry me. It is the growing number of exceptions that disturbs and worries me as a clinician, because I have had the unfortunate experience of seeing too many of them. Because of these people, I originally wrote the first edition of *Marijuana* four years ago as a commentary on the scene as it appeared then. Now, as I write the revised and enlarged edition, I do so with increased concern about the rapid growth of pot in our culture, and the frequency with which adverse reactions are now being reported. As research progresses, I become more, not less, worried. As investigator after investigator turns up new material that reenforces the apprehension that all is not well with the use of pot, it becomes apparent that caution, not a "let's-give-up-we're-licked" attitude, is indicated.

I think there is a solution to the pot problem, at least an interim one until we are certain whether the protagonists or the antagonists, if either, are correct. As is true of the "solutions" offered by others who dare to attempt to resolve critical social problems, mine has yet to be tried. Others may find it full of holes, as I have vigorously objected to John Kaplan's "solution." Yet, I hope that as critics dissect these suggestions, they will have the same respect for my attempts that I have for Kaplan and others, whom I praise for trying, even though I am in marked disagreement with some of their conclusions.

I view the current cannabis dilemma as a public health problem, and I feel that the usual triad of interacting factors seen in other epidemiological situations is present here—namely, a *host* (user), an *agent* (the drug), and a *carrier* (the distributor). I propose, therefore, that the cannabis crisis may be reasonably attacked as an epidemiological problem, with certain modifications from the approach usually used to combat contagious disease.

The *agent* in the case of cannabis is the highly versatile, unpredictable group of chemical substances present in the resin of the plant Cannabis sativa. It differs from a bacillus in that it must be sought and employed in order to achieve its effect— i.e., cannabis drugs are not aggressive but wait to be used.

As is true with all agents if they are controlled or if the subject does not come in contact with them, the cannabis drug(s) will not harm human beings. Thus, if the agent is eliminated or barred from contact with the subject, problems associated with its effects will not occur. One cannot eliminate cannabis, a wild, self-perpetuating weed, but this does not mean that one should give up attempts to control it *if that is the will of a given society*. If the society is uncertain or indifferent in its attitude, the pro-pot people will soon control the situation. If pot use is kept on the run through proper assault, it may be present but its effects will be muted.

Step one in controlling the agent, then, requires that the adult population make a decision about pot. Society (speaking of the over-thirty group) hasn't really made this decision. They grumble and pass laws and, providing their own children aren't involved, begrudgingly and halfheartedly support the police, who are expected both to do the dirty work and to take the blame for the inadequacies of their employers. They also shift the burden of decision on youth, and then when youth decides, frequently in favor of pot, they assert that the incoming generation is irresponsible and degenerate.

The fact that many youths have tended to favor legalization of pot should not be considered an indictment of young people. It is a scathing exposé of the vascillation of older people not yet committed to educate, *preferably by example*, those who follow in their footsteps.

If society decides to accept and legalize pot, even with an awareness of the Pandora's box they may be opening, nothing further need be said about preventative medicine where cannabis is concerned.

If, on the other hand, society wishes to exercise caution until it is sure the drug is safe (not just uncertain it is dangerous), an attack must be made on the agent itself.

Such an attack must involve education of *all* citizens as to the potential, *both good and bad*, of the use of pot. If a question exists as to its safety, prudent men will urge caution. Notably, evidence of questionable safety of cannabis exists in abundance for those who choose to seek it out. The attack must also include adequate enforcement to control the growth, harvesting, and distribution of the weed, and the utilization of the courts in managing those who choose to flaunt social dictates.

At this point we have several needs. First, we need to stop spending endless hours of useless debate as to whether marijuana is a sedative, hallucinogen, or stimulant, and accept it for what it is: *cannabis,* a unique plant containing unique drugs.

Second, we need to create a new category of violation or set of violations, with appropriate laws to deal with problems associated with cannabis use, distribution and sale. Since this is a public health problem, such laws should follow the same design as other similar laws enacted to protect public safety. (As an example, if a man has a contagious disease, whether open tuberculosis, syphilis, or a similar problem, and will not comply with public health laws or cease spreading the disease, law enforcement is called in to limit his activity until he can be treated.) Physicians do not have the facilities, the training, or the emotional bent to enforce such laws. Their job begins when the violator of public safety, because of his *abuse* of the drug, is placed where—willingly or not—he can be treated. The doctor's job consists of treating his patient's illness—which is, in the case of cannabis *abuse,* a socio-emotional problem—thus eliminating it or making it impossible for him to involve others. One would also hope to educate the abuser as to the unreasonableness of his activity in the face of society's disapproval. If the subject refuses to cooperate, becomes reinvolved and starts the epidemiological cycle all over again, society must then decide whether to tolerate his activities or place him where he can no longer communicate his problem to other nonusing but susceptible persons. This will require special institutions if society is to properly manage the problem.

Third, we need proper facilities to handle the distributors or producers of the agent and, in particular, its victims (if this is the proper term) once enforcement disrupts their abuse patterns. Psychiatric and medical treatment must be made available, along with rehabilitation facilities *when they are needed.*

There are those who say that since we can never eliminate the weed, we should attempt to tax it. In rebuttal, I ask, if we can't control the illegal production of alcohol, which requires a distillery, how can we tax (and thus control) marijuana, when Mother Nature spreads it in profusion all across our nation, and an increasing number of pot-oriented "Johnny Appleseeds" help the mother along? So we don't totally control it. We aren't controlling cancer, either, but clinicians keep up the battle.

The second element of the triad is the *distributor* of the drug, the wholesale dealer who properly belongs under police jurisdiction. Unfortunately, the control and management of dealers is not a simple matter, for reasons discussed earlier—i.e., that most marijuana is distributed by small-time users who buy, use, and sell or give the drug away. If, indeed, a youth or adult sells for profit, or if his drug ideology seriously conflicts with that of the majority, society may choose to control him in order to curtail distribution of the drug. A properly experienced court must make the decision as to whether criminal sanctions should be applied. As it is today, cases involving commercial dealers are frequently handled the same as those against casual user-dealer-donators. Further, under our present laws and system, those with adequate funds or highly trained legal assistance (who tend to be the large dealers) seem to have a much better chance of "beating the rap" than do less affluent, casual users who frequently take the brunt of the punishment for others. This, too, should be changed.

As for the third element, the human *subject,* it must be noted that *the majority of the contemporary "violators" of society's dictums against the use of cannabis need neither treatment, psychotherapy or rehabilitation. They are not sick, neither are they antisocial.* They may be curious and may play the same game others play with laws for which they have contempt, i.e., indulging in the belief that their activity is justified and that they will not get caught. In this belief they are no different from other Americans who choose to enjoy socio-recreational drugs.

Most of these young men and women seem to try pot, get their kicks, and move on to something else. Most, therefore, unless they are incredibly unlucky or inept, do not come into contact with the law. Those who do, if this is their only "crime," should not be condemned by statutes which now treat the curious or the disrespectful as criminals.

If society chooses to put some teeth in its laws and make the casual user reluctant to repeat an infraction, it should do so

through fines, work camps, or through the use of institutionaliza-
tion for varying periods in *environments that will not be training
schools for crime*. Furthermore, such individuals should be
found as violators of the cannabis laws per se, and not as guilty
of a felony.

The joker here is that we haven't the institutions, the laws, or
the public attitudes necessary to accomplish this. To obtain
them will cost money, it is true. But the health and safety of
American youth is at stake. Even with adequate funds, it is improbable that the drug problem can be completely resolved. To
do so would demand a social revolution inaugurated by a new
and knowledgeable generation.

This, then, is one physician's viewpoint. It is my hope that
others will build on this attempt to assist youth in trouble rather
than compound their difficulties. I do not feel we should, at this
time, legalize cannabis. I think that to do so would obviate any
attempt on the part of conservatives to encourage youth to "play
it cool." I feel that if future research shows the drug to be dangerous after it has already been legalized, the battle to prevent
serious problems associated with cannabis use and abuse will be
severely complicated. This would be particularly true once
irresponsible, profit-motivated companies were granted the fran-
chise to sell and legally produce cannabis.

We should learn from the lessons of history. Sadly, each
generation wants to spend its own time on "fool's hill." Sometimes this experience is permanently crippling. One thing history has taught us is that humans cannot validly escape from
reality for more than brief periods of time without losing control
of their environment. Another lesson we tend to ignore is that
there are no simplistic solutions to complex problems.

America has had two tragic lessons where drug abuse is concerned. The first involved the legalization of alcohol and the
chaos resulting from this decision. The second involved addiction to opium which, when it got out of control, was "treated"
with a "safe substitute," morphine. When morphine proved to
be as addicting as opium, another approach was instituted: a
replacement drug named heroin (so called because the therapy
was considered "heroic"). Now that heroin has proved to be a
social menace, another pharmacological substance is being substituted in its place. The new drug is methadone, less crippling

than heroin as far as science knows at the moment, but far from the answer to opiate addiction.

The problems of life can never be satisfactorily solved through evasion of reality. On the other hand, unfortunately, no man seems capable of existing in today's society without some sort of "safety valve" through which he can occasionally vent his pent-up emotions. America is apparently in desperate need of a cheap, safe, effective tranquilizer. To date, none has been developed. Currently, some suggest that the answer may be found in the chemistry of cannabis. Perhaps. But it is possible that once again, with professional assistance, we may be climbing "fool's hill."

THE WIZARD OF ID

potpourri

A GLOSSARY
OF THE JARGON
OF THE DRUG WORLD

The following list does not aim to be an exhaustive glossary but is confined to those terms directly related to the use of drugs. Since the special language of the drug subculture constantly changes, some of these terms may already be passing out of currency as new ones come in, but a great many of them have endured for many years and give prospect of continuing in use for a long time.

A—amphetamines
A-Head—amphetamine abuser
A Bomb—mixture of marijuana and heroin
Acapulco gold—high potency cannabis from central Mexico
Acid—Lysergic acid diethylamide (LSD), a powerful hallucinogenic substance that was at one time the mainstay of the psychedelic drug users and was used as a medium for obtaining very high intoxications and unpredictable psychological excursions

Acid freak—a chronic user of LSD

Acid funk—an LSD induced depression

Acidhead—a regular user of LSD

Acid rock—rock and roll music with a psychedelic orientation

Acid test—a rock and roll dance performed to multiple light and sound effects.

Amyl nitrate—a medicinal used to dilate coronary vessels (heart), used illicitly (a) to increase the effect of sexual orgasm; (b) to bring down a user on a high marijuana trip

Amys—amyl nitrate pearls (i.e. glass capsules); see Snappers

Angel Dust—see P.C.P.

Artillery—equipment for injecting drugs

Astral—a situation where the mind takes a trip and the body stays there

At—where drug or other action is taking place

B bombs—amphetamine inhalers; (occasionally the inhaler is emptied and used to sniff amyl nitrate)

Baby—marijuana

Babysit—to guide a person through his drug experiences; baby-sitters are usually experienced drug users; see Guide

Backtrack—to withdraw the plunger of a syringe before injecting drugs to make sure needle is in proper position

Backwards—a term applied to tranquilizers

Bad trip—a freak out or panic reaction on hallucinogens

Bag—(a) one's particular interest or mood; if one is attracted to cannabis, then cannabis is his bag, and so on; (b) a quantity of drugs —i.e., a "nickel bag"

Bagman—a dealer in drugs, usually heroin

Bale—a pound of cannabis

Ball—a pleasant happening; the term may refer either to events in general or to a sexual experience

Balloon—rubber toy balloon used for storing or delivering narcotics, usually heroin

Bang—(a) to give an intravenous injection of a drug; (b) the pleasurable flush occurring as an intravenous drug is injected; (c) to have sexual intercourse

Bar—a solid brick of marijuana, usually stuck together with some sticky substance such as honey

Barbs—barbiturates

Beaming—under the influence of marijuana

Bean—Mexican person or person of Latin or South American descent

Beast—heroin

Beautiful—a term of approval; often an exclamation

Behind—(a) under a drug's influence; (b) to be addicted to a drug

Behind juice—being drunk on alcohol

Be-in—a collection of people meeting for some specific purpose. Usually this term applies to hippie conclaves or at least to assemblies of "in" people who gather for various activities

Belly habit—withdrawal symptom-causing drug, i.e. barbiturates, or heroin

Bennies—the term may refer to any amphetamine, but specifically denotes amphetamine sulfate or phosphate. Obese people take these to lose weight, since bennies tend to depress appetite. Drug users take them to promote alertness and for various types of drug trips. The latter experiences are usually followed by depression. If used chronically, bennies may cause physical and mental deterioration.

Bent—under the influence of drugs, i.e., high

Berkeley barb—underground newspaper, printed in Berkeley, California

Bernice—cocaine

Big chief—mescaline

Big D—LSD 25

Big John—the police

Big man—dealer

Bindle—a small packet of drugs, usually heroin

Birdseye—an extremely small amount of various narcotics

Bit—time served in an institution, usually jail

Bitch—(a) female; (b) complain

Bitchin'—goodtime, nice

Biz—equipment for injecting drugs

Black and whites—marked patrol cars

Blade—knife, razor, dagger, sharp instrument

Blanks—poor quality narcotics

Blast—smoke marijuana

Blasted—intoxicated by marijuana, or intoxicated by any drug

Blaster—marijuana smoker, grasshopper

Blind—(a) to be severely under the influence of a drug; (b) uncircumcized

Blood—a Negro person

Blow—(a) to leave willingly; (b) to invite to leave, usually because of disapproval of one's conduct; (c) to do a poor job in a given endeavor.

Blow a joint—smoke a marijuana cigarette

Blow a stick—smoke a marijuana cigarette

Blow dart—hypodermic needle

Blow one's mind—on the positive side this may be an astonishing or fascinating experience; on the negative, it may denote a bad trip or an experience that causes one to become upset or depressed

Blue bands—carbrital (Pentobarbital Sodium-Carbromal)

Blue birds—amytal (Amobarbital Sodium)

Blue cheer—type of LSD

Blue devils—amytal (Amobarbital Sodium)

Blue Fascists—one of the milder synonyms for the police

Blue heaven—amytal (Amobarbital Sodium)

Blue velvets—an antihistamine, (Pyrabenzamine) usually taken intravenously for effect

Blues—amytal (Amobarbital Sodium)

Body drugs—narcotics (not psychedelic drugs)

Bogue—very, very bad

Boo—cannabis

Boo hoo—a "priest" in the hippie Neo American Church

Book, the—*The Physician's Desk Reference,* a book describing drugs and drug effects, published for physicians

Bomb—(a) a fat marijuana cigarette; (b) high potency heroin; (c) to overdose on a drug; (d) to fail; see Blow

Bombed—intoxicated on drugs

Bombido—injectible amphetamine

Boss—originally a surfing term; roughly synonymous with "groovy"

Boost—to shoplift

Booster—(a) consumption or injection of additional dosage to continue or prolong a "trip"; (b) a shoplifter

Boot—to pump blood and/or fluid back and forth in an eye-dropper or syringe

Box—(a) hi fi set; (b) female sex organ

Boxed—in jail

Bottle dealer—a person who sells drugs in 1000 tablet or capsule bottles

Bread—money, usually a large sum, in contrast to "crumbs," which means change or small bills

Broad—girl, woman

BLTC—better living through chemistry

Brick—kilo of marijuana in compressed brick form

Bridge—see Crutch—usually alligator clamp or like device used to hold marijuana cigarette while smoking

Bring down—to cause loss of intoxicated, drugged state; also to cause depression

Bug—to bother or pester someone

Bull—(a) a federal narcotic agent or a police officer; (b) lesbian

Bum trip—a bad experience; usually used in connection with the use of mind-affecting drugs, but also employed to describe any emotional experience that was depressing or disturbing

Bummer—an unpleasant trip

Burn—(a) to sell bad drugs; (b) to sell placebos as drugs; (c) to cheat out of money or drugs; (d) to kill; (e) to burn the skin while injecting drugs

Burned—used to describe the acquisition of bad drugs, diluted drugs, or no drugs at all, even though cash has been exchanged

Bust—an arrest; usually this implies that the police have descended upon a gathering and rounded the participants up for questioning or arrest

Busted—arrested, specifically for drugs, but also for any other criminal activity

Button—peyote

Buy—to purchase narcotics or other drugs

Buzz—an early high on a drug

Cabbage—money

Cache—see Stash

Can—one ounce of marijuana; term derived from tobacco can in which marijuana was commonly sold in the past; (now it is more frequently sold in small paper or plastic bags); see Lid

Cannabis—the genus name for all the tetrahydrocannabinol-producing weeds

Candy—barbiturates

Cap—an empty gelatin capsule used to take narcotics or drugs

Carrying—transporting drugs or keeping them on one's person while in transit; see Holding

Cartwheels—amphetamines, usually Mexican in origin; tablets are white and cross scored in quarters

Cat—an informed person who knows where the action is; usually said of the male; see Chick

Catnip—bogus marijuana or a substitute mixed with part marijuana

Chalk—methamphetamine

Champ—drug abuser who won't reveal his supplier, even under pressure

Changes—a new scene, usually a new perception noted on a drug trip; specifically, a "change" is a transient disorientation followed by a resolution

Charge—the effect of a drug

Charged up—under the influence of drugs

Chick—a sexually desirable young female

Chicken powder—amphetamine powder for injection

Chicano—person of Mexican or South American extraction

Chief—LSD 25

Chill—(a) refusal to sell or give drugs to someone; (b) to kill; (c) to turn down or turn off someone socially

Chip—to play around with a drug; to use drugs sporadically

Chipper—one who chips

Chippy—an occasional user of heroin or other drug

Chiva—heroin

Christmas Tree—tuinal (a mixture of amobarbital sodium and secobarbitol sodium)

Clean—(a) removing stems and seeds from marijuana; (b) an addict who is free from narcotic injection marks, as in "I'm clean, man;" (c) off drugs

Clear light— one stop on the LSD trip, during which time one is receptive to information and enlightenment

Clear-up—to withdraw from drugs

Clocked—doing time in jail

Coast—to nod or dream on drugs, usually opiates

Coke—cocaine

Coke head—cocaine user

Cocktail—a regular cigarette with a joint stuffed in one end

Cold turkey—to kick an addicting habit without help of additional drugs to ease withdrawal

Collar—to arrest

Come down—permit the effects of drugs to wear off, to come back to reality

Commune—a communal apartment; see Crashpad

Connect—(a) to find a source of drugs; (b) to purchase drugs

Connection—(a) the source of illegal drugs, usually a seller; (b) a source who can direct one to a seller, but who may not sell, himself; (c) a person who gives or sells information

Contact—(a) to meet someone to buy drugs; (b) the man who sells drugs or directs one to a seller; (c) a source of drugs

Contact high—a trip caused by the emotional experience of observing or being near someone who is high because of actual drug indulgence; the idea is the same as the empathetic response occurring when one sees another yawn

Cook—to prepare an injection of drugs by heating

Cook up a pill—to prepare opium for smoking

Cooker—equipment to "cook" drugs

Cool—(a) in tune with what's happening; also refers to being unusually adept in moving within the drug scene and coping with its problems; (b) all right, safe.

Cool it—(a) to be quiet, peaceful, tranquil; (b) to stop and reevaluate a situation; (c) a term that once referred to jazz musicians' habit of pulling in cool air on top of already-inhaled marijuana smoke, to increase the efficiency and effect of smoking pot

Cop—(a) police; (b) to buy or obtain drugs; (c) to steal

Cop out—(a) see Fink; (b) to drop out of the drug world and return to the world of the Establishment; (c) to give up

Copilot—(a) a baby sitter or guide on a trip; (b) amphetamines

Cope—to maintain while intoxicated on drugs, i.e., to handle oneself effectively while under the influence of drugs; this ability varies from person to person and takes practice to acquire

Corine—cocaine

Cottons—bits of cotton saturated with narcotic solution, used to strain foreign matter when drawing solution up into hypodermic syringe or eyedropper; these "cottons" are often saved by addicts for an emergency, as they contain a residual amount of the drug

Crap—bad drugs

Crash—(a) to fall asleep; may be said for those who are up on drugs, but also denotes any sudden falling asleep; (b) a comedown from a drug episode, usually a precipitous and unpleasant one; for example, crashing in the middle of a drug episode because of an arrest

Crashpad—a place to sleep

Crater—an ulcer in the skin caused by shooting drugs

Crazy—(a) exciting, in the know, enjoyable; (b) a general form of approval, especially of happenings in the drug world which are presumed to by annoying to the Establishment, i.e., "that's crazy, man!"

Creep—an undesirable

Crib—a house, apartment or residence

Croaker—a doctor that chums with or treats the underworld

Crumbs—small amounts of money

Crutch—(a) an aid (e.g., drugs) one must have to cope with daily existence; (b) a split match which is used as a roach holder

Cube—non user of drugs

Cube head—acid user

Cut—to dilute a drug

Cut out—to leave, depart

Crystal—methedrine (speed)

Dabbling—to play around with drugs

Deal—to sell drugs

Dealer—a heavy supplier of illegal drugs; also called the "man," or the "connection." In contrast to the pusher, the dealer is a merchandiser and usually does not proselyte customers

Deck—a small package of drugs, usually heroin

DET—diethyltryptamine (a hallucinogen)

Deuce bag—a two-dollar container of a drug

Dexies—dextroamphetamine sulfate (a mixture of barbiturate and amphetamine)

Dig—to understand, usually to appreciate, approve or enjoy

Digger—a hippie father figure who tries to obtain beds, food, money, or employment for needy hippies

Dime bag—ten dollars worth of drugs, usually cannabis

Dirty—(a) on drugs; (b) carrying or holding drugs; (c) non-manicured marijuana

DMT—dimethyltryptamine, a short-acting hallucinogenic drug. Sometimes called the "business man's trip" because the entire episode can be achieved during a lunch hour

Do—to take a drug

Doing—may be any "happening," but specifically the taking of a drug

Doing one's own thing—indulging in one's "bag"; participating in action notably pleasurable to the doer

Dolls—barbiturates

Dollies—dolophine (methadone) a synthetic narcotic named after Adolph Hitler, used in America to assist withdrawal from heroin or to substitute for heroin in therapy

Domino—to purchase drugs

Dope—(a) to drug or give any drugs to a person; (b) specifically, opiates and opiate narcotics; (c) a synonym for glue used for glue-sniffing; (d) occasionally used to describe any drug

Doper—addict

Dope fiend—usually any drug user, originally a heroin addict

Dotting—placing LSD on a sugar cube

Double cross—(a) amphetamine tablets (double scored); (b) to fink; see Burn

Double trouble—tuinal (brand name of amobarbital sodium and secobarbital sodium capsules)

Do-up—smoke a marijuana cigarette

Downs—barbiturates

Downer—(a) a down trip, a bummer, a bad drug experience; (b) a synonym for depressant drugs such as barbiturates

Drag—a boring happening, a meaningless situation

Dreamer—(a) morphine or opiate narcotics; (b) one who takes opiates

Dried out—withdrawn from drugs

Drop—to take a drug by mouth

Drop out—(a) one who withdraws from society or dispenses with its social mores; (b) the ultimate happening in the psychedelic experience; the term is used both as a noun to denote the doer and as a verb to describe the experience

Dropped—arrested

Dropper—an eyedropper used as a syringe substitute for intravenous injection of drugs

Dummy—a placebo; see Burn

Dust—cocaine

Dynamite—boss, groovy, especially in discussing the effects of cannabis, i.e., "This weed is dynamite."

Ego games—a deprecative term applied by LSD users to social conformity and to the normal activities, occupations, and responsibilities of the majority of people

Electric—having psychedelic powers

Electric koolade—koolade spiked with LSD

Establishment—people over the age of 30 (or, generously, 35), usually straight, more often square

Experience—an LSD trip

Factory—(a) a processing place for drugs, usually amphetamines or acid; (b) equipment for injecting drugs

Fag—(a) not accepted by the group; (b) undesirable; (c) homosexual; (d) tobacco cigarette

Fall out—to sleep, usually after taking a drug

Far out—(a) authentically bizarre; (b) avant garde, new, unusual

Fat—describing someone who has a good supply of drugs

Fatty—fat, or thick, marijuana cigarette

Fed—a federal narcotics agent

Fiend—a chronic user of drugs; see Freak

Fit—equipment for injecting drugs

Fix—a shot of drugs, usually heroin, but also applied to speed

Fink—to give information, usually to the Establishment

Flake—cocaine

Flash—(a) a sudden idea; (b) an onrush of pleasant effects from taking a drug, usually hallucinogens; see Rush

Flashback—the return of a hallucinogenic drug-induced experience without the taking of drugs at the time of the flashback

Flashing—(a) thinking; (b) feeling the effects of drugs; (c) experiencing a high, but not necessarily on drugs

Flip—to express unusually strong emotion that may range from untoward enthusiasm to psychotic behavior

Flip out—to become panicked by drugs or to be overcome in a negative manner by their effects

Floating—under the effects of a drug, pleasant

Flower people (children)—those who opt or belong to the subculture espousing peace, love, who usually utilize hallucinogens either for effect or as a sacrament in their faith

Flower power—the influence and power of love and peace

Flush—the initial feeling the user gets when injecting methamphetamine; see Rush

Flying—on a trip, on the effects of drugs (hallucinogens)

Footballs—amphetamine tablets (oval shaped)

Forwards—pep pills, specifically amphetamines; see Backwards

Freak—(a) one who has flipped, i.e., one who uses drugs to the point of transcending reality; (b) used to describe a special type of intense abuser of a particular psychedelic drug, such as "speed freak," or "acid freak"

Freak out—(a) truly to lose all contact with reality; (b) a psychotic episode

Freak rock—acid rock music

Front—(a) one's external appearance; (b) to cover for someone

Fruit salad—a game in which participants pour available pills into a bowl and take them, each in turn, to see what kind of effect will occur

Full moon—peyote

Fuzz—the police

Gage—marijuana

Game—an unnecessary type of behavior designed to impress others

Gangster—marijuana

Gassing—sniffing glue and/or other fumes

Garbage—bad drugs

Gay—(a) high on drugs; (b) homosexual

GB—goof balls, i.e., barbituates

Gear—equipment for taking drugs

Gee-head—paragoric user

Geezer—an injection of narcotics

Gestapo—the police

Get high—smoke marijuana

Get into something—to enter into the action, to be involved

Ghost—LSD 25

Gig—someone's "thing"

Giggle-smoke—cannabis, or cannabis smoke

Gimmicks—equipment for injecting drugs

Glad rag—a piece of cloth saturated with a chemical

Glow—a high, the effects of a drug (pleasant)

Gluey—glue sniffer

Gold dust—cocaine

Go—(a) to swing, to participate freely in the drug scene; (b) to perform unusually well; (c) used as a shout of encouragement

Good Go—a good or reliable dealer in drugs

Good H—a good quality of heroin

Good people—those who can be trusted with drugs

Goods—narcotics

Goofballs—barbiturates

Goofer—one who drops pills

Goofed up—under the influence of barbiturates

Goofing—on barbiturates

Going up—taking drugs to obtain their effect; said of smoking cannabis or injecting speed, etc.

Grapes—wine

Gram—gram of heroin (approximately 10 capsules)

Grass—marijuana

Grass brownies—cookies containing cannabis

Grasshopper—marijuana user

Gravy—the blood-fluid mixture obtained from sticking a needle on a syringe or dropper into one's vein

Gray boy—Caucasian

Green—(a) cannabis; (b) money

Greenies—green, triangle-shaped tablet of dextroamphetamine sulfate and amobarbital; see Dexies

Griffo—cannabis

Groove—to concentrate intensely on an object or activity, usually with pleasure

Groovy—an enjoyable activity or person; swinging; with it

Groover—one who grooves

Guide—one who babysits a novice when he goes up on a psychedelic substance; see Babysitter

Gun—hypodermic needle

Guru—one who acts as a teacher and guide in matters of fundamental and intellectual concern

H.—Heroin

Habit—physically or psychologically dependent on drugs

Hallucinogens—psychotropic drugs that affect the mind in such a way as to produce sensations that are distorted and abnormal in content; the term is strictly Establishment in that users frequently deny that drugs such as LSD actually produce psychotic or pseudo-psychotic episodes

Hand-to-hand—delivery of narcotics person-to-person

Hangup—a habit or idea which causes one discomfort; see also Hung up.

Hang tough—stay cool; stay with it

Happening—action; what's occurring at the moment of interest to the drug group; an exciting or pleasurable event

Hard drugs—narcotics or other addictive drugs

Hard stuff—morphine, cocaine, or heroin

Harness bulls—uniformed officers

Harry—heroin

Hash—hashish

Hashbury—colloquial term for the Haight-Ashbury area in San Francisco

Hashish—resin from the Cannabis indica plant which contains a very high THC content

Hassle—(a) an argument or unpleasant discourse between people; (b) any unpleasant situation or duty which disrupts the tranquility of doing one's own thing

Hay—marijuana

Head—(a) a user of a drug or drugs, e.g., pothead, acid head, etc.; within the drug subculture this term is identifying only; within the Establishment it is identifying and derogatory; (b) mood, thoughts

Hearts—amphetamines, specifically dextroamphetamine and benzedrine sulfate

Heat—police

Heavenly blue—a morning glory seed that contains psilocybin

Heavy—(a) heroin; (b) desirable; (c) influential; see Righteous

Hemp—marijuana

High—being intoxicated, turned on, exhilarated, particularly by the use of drugs such as cannabis

Hip—aware, in the know, informed

Hit—(a) an arrest; (b) to smoke a joint of marijuana; (c) one dose of a particular drug; (a) to kill

Hocus—a narcotic ready for injection

Hog—(a) an addict who uses all the drugs he can get his hands on; (b) P.C.P.

Hold—to keep cannabis or other drugs on one's person for use, transit, or sale; one may also hold by storing drugs in his house; see Carrying

Hookah—a pipe of Indian origin used for smoking cannabis

Hooked—addicted

Hophead—narcotic addict

Hopped up—under the influence of drugs

Horning—to sniff powdered narcotics into nostrils

Horse—heroin

Hot—wanted by the police

Hot shot—an overdose of drugs, usually heroin

Hung up—trapped in a snare of emotional, psychological, or interpersonal problems that prevent one from enjoying drugs or life in general

Hustle—(a) to precipitate a happening of any kind; (b) to prostitute

Hustling—(a) stealing, prostitution, or using other illicit means to obtain money for drugs or other endeavors; (b) working hard or feverishly

Hype—one who uses intravenous drugs, especially heroin or speed

Hype outfit—equipment for injecting drugs

Ice Cream Habit—sporadic use of drugs; see Chip

Indian Hay—cannabis, specifically Cannabis indica, or hashish

In front—giving money to a person for drugs before the exchange takes place, or "in front" of the exchange

Into—using, as to be into pot; also, involved, as in music

J. or Jay—joint or marijuana cigarette

Jack—money

Jack off—(a) to masturbate; (b) to boot

Jack up—rob, steal, hold up

Jag—an intoxicated state due to the influence of drugs

Jay smoke—cannabis cigarette

Jar dealer—a person who sells drugs in 1000 tablets or capsule bottles

Jam—(a) to have intercourse; (b) to play instrument fervently; (c) lose one's cool

Jammed up—overdosed on drugs

Jefferson Airplane—(a) a popular rock group; (b) a roach holder made out of a split match

Jerk off—(a) to boot; (b) to masturbate

Jive—marijuana

John—(a) a bathroom; (b) a prostitute's customers

Joint—(a) a marijuana cigarette; (b) a place where the action is

Jolly beans—pep pills

Jolt—an injection of narcotics

Joy pop—to inject small amounts of drugs irregularly; see Chip
Joy powder—heroin
Juice—(a) wine, whiskey; (b) liquid for intravenous drug injection; (c) stamina; (d) power; (e) influence
Juicehead—an alcoholic
Jug—1000 tablet or capsule bottle
Jump—dance
Junk—heroin
Junkie—heroin user
Juvies—juvenile officers

Karma—a term borrowed by the counterculture from the Hindu and from Buddhism. It denotes one's destiny, particularly as it is determined by the ethical consequences of one's acts in this life as they affect his existence in the hereafter.
Key—a kilogram (2.2 pounds) of cannabis
Keyster—buttock
Keyster plant—narcotics secured in the rectum
Kee—Kilo
Keg—25,000 amphetamine capsules or tablets, or more
Kick—to stop or withdraw from a habit or addiction
Kicks—the pleasant effects of drugs
Kif—cannabis (Morocco)
Kilo—2.2 pounds of drug substance, almost always cannabis; usually this amount is compressed into brick form for transport
Kiss in—be in
Kit—equipment used for taking drugs

L.—LSD
Lab—equipment used to manufacture drugs illegally
L.B.—spoken as two letters, referring to a pound (lb.)
Lace—to cut, or add drugs; to increase the effect of one drug by the addition of another
Laid out—being informed on
Lame—not very smart; dumb or green, not street wise
Lame ones—those who need a crutch to cope with reality
Lard—police
Laughing gas—nitrous oxide
Lay on—(a) to give someone something (frequently drugs); (b) to communicate
Lay up—acquire a large supply or stash of drugs
Layout—equipment for injecting drugs
Lean on drugs—drug dependency

Leg—girl

Lemonade—poor quality heroin

Let it all hang out—to give the facts, to hide nothing

Lid—approximately an ounce of marijuana; also called a can

Lid propers—amphetamines

Lid poppers—amphetamines

Lift up—under influence of drugs

Light up—smoking marijuana

Lipton tea—poor quality narcotics

Lit up—under the influence of drugs

Loaded—under the influence of drugs

Locoweed—Astragalus Mollissimus, a weed that causes psychotic reactions in animals; not to be confused with cannabis

Love-in—a be-in dedicated to peace and love and, on occasion, cannabis smoking and sex

LSD-25—Lysergic acid diethylamide, derived originally from rye ergot. It was discovered in 1943 by Hoffman, kept a relative secret until recent years when it became the "sacrament" of the hippies. At the time of this writing it is not manufactured legally in the United States.

M.—morphine

Machinery—equipment for injecting drugs

Magic mushroom—the Mexican mushroom containing psilocybin

Make—(a) to take a drug; (b) to have sexual intercourse

Make a buy—purchase drugs

Make it—(a) be a friend; (b) to go away; (c) to have intercourse with

Making the scene—to be involved in what's happening

Man—(a) a drug connection; (b) the police; (c) a term of address

Manicure—to clean cannabis of its stems and seeds

Mainlining—to take drugs intravenously

Matchbox—a small amount of cannabis sufficient to make between five to eight cigarettes; about a fifth of a lid

Marijuana—cannabis sativa, usually Cannabis americana or mexicana; specifically, the flowering tops of the female plant which contain the majority of the plant's THC content

Mary Jane—cannabis

MDA—hallucinogen, methyl-3, 4-methylenedioxyphenethylamine

Mellow yellows—(a) pale yellow LSD powder purportedly

manufactured by Augustus Owsley Stanley III; (b) dried banana skins for smoking, labeled "The Great Banana Hoax" by California medical researchers, as the substance has no hallucinogenic properties

Mesc—mescaline

Meth—methamphetamine; see Speed

Mexican brown, green—grades of marijuana

Mike/Micro—a microgram (a millionth of a gram); used to measure LSD

Mickey—chloral hydrate

Mickey finn—chloral hydrate in an alcoholic drink

Mindblower—(a) an experience or a drug which upsets one's emotional and/or psychological equilibrium; (b) pure, unadulaterated drug

Mind trippers—those who take drugs for self therapy or introspection

Miss Emma—morphine

MJ—cannabis

Mohasky—cannabis

Monkey—a drug habit where physical dependence is present

Morning glory seeds—specifically Heavenly Blues, Flying Saucers and Pearly Gates, commercial names for morning glory seeds that contain psilocybin, a hallucinogen

Mota—marijuana

Mother—(a) an adjective meaning difficult; (b) a dealer or peddler of drugs

Mu—cannabis

Mud—opium

Muggles—cannabis

Mule—a person who delivers or carries a drug for a dealer

Nab—to arrest

Nail—a hypodermic needle

Narghile—a Turkish water pipe used for smoking cannabis

Nark/Narco—narcotics agent

Needle—hypodermic needle

Needle habit—to enjoy the effects of sticking a needle in one's veins, with or without drugs

Nickel buy—a $5.00 purchase, generally makes between five and eight joints, i.e., a nickel bag

Nod—to be under the effects of a depressant, usually an opiate

Nodding out—to be sleepy or "nodding" one's head from the influence of drugs

Nowhere—not acceptable, strange

OD—an overdose of drugs

Off—withdrawn from drugs

Old lady—girl friend, common law wife, wife

On—to be under the influence of a drug

On a trip—under the influence of LSD or other hallucingens

On the nod—under the influence of a sedative-hypnotic drug

Oranges—amphetamine sulfate tablets

Out of it—not in contact, not part of the drug scene

Outfit—equipment used to take drugs, usually intravenously

Out of sight—tremendous, superb, so good it can't be believed

Owsley's Acid—LSD purportedly manufactured by Augustus Owsley Stanley III, also infers that it is good quality LSD

Overdose—to accidentally (or suicidally) take a larger drug dosage than the body can handle

Overjolt—same as overdose

OZ - ounce—refers to ounce of drugs, usually heroin

P.—peyote

Packin'—to carry a pistol, knife, any weapon

Pad—apartment, room, house, where one resides

Paddy—caucasian

Panama red—a potent type of South American cannabis

Panic—the emotional response when a drug supply has been cut off

Paper—a small package of narcotics, usually heroin

P.C.P.—hallucinogenic substance, sernyl (phencyclidine HCL); also called hog or peace pills

PDR—*Physician's Desk Reference*; see Book

Peaches—benzedrine (brand of amphetamine sulfate tablets)

Peanuts—barbiturates

Pearls—amyl nitrate capsules

Peace Pill—hallucinogenic substance, sernyl (phencyclidine HCL)

Pellets—tablets of LSD

Pep pills—stimulants, specifically amphetamines

PEZ—PEZ candies impregnated with LSD

P.G. or P.O.—paragoric

Pick up—(a) buy drugs or anything else; (b) to appreciate, try to understand

Piece—an amount of drugs

Pig—police

Pill head—amphetamine or barbiturate user

Pill freak—see Pill head

Pin—a skinny joint (marijuana cigarette)

Pinks—seconal (brand name of secobarbital capsules)

Pinned—under the influence of heroin (pin point pupils)

Places—where one is; on a trip this is divided between good places (pleasant) and bad ones (freakouts)

Plant—(a) a hiding place for drugs; (b) to put drugs on a person so he will be caught and blamed

Plastic—a person who pretends to be involved in the hippie philosophy but who is actually along for the fun, notariety and/or the ride

Pod—cannabis

Point—hypodermic needle

Poke—(a) a puff on a joint; (b) wallet; (c) stash; (d) to jab a needle into oneself

Pop—(a) a subcutaneous injection, usually referred to as "skin poppin'"; (b) to swallow drugs; (c) to have intercourse; (c) to be arrested; (e) to inject drugs

Pops—an older male person

Popped—to have swallowed a pill

Poppers—amyl nitrate capsules

Popping—to inject drugs under the skin

Pot—cannabis

Pot likker—cannabis tea, usually made with regular tea boiled with cannabis leaves

Pothead—a chronic cannabis user

Potsville—(a) the effects of cannabis; (b) the cannabis counter-culture

Pounds—money, $25.00

Powder—amphetamine powder

PR—initials for Panama Red, a reddish brownish variety of cannabis sativa mexicana

Prince Albert—see Can, Lid; pot was once packaged in Prince Albert tobacco cans

Psyched up—excited, anticipatory

Psychedelic—that which enhances or expands consciousness

Psychedelphia—Herb Caen's nickname for the Haight-Ashbury district in San Francisco

Psyching—(a) to try to understand a person's thinking or attitude; (b) to use psychology on a person to obtain a result

Punk—(a) poor grade marijuana; (b) unimportant individual; (c) petty criminal

Pusher—drug peddler to users; one who seeks more business from regular customers, in contrast to a dealer who passively merchandizes

Pushing—selling drugs

Pure—pure heroin, prior to adulteration

Push—(a) to sell, specifically narcotics and dangerous drugs; (b) to attempt to manipulate one's environment or to encourage things to happen

Put somebody on—(a) try to fool someone; (b) to give someone drugs

Quill—a folded matchbox cover from which narcotics are sniffed through the nose; also see Crutch

Quarter—quarter of an ounce of either heroin or methamphetamine, usually 4 to 8 grams

Quarter bag—$25.00 bag of marijuana

Quarter Deck—(a) ¼ of a deck; see Deck; (b) paper containing heroin or amphetamine

Rainbow—a barbiturate (tuinal)

Rainy day woman—a marijuana cigarette

Rap—to communicate peacefully and/or with purpose

Reader—a prescription

Reds—seconal (secobarbital sodium)

Reds & Blues—tuinal (amobarbital sodium and secobarbital sodium)

Red birds—seconal (secobarbital sodium)

Red devils—seconal (secobarbital sodium)

Red dirt marijuana—wild marijuana

Red Oil—the sap of the cannabis sativa plant

Reefer—(a) marijuana cigarette; (b) a quantity of cannabis

Rep—one's status or reputation

Riff—(a) an extraneous bit of conversation; (b) a fight

Righteous—(a) good quality drugs; (b) desirable; see Heavy, Boss, Cool

Rip off—(a) to steal; (b) to forcibly rob a peddler of his drugs or money

Ripped—highly intoxicated on drugs

Roach—the butt end of a marijuana cigarette which contains a high THC content that accumulates as the cigarette is burned

Roach holder—a device that enables the smoker to hold a joint so it can be consumed to the very end; often these holders are elaborate, jeweled items, but they may be made of broom straws or match sticks

Roll—a tin foil wrapped roll of tablets

Roll dealer—a person who sells tablets in rolls

Roll deck—same as Roll

Root—a marijuana cigarette

Rope—marijuana

Roses—benzedrine (brand of amphetamine sulfate tablets)

Rough stuff—marijuana as it comes from plant

Run—(a) an amphetamine trip, usually denotes a series of intravenous injections; (b) to take drugs continuously for several days

Rush—the beginning of the effects of a drug, usually from intravenous injection

Sack—jacket or coat

Sam—federal narcotics agent

Satch cotton—cotton used to strain narcotics before injection

Scag—heroin

Scars—healed wounds from needle punctures

Scat—heroin

Schoolboy—codeine

Scene—the place where the action is, as well as all that is happening at the time. Similar to the scene of a play which portrays all the events of the moment

Scoff—(a) to eat; (b) to swallow a drug

Score—(a) the important facts about a given event or subject; (b) to buy or acquire drugs or sex; (c) to acquire recognition for an accomplishment; (d) sexual intercourse

Scratch—money

Script—prescription (a) stolen from a doctor's office; (b) issued by a doctor

Session—(a) the duration of a trip, usually on acid; (b) a meeting; see Rap

Set—one's attitude toward taking drugs and the anticipated trip

Setting—the environment surrounding the drug taker

Set up—(a) to entrap for arrest; (b) equipment for shooting drugs

Shades—sunglasses

Shakedown—(a) arrest and search; (b) blackmail

Shakin'—(a) happening; (b) goings-on; (c) news, news event

Sharp—stylishly dressed, in vogue

Shine—reject

Shine-on—(a) to con; (b) to "get it on," i.e., do something vigorously; see Put on

Shit—(a) bad drugs; (b) a term for heroin; (c) a term for cannabis; (d) any drug

Shiv—knife, razor, sharp instrument

Shooting gallery—place where users can purchase drugs and inject them

Shoot up—to inject drugs

Short—(a) car, automobile, wheels; (b) having an inadequate supply of drugs or money

Shrink—psychiatrist

Sick—to suffer withdrawal symptoms

Sitter—experienced LSD user who helps or guides a new user

Siva—the Hindu god who gave man cannabis

Skin—(a) paper for rolling marijuana cigarettes; (b) to cheat; (c) a prophylactic

Skinning—skin popping, i.e., shooting drugs under the skin

Skin popping—intradermal or subcutaneous injection of a drug

Slammed—in jail

Sleep walker—heroin addict

Sleepers—a depressant type drug such as barbiturates

Smack—(a) heroin; (b) drugs, especially powdered drugs in the form of snuff

Smash—(a) wine; (b) hit or strike

Smashed—intoxicated; see Stoned

Smoke—cannabis (particularly on the East Coast)

Snappers—amyl nitrate capsules

Sneeze it—attempt to break the habit

Sniffing—using narcotics by sniffing through nasal passages, usually heroin or cocaine; this is taking it "rare"—not in solution

Snith—informer, stoolie

Snort—see Sniffing

Snow—cocaine; also used to mean heroin

Snowbird—cocaine user

Sock it to me—(a) to tell the straight facts, to speak plainly and honestly; (b) sexually, the term denotes assent on the part of the speaker for mutual participation

Soda jerk—small irregular drug habit; see Chip

Soft drugs—hallucinogens

Solid—agreeable, good, most desirable

Source—supplier of drugs or narcotics

Space out—in a daze, particularly a daze resulting from a trip due to the use of psychotropics

Spade—Negro

Speed—stimulants, specifically methamphetamine (or desoxy-ephedrine), a drug capable of producing intense highs with, in most cases, subsequent severe crashes

Speedball—a mixture of heroin and cocaine

Spike—hypodermic needle

Splash—speed

Spook—Negro

Spoon—(a) a measure for a drug in powder form; there are 16 spoons per ounce; (b) a container for cooking heroin

Split—to depart or leave

Spring—(a) to pay a person's way or to let him smoke marijuana at no cost; (b) to free from jail, usually on bond or writ

Square—not with it, straight-laced, narrow-minded, unimaginative, anti-hip

Stanley's stuff—LSD purportedly manufactured by Augustus Owsley Stanley III

Stardust—cocaine

Stash—place where narcotics or the "outfit" is hidden; also, place where a drug peddler will secrete various quantities of narcotics

Steamboat—a hollow tube, such as the center of a toilet paper roll with a hole in the top, where a marijuana cigarette is placed; the steamboat permits intake of air along with the smoke for quicker effect

Stick—a marijuana cigarette

Sting—to cheat or rob

Stone—the ultimate, the best

Stoned—very high on drugs, usually to the point of being unable to cope with reality

Stool—to inform, usually on a fellow user to the police

STP—4-methyl-2,5-dimethoxy-alpha-methylphenethylamine, a synthetic hallucinogen developed by the army, related to amphetamine and mescaline

Straight—(a) one who does not use drugs; (b) more broadly, one who is not connected with the drug or swinging sex world; this is not usually a derogatory term but is used to identify one's social association in contrast to the word "square," which is not a complimentary term; (c) a tobacco cigarette

Straighten out—to withdraw from addiction to drugs

String out—regular use of narcotics

Stroke—disappointment, not pleasurable

Strung out—(a) badly addicted to a drug; (b) to be out of drugs and craving them; (c) to be sick from excessive use of drug; see Spaced out

Stuff—cannabis or other drugs

Suds—beer

Suede—Negro

Sugar—powdered narcotic

Super—(a) great, exceptionally good; (b) used with another word to denote a special evaluation

Superpot—cannabis soaked or laced with another drug

Swing—to be an active and effective participant in the action or happening in the drug and/or the liberal sexual world

Swinger—one who is an active participant in the drug and/or sexually experimenting world

Swing man—drug supplier ·

Tabs—LSD 25

Take off—(a) to inject narcotics; (b) to steal drugs

Tall—good

Tar—opium

Taste—a small quantity of drugs or narcotics—a sample

TD caps—time disintegrating capsules

Tea—cannabis

Teashades—sunglasses; (it was once believed that cannabis dilated the pupils, and thus "shades" were needed to protect the users' eyes from the sun.)

Tell it like it is—(or tell it the way it is); to tell the truth without embellishment

Teenybopper—a preadolescent fan of the hippie or drug subculture

Tetrahydrocannabinols—identified as the group of substances which are responsible for the psychoactivity and many of the other pharmacological effects that accrue from the use of cannabis

Texas tea—marijuana

THC—tetrahydrocannabinol

Thing—(a) someone's true nature; (b) an item or pastime of special interest

Third eye—(a) the inner self or inward-looking eye; (b) the vision one obtains of oneself on hallucinogens

Thoroughbred—a high type dealer who sells pure narcotics

Threads—(a) clothes; (b) bad luck or rough situation

Thumb—a fat marijuana cigarette

Tighten up—to turn on, to smoke cannabis

Tin—a small amount of opiate

TJ—Tijuana, Mexico

Toast—good, fine, acceptable

Toat—smoke marijuana cigarettes

Together—nice, stylish, pretty

TMA—a hallucinogen, quite potent but not as potent as LSD (3, 4, 5-trimethoxyphenylbeta-aminopropane)

Toke—to smoke a marijuana cigarette

Toke pipe—a small marijuana pipe

Toke up—(a) to drag on a cannabis-filled cigarette or pipe; (b) to go up significantly on cannabis

Tools—equipment for taking drugs

Torch—a match

Torch up—light marijuana cigarette

Torn up—intoxicated, stoned

Tossed—to be searched for possession of drugs

Tour guide—travelling, experienced LSD user who helps out a new user; see Sitter

Tracks—needle marks along one's veins from intravenous use of drugs

Trap—(a) hiding place for drugs; see Stash; (b) to set up a person for arrest

Travel agent—a dealer in hallucinogens, especially acid

Trey—a $3.00 purchase

Trick—an easy mark, sucker, patsy

Trigger—to smoke a marijuana cigarette immediately after taking LSD

Trip—an emotional excursion into unknown psychological realms involving heightened sensual perception and concentration; in drug parlance this is the result of taking drugs and obtaining their effects

Trip out—(a) to immerse oneself in a happening; (b) to become intensely involved

Tripsit—one under the influence of LSD

Tripsville—the Haight Ashbury section of San Francisco

Truck drivers—amphetamines

Tuned in—(a) to become markedly aware of oneself as a result of mind expansion due to drug use; (b) generally, to be aware of the scene and usually part of it

Turkey—a capsule purported to be narcotic but filled with a non-narcotic substance

Turn off—(a) to dispel interest, to bore, to cause indifference; (b) withdraw from drugs

Turn on—(a) in the limited sense, to smoke marijuana or take another hallucinogen; (b) in the general sense, to acquire expanded appreciation of an event or experience as a result of being highly pleased by it; (c) to come alive, to enter the drug society; (d) to encourage another to use a drug; (e) a good thing or experience

Turned out—to be introduced to the drug subculture

Turning tricks—prostituting

Turps—elixir of turpin hydrate with codeine (cough syrup)

Twisted—(a) suffering from withdrawal symptoms; (b) a quasi-trance induced by drugs or alcohol; (c) to have a case pending on a person to help persuade that person to cooperate with police

Twenty-five—LSD-25

Tying up—to put a tourniquet on one's veins in order to facilitate intravenous injection

Uncool—one who is aware but incapable (because of hangups or comparable problems) of participating fully in the action. An uncool person may endanger a cool scene because of his lack of self-control and inability to maintain; this is a most uncomplimentary term

Uncle—federal narcotics agent

Underground—this is the whole drug, sex and anti-Establishment subculture, its inhabitants, its activities, its philosophies

Underground railway—system which supplies food and lodging to juvenile runaways

Up—to be under the influence of a drug; usually not in full control of oneself; the person who is "up" is usually sympathetically protected by others in the drug community until he comes down

Uppers—stimulants

Up tight—nervous, anxious, tense

User—one who uses narcotics

Vibrations (Vibes)—extra-sensory perceptions, feelings between people, may be good or bad vibes

Wasted—high, or drunk, badly involved with a drug

Wedges—(a) small tablets; (b) LSD

Weed—marijuana

Weed head—marijuana smoker

Weekend habit—irregular habit

Weight—a large amount of drugs, usually marijuana

West coast—amphetamine tablets or capsules

Wheels—car, automobile

Where it's at—the place, real or imagined, where the action is; to know "where it's at" is to be aware of the drug scene

Whites—amphetamine tablets

White light—the high stop on the LSD trip during which time one fuses with infinity

Wig—one's mind

Wig out—to blow one's mind; see Freak out

Wings—mainline shots of drugs, usually applied to the first such trip

Wiped out—see Wasted

Works—equipment for shooting drugs

Wrap—the cover, usually a deceptive one, over a package of drugs or cannabis

Yard—$100.00

Yellow jackets—nembutal (pentobarbital sodium)

Yellows—nembutal (pentobarbital sodium)

Yen—opium

Yen shee babies—the constipated products of one's stool caused by the marked depression of bowel activity occurring with opiate addiction

Yenning—(a) withdrawal symptoms; (b) a desire for drugs

Youngblood—young person starting to use marijuana

Zap—borrowed from Buck Rogers gun noise (a) to defeat someone; (b) to overcome someone; (c) to kill someone

Zen in— to be able to read someone's mind, to be intuitive or have extrasensory perception

Zig-zag—roll-your-own cigarette paper

Zig zag man—symbol that portrays man smoking cigarette on a brand of paper frequently used to roll joints

Zonked—highly intoxicated by a drug

BELOW OLYMPUS   By Interlandi

Note: Cut along dotted line and pin on wall!

appendix

ARGUMENTS PRO AND CON:
QUESTIONS AND ANSWERS
ON THE USE OF CANNABIS

In the body of this book, we have discussed the major con-troversies surrounding the use of cannabis—those comparing its effects to those of alcohol and tobacco (on the pro-pot side), and exploring possible connections between cannabis and crime and violence (on the anti-pot side). These by no means exhaust the issues and problems associated with marijuana use; many others have been touched on in this book.

Certain questions seem to be raised repeatedly: What about "religions" that claim pot as a sacrament? What about the claim that prominent people smoke grass, as an excuse for its use? What connection does cannabis *really* have with the more dan-gerous drugs? These and other very common questions have been gathered here in question and answer form. For the most part the questions are phrased from the pro-cannabis side, as though they were being posed by those who have used or would like to try cannabis. The answers, although tending to discourage cannabis use are, above all, attempts to present such facts as are known in each case. We hope the reader will find the questions, and the answers, he is looking for.

Isn't pot the "in" thing today. Aren't all the "cool" kids using pot?

Not really. Although statistics will vary from study to study, the actual number of true *users* is relatively small. Users in this sense, however, have to be defined differently from those who play occasionally. The users and players are noisy about their habit and attract attention and publicity that causes many to believe their number is much greater than it actually is. Additionally, because they feel that current cannabis legislation is an intrusion on their friends' personal liberties, many nonusers join the crusade. This combination tends to help swell the continuing flood of publicity which, in truth, causes others to try the drug out of curiosity.

Some journalists have not been helpful in presenting an unbiased picture of cannabis use in this country. The various "guestimates" available concerning the number of youngsters who are turning on are just that, and for the most part are unreliable. It is true that a growing number of youths, urged on by favorable publicity and reassurance from "experts" that the drug is safe, are *trying* the drug. At the same time, an unknown number of youths, who have tried it, have put it down as unnecessary or undesirable, and will never return to its use. These people, unlike those who continue to use or who think it's "in" to be pro-pot, do not always talk about their experience.

The situation hasn't changed too much from the observation made by *Time* magazine in 1965 that "statistics on the problem are non-existent and its extent is tough to gauge. School officials normally ignore it or hush it up; students with first-hand knowledge are prone to boastful exaggeration . . ."[1] Further, usage is not the same throughout the country. There are sections of America where kids are only now really awakening to the prospects of "better living through chemistry" because their local media have chosen to take a negative view towards drugs, pot in particular. This influence, however, is being watered down by the incessant pounding of pro-pot motion pictures, magazines, and television writers and producers. Such people may take the "turn on" viewpoint for any of several reasons: they may use and enjoy pot, themselves, and be convinced there are no problems associated with it; they may have found a new commercial market and a way of making a fast buck (one producer, having been advised that his picture painted an unrealistically happy side of the drug scene, told this author, "To hell with the kids . . . this is what they want to hear and pay to see, and I'm in business to make money." Or they may be in no position to argue with a superior who favors a pro-drug policy, and so write or produce as they are told.

There is, of course, the "fad" appeal, especially when youth's heroes are depicted as being part of the scene. But a significant number of these highly talented kids, who are deeply involved in the drug scene, are dying off at tragically young ages. As one young friend of the author recently put it, "I guess I'll never have any contemporary heroes in my peer group that will outlive the age of thirty."

Aren't all sorts of really intelligent people using cannabis? I can give you names of doctors and lawyers and ministers and teachers, not to mention top students, who use it without any harm.

Of course. In rebuttal, consider the following from Los Angeles Judge Arthur Alarcon: "It is my opinion that marijuana use, especially among college students and their pseudo-intellectual leaders from the professional ranks, is a symptom and not the cause of preexisting profound psychological disturbance which is magnified by marijuana."[2]

There are, to be sure, a number of people who can use marijuana at frequent intervals and not be impaired by the drug's effects. This should not be surprising, knowing as we do the tremendous variables involved in the use of cannabis. The effects of consuming cannabis, note Drs. David Maurer and Victor Vogel,[3] "differ widely with the culture, with different racial stocks, with various religious groups, and with varying social status of the individuals who consume it. Furthermore, hemp raised in different parts of the world, while consistent in producing the essential cannabinol or intoxicating principle, varies widely in the content and strength of the drug produced; soil, climate, light intensity, latitude, etc., have a profound effect on the hemp plant. Also, the effects vary widely with the part of the plant consumed, and with various methods of consumption."

The end result of this tremendous variability is that, first, we cannot predict just what will occur when a given person takes the drug, because mood, ideation, inclination, external stimuli, and other variants influence the outcome. Second, it can be assumed that while much of the time the use of milder forms of cannabis available in this country will not produce adverse effects, we are not sure this will always be the case, or that the milder forms will not give way to stronger ones as use spreads.

As for the "top students" of cannabis legend, Yale psychologist Kenneth Kenniston[4] states that these users are "a small but talented minority. They are generally very bright, hard-working students who maintain A and B averages." But these users are not dependent upon cannabis in the true sense of the word. They are "chippers," and lack the addict's compulsive need to relieve intolerable tension and depression. Unlike the true addict they remain in the mainstream of life *despite*, (not because of), their use of the drug. They continue to be achievement-oriented and competitive. The true problem presented by this small minority is that by example they encourage others who may lack their stability and drive to try marijuana. The results can be disastrous. There may even be some naive enough to imagine that cannabis will *help* them to get good grades; but that's being very naive indeed.

It should be clear, then, that marijuana use is a kind of chemical Russian roulette. The risk is great. That one person spins the revolver and comes up with a blank is no guarantee that the next will be so fortunate. Those who do become dependent on the drug resemble one another enough so that their emotional characteristics and behavior patterns can largely be predicted; the description of such persons often fits not the top students, but the dropouts.

Commenting on young Moroccan kif (cannabis) users, Benabud[5] notes they are immature young people who are "tuned in" more to the imaginary than to the real; they live for today instead of worrying about the future; they demonstrate a compulsive need to satisfy their desires right now, and are frustrated if they cannot. Benabud concludes from this syndrome that some users are more or less destined to become addicted to kif because of an emotional predisposition that makes the effects of the drug attractive to them. This, he says, justifies an old Moroccan saying that "You are a kif addict long before you smoke your first pipe." The sad thing is that most of these future "addicts" are unaware of the impending danger. Their psychological predisposition to respond positively to the effects of the drug is so strong that one exposure, one puff, starts them on the road to drug oblivion.

Maybe it's true that some professional people have problems, just as young people do, but if they can smoke cannabis why shouldn't young people?

Some professional people do smoke pot. To deny this would be less than honest. But let's take a closer look at the adults who use marijuana in the tightly guarded privacy of their homes or offices.

One of the more damaging of these episodes happened in a small northern California town in 1967.* None of the principals, least of all the central figure, ever thought they would come to public attention. The case in point involved one of the town's more prominent citizens, who lived near the little three-room schoolhouse that serves the children of the area. The citizen: Mrs. Garnett Brennan, a cheerful, wide-eyed, blithe spirit, an accredited California teacher for thirty years, who was the teaching principal of the town's elementary school.

Nearing age sixty, Mrs. Brennan was recently fired from her job because she signed an affidavit to help a young friend who was arrested for selling marijuana. In this affidavit she stated she knew cannabis was not harmful because she had smoked it almost daily herself for nearly eighteen years. The experience, she said, was quite beneficial, relaxing, and a great aid in staying up late to correct papers. Discreet, Mrs. Brennan never smoked in public, only at home. In public, she used tobacco, which she recently affirmed she wished she could quit.

According to *Life* magazine writer Shana Alexander,[6] Mrs. Brennan began her habit in 1947 when she was visiting at Big Sur, California, now famed as a hippie mecca. "I remember the first time someone turned me on back there," the teacher told the the columnist, "I felt just like Alice in Wonderland. I'd stand up and grow taller and taller. I'd reach out my arm and watch it grow longer and longer. I wondered why I didn't fall into the Pacific Ocean. Then I thought: how crazy reading is. . . ."

Things are no longer the same for Mrs. Brennan. The tiny zinnia bed where she grew her own supply of cannabis fails

---

*This account is reprinted from *Marijuana* (first edition), by E. R. Bloomquist (Beverly Hills: Glencoe Press, 1968).

to sprout her plants now, by law. She no longer uses cannabis, having renounced it until "it becomes legal," chiefly to prove that she can give it up. She is not now in charge of the school; she was fired when her use of cannabis became public knowledge.

It happens that Mrs. Brennan was but one of nearly two thousand solid citizens living in the San Francisco area who came to the aid of the young man facing a jail sentence for selling cannabis. The signers of the petition were warned ahead of time by their attorneys that they did not have to say they personally smoked marijuana; all they had to do was certify from firsthand experience or observation that they knew it was not a dangerous drug. Even this testimony might place them in jeopardy. Mrs. Brennan thought it over and said to herself, "Shoot, it's no worse than having to be cool all the time. So," she continued, "we all took our copies home from the court and that night I got high and wrote mine out." The affidavits were given to the judge in San Francisco at 2 p.m. that fateful Friday. Less than an hour later the administrative axe fell.

"She didn't intend to play Snow White," Miss Alexander reflects in her story, "only to help a friend in trouble. She did not even anticipate that her endorsement of pot would ever be made public. At such naïveté I am moved to say, 'Wow'."

Now, let us see what can be culled from this unfortunate experience. First, it is obvious that stable, intelligent, capable, socially valuable people can use cannabis and that such use can be maintained for long periods of time by these people without any visible adverse effects. It would be a mistake to assume that such practice is commonplace, but it obviously occurs. But let's consider another point. Mrs. Brennan did not sign her devastating affidavit while she had good control of her reasoning power. By her own testimony she took the affidavit home and "that night . . . got high" and wrote it out. For years her common sense kept her from discovery. Then, one night, the very drug she was defending tripped her up and destroyed her career. Had she remained cool and thought the situation over when the haze of the cannabis smoke had blown away, she might well still be teaching school.

Mrs. Brennan got by with using the drug over a long period of time. Most do not. Some will either become dependent on it or go on to something stronger. Most will give it up altogether, saying it was fun while it lasted, but life has more to offer than drug trips, particularly when the risks are so high.

We've seen what happened to Mrs. Brennan. Now let's take a look at another experience, this one by a woman two years the teacher's junior. It is not a pleasant story. Worse, while it began somewhat like Mrs. Brennan's, it ended in sheer tragedy. Contrary to Mrs. Brennan's reassurance that she found cannabis pleasant, relaxing, and "cool," this second woman has dedicated the remaining years of her life to warning parents and youth about the dangers of this drug. "Society must say: do not touch it," she says; "leave it alone!"[7]

As of September, 1967, her son was a brilliant student. "Very bright, very able, with prospects of a fine career as a teacher," said his major professor in college. The young man held a master's degree in psychology and was studying for his doctorate in psychology under a federal grant. Then, one day, a friend introduced him to cannabis under the aegis of researching the drug and expanding the mind. Because the effects of the cannabis plant weren't as effective as mind-expanders as the young man had hoped, he soon turned to LSD. "Later," says his mother, "one of his kooky friends gave him STP and this caused his tailspin. This is the horrible part—a fellow student gave him STP knowing he had had a nervous breakdown." The breakdown had occurred after the youth had been on several cannabis trips. At this time, despite a happy marriage and a successful career, the young man began to question the validity of life. He became so depressed he attempted suicide. Failing this attempt, he voluntarily entered UCLA Hospital for psychiatric therapy.

The mother had frequently discussed her son's experiments with him, trying to persuade him to give them up. "We knew all about it," she said. "He told us all about it. We warned him, 'Son, if you smoke marijuana it will lead to something else,' but he pooh-poohed all our warnings." Instead, he insisted, "They've been using it for thousands of years without harm. There's nothing to it. It's actually not as bad as alcohol."

Near the end of September the youth, obsessed by his drug-induced philosophies, entered the photo lab in Franz Hall at UCLA. He wrapped his head and face with gauze, put a plastic bag over the gauze, and taped it around his neck. A scuba diver's mask was placed over his mouth. From it ran a hose that was connected to a nearby open gas jet. A roll of masking tape lay near the body. On it, written in blue ink, were the words, "I shall return." The following morning his professor found him dead of asphyxiation.

The mother lamented, "What they don't realize is that the effects are cumulative. If they don't get the results they think they should, they move on to something else."

In other words, social prominence or obscurity is not the important point. The important point is that potential users should know the whole range of evidence. It is not rational to consider only evidence that supports one's convictions. Look at it all and then decide.

Does cannabis cause sexual excitation and increased sexual powers? Is it an aphrodisiac?

"It is true that some individuals experience a marked stimulation of [sexual] desires," Walton says, "but in a great proportion of other instances, no such impulses are evident. The effect, again, is very probably due to removal of the usual restraints and correspondingly to the release of the more primitive impulses."[8] Vogel[9] notes that some people actually take the drug in the hope that it will preserve, improve, or maintain their sexual powers. Since strong expectations may exist in that direction and since cannabis creates receptivity to suggestions, use of the drug may actually influence sexual performance. This, however, is temporary at best.

The ability of cannabis to enhance sexuality lies in its peculiar alterations of time-space relationships and its propensity to increase the acuity of the senses. Additionally, by removing normal restraints and releasing inhibitions and by making the individual more susceptible to suggestion, cannabis use makes participation in sexual activity not only pleasant, if this happens to be what the user has in mind, but the obvious thing to do. Ausubel notes:

> The apparent erotic stimulation induced by marijuana in certain individuals, therefore, corresponds essentially to the release of inhibited personality trends. These persons prior to drug use tend to be excessively preoccupied with sexual gratification. Many also exhibit infantile and homosexual tendencies. In addition, the drug increases self-confidence and eliminates apprehension about

the receptivity of the contemplated sex partner. Many [users] report that the sensual aspects of sexual enjoyment are prolonged as a consequence of the exaggerated perception of elapsed time. Exhibitions of perverted sexual practices ('circuses') are not an uncommon feature at 'tea parties'.[10]

Arguing against the concept that cannabis can enhance sexuality, some people note that Eastern monks and fakirs have used hemp from earliest times to turn off their sexual desires and heighten their visual and auditory contemplations of eternity. Of course they have; some still do. This is the remarkable thing about cannabis. Whatever you were before you took the drug, whatever you had in mind as the goal to reach while on it, is increased and enhanced by the use of the drug. If one wishes to pray, one may think he is in intimate contact with the Eternal; if one wishes to copulate, he can pretend he is a satyr or she a nymph. Cannabis enables one to regress to an earlier stage of life when the very innocence of being young and uninhibited makes it possible to do things that the adult ego-censorship would prohibit. Whether or not this is a good thing is open to debate.

It is well to reflect that most of the cannabis users in this country are youths between the ages of fourteen and twenty-five. In general, individuals in this age bracket need no aphrodisiac to stimulate either interest or capacity to perform. If a young man has sex in mind when he uses the drug; he will probably move toward a selected partner. The woman may find it easier to acquiesce. As for homosexuals, a growing number have found this drug an ideal releaser of restraints, and use it to sidetrack the usual inhibitions, suspicions, and guilt associated with socially unapproved sexuality.

The interesting thing is that extensive sexual activity by young people while on marijuana is very largely a projection on the part of adults. Cannabis users have a lot to do while high and sex is only part of a long list. As for those who "wouldn't touch a girl while up on pot," let's face it: they probably wouldn't have touched her while off pot either.

How does cannabis affect the mind?

This depends on a number of factors. The La Guardia Report (which is not, as some claim, pro-cannabis, if one reads the clinical section) states, "The conclusion seems warranted that given the potential makeup and the right time and environment, marijuana may bring on a true psychotic state."[11] But psychosis is not at the moment one of our pressing problems in America. Apathy and drug-induced loss of motivation is the real issue. Psychic dependence is serious, says Dr. David Smith.[12] There is such a thing as a chronic-abuse syndrome, and such a syndrome can impair a user's growth. Some users may take years to amotivate and not show it readily because the process takes so long. But others may amotivate in a short time.

Cannabis opens the mind and enhances creativity. Right?

It again boils down to a matter of value judgments and to what one appreciates as art. If one enjoys freeform, boundless, unconventionally organized expression that is endless and seemingly without the usual forms of structure, the use of pot may enhance production of such works. If one conforms to organization and boundary, however, pot use seems to interrupt rather than assist creative activity. Classically this is exemplified by an ancient story. Once upon a time some six centuries ago there lived a man by the name of Nasreddin Hodja, whose feats were so remarkable that he became a legend in the Middle East. Hodja was very curious about hashish. He had heard all the fourteenth century talk about how much fun it was, and how it wouldn't hurt him, so one day he bought a stash, smoked it, and wandered off to the Turkish bath to enjoy the effects in a swirl of steam. After a while, Hodja became a bit irritated. He experienced absolutely nothing. Convinced he had been cheated he rushed out on the street, headed for the druggist's. Midway a friend stopped him and asked what was going on. "I thought smoking hashish would do something to me," Hodja replied, "but as you can see I'm still what I was. I'm going to get the real stuff from the apothecary. I have a feeling he's cheated me." The friend smiled and nodded his head, then gave Hodja some advice. "Before you go all the way, Hodja, old friend," said the man, "go back to the bath and put on your clothes."[13]

Henri Michaux puts it a little more scientifically. "Don't forget," he warns his readers, "that you have swallowed poison. Psychological explanations are all too tempting. Tracing everything to psychology is poor psychology." Michaux continues:

The modulations, indeed, which "hemp" is able to achieve from such neutral beginnings are so astounding, so wondrous, so demonstrative of its superhuman power, so luminous, that no metaphysical brain, even with the most magnificent idea, could equal them.... There is no greater miracle of the "grasping intellect." Thus it is not surprising that these prodigious "exchanges" have given many a drug addict, even among the most mediocre, a somewhat exalted idea of his intelligence. No one, in fact, has a greater density of ideas than they do at certain moments, nor is capable of more unexpected association of ideas—of which they subsequently have not the slightest recollection.[14]

Where music is concerned, the myth exists that jazz musicians play much better when on cannabis. It is true they are less inhibited and probably tire less easily, but there the effect stops. The habit is so common among musicians, Walton writes, "that it may properly be considered a special occupational hazard.... There is very little probability that an individual's performance is in any degree improved over that of his best capabilities. As judged by objectively critical means, the standards of performance are no doubt lowered."[15]

In 1934 Gerard Piel wrote an article for a national magazine about the use of cannabis by musicians and included the blatantly false assertion that while on cannabis the "swing musician ascends to new peaks of virtuosity."[16] This interested Dr. C. Knight Aldrich, an assistant surgeon for the United States Public Health Service, who gave cannabis (synthetic THC) to twelve musicians, then administered a group of tests that experts refer to as "outstandingly the most important battery of tests in the field of music." Aldrich suspected that the release of inhibitions by cannabis use might bring out latent talents or evoke a more intense emotional performance. Yet he also recognized that one could not trust the using subject's evaluation of his own performance. So he ran his own careful tests. Here is his conclusion: "No improvement was observed in the musical capability, as tested by the Seashore measures of musical talents, of twelve former users of marijuana after ingestion of satisfying amounts of parahexyl compound, a synthetic marijuana-like substance. Although nine out of the twelve subjects achieved poorer scores after using the drug than on the previous trial, eight out of twelve expressed the opinion ·that their scores had improved, and none recognized a loss of efficiency."[17]

"The very common idea of improved performance is based on several features which can give considerable apparent support to such an impression," Walton notes.[18] "There is an increased sensitivity to sound and a keener appreciation of rhythm and timing. These phenomena, as judged by objective criteria, probably do not exist except during certain early phases of the drug's effects. The release of inhibitions may uncover latent talents which previously had been subject to personality restraints. The wild, emotional character of performance can be intensified and for certain audiences this may represent improvement although it would not be so acknowledged by an individual of cultivated musical appreciation."

In addition, we have the testimony of author William Burroughs: "Unquestionably this drug is very useful to the artist, activating trains of association that would otherwise be inaccessible, and I owe many of the scenes in *Naked Lunch* directly to the use of cannabis."[19] In a previous edition we marveled at Burroughs' comment, finding it difficult to understand, considering the content of *Naked Lunch*, why Mr. Burroughs would imply this was an endorsement for using pot. Goode roundly criticized this observation, and suggested again this was a matter of value judgments. "The sociologist of knowledge," he commented, "seeks to understand and explain the bases from which man's intellectual efforts spring. He will notice the prominent place in this debate of the manner in which matters of taste, such as artistic esthetics, are intimately and inseparably bound with views of the empirical reality of the drug [cannabis]."[20]

As a matter of fact, Goode has a point and a valid one. Much of the argument, as has been noted in Chapter Eleven, is not centered around cannabis at all where debate is concerned. Much of the comment is involved in defending values and ideas. If Burroughs feels his material is art (and there are those who follow him in agreement), it indeed becomes not only a matter of value judgments but a conflict of interests which may ultimately distinguish art from social anathema.

On the other hand, where cannabis is concerned in relationship to creativity, it is interesting to note that on a different day and in a different mood Mr. Burroughs, writing in the *British Journal of Addiction* in 1956, had this to say about pot: "Marijuana is a sensitizer and the results are not always pleasant. It makes a bad situation worse. Depression becomes despair;

anxiety panic. I once gave a marijuana cigarette to a guest who was mildly anxious. After smoking half a cigarette he suddenly leapt to his feet screaming, 'I got fear' and rushed out of the house."[21] Thus, while Mr. Goode may be justified in stating that sociologists of knowledge have to take a varied approach to evaluating the empirical reality of the drug, it is only fair to ask that they note the bad with the good. This is particularly desirable where they are influencing the thinking of young minds who are trying to relate themselves to this problem (realizing, of course, that referring to pot as a "problem" is another value judgment.)

American cannabis is so weak and lasts for such a short time that none of the effects described by hashish ever occur. Why do some people keep attacking marijuana when it is not the same as hashish and, in fact, comes from an entirely different plant?

The truth about marijuana, hashish, and any number of synonyms for this plant, or its product, is that it all comes from the same source. There is only one marijuana (hashish) plant. It is *Cannabis sativa*. One genus, one species. All the rest of the subdivisions are *varieties* of the mother plant. They differ in potency for reasons previously described, essentially (a) varied geographical locations and climatic conditions, (b) the plant's genotypic ancestors, and (c) possible differences in the chemical content of the varieties of the plant.

American marijuana is a cousin to hashish, the latter being some five to six times more potent because the cannabinol content of the resin of *Cannabis indica* is more toxic than that found in the resin of *Cannabis americana* and some *mexicana*. If cannabis use in the United States were static, there might be less cause for alarm than there is, but Americans do not seem content to continue to use poor-quality cannabis. A growing number of users keep on the lookout for increasingly powerful types of "good" grass." Because of this, "Acapulco gold" or "Panama red" have become very popular. For the same reasons, the hashish market is steadily expanding in America. Users no longer just buy "pot"; they are becoming selective. This may not be true for the unsophisticated user who is curious to try once and will probably not return to the drug again, but it applies to a significant segment of the experienced repeating users.

Today's buyer can obtain almost any effect he wants

wrapped into the prepared "joint." If he wants to nod he gets marijuana soaked in opium. The smoker who wants a psychological trip, on the other hand, dips his reefer in DMT or any of the readily available drugs that provide bizarre mental experiences and are compatible with marijuana.

One does not have to resort to these esoteric compounds, however, if he really wants to hallucinate and "mindblow." He can start with "mild" American or Mexican cannabis and if he persists he can obtain the same effect acquired from any of the stronger hallucinogens. How much he will need to do this is unpredictable because of all the variables. Some users can obtain the effect with just a few cigarettes; others have to take pipefuls in order to reach the same high. But this much we know: cannabis may produce most if not all of the weird emotional and mental effects that can be obtained with other hallucinogenic substances, including those experienced from the use of LSD. The difference between the mild form of American cannabis and the more potent forms of hallucinogens is primarily one of use pattern and amount of drug. It is true most American users are now staying on the conservative side of cannabis use. But if experiences in other countries are any indication, we can expect that a segment of American users will do everything they can to increase the potency of their drugs until the preferred products will resemble those found in countries where resin with high cannabinol content is readily available.

Is there a "typical" cannabis user, and can he be expected to behave in a given manner if he is dependent upon the drug?

Once there might have been a single typical cannabis user. No more. Elsewhere in this book we have tried to categorize loosely today's users, but it is recognized that even a loose categorization is inadequate. Perhaps we should here refer to Dr. David Ausubel's[22] classification. Ausubel employs the etiological headings used by some authorities for opium addicts and applies them to cannabis users. These are: primary users, symptomatic users, and reactive users. In addition there are some subdivisions that are found in all three categories: recreational users, who use it simply for fun, habitual users, who are usually inadequate personalities, and two less frequently encountered groups—those who use the drug to augment their appreciation of artistic and creative activity, and an even smaller group of those who use it to help them in the performance of premeditated criminal activity.

The primary users, Ausubel says, are those who need the drug to help them adjust. These are inadequate personalities, anxious, neurotic people, and those who are depressed. The symptomatic users are antisocial people who use the drug to aid their already antisocial activities. The reactive users are preponderantly normal, usually teenage, youths who use it as a status symbol or to keep up with the rest of the group.

The interesting thing about Ausubel's discussion is that he emphasizes, as do most students of cannabis abuse, the importance of understanding the inadequate personality, because it is this group that constitutes the major social problem where the legalization of cannabis is concerned. The hazard in this instance is that the inadequate personality is drawn to the use of drugs and, being marginally adjusted, he will often fall into overt antisocial behavior, although previously he was in reasonable, if not total, control.

Ausubel believes that the inadequately adjusted group constitutes the habitual user segment of cannabis society. He calls them immature, emotionally unstable people who are unable to face reality or endure any stress or deprivation. They have a low frustration threshold and they cannot stand to be disciplined. Whenever they face conflict they attempt to resort to hedonistic behavior which pacifies them much as a bottle or nipple will pacify an anxious infant. If they cannot obtain adequate pacification, or if the drug they choose makes it easier for them to be aggressive, they can become socially disruptive.

Hedonism is the concept that best describes this group of inadequate personality drug users. It may be defined as the philosophy that pleasure and/or happiness is the sole or chief good in life. It is reiterated in the drug user jargon of the day that says, "What's the harm in doing your own thing if you don't hurt anybody?" Characteristically, the hedonistic cannabis user comes from a broken home, a poverty stricken home, or one in which there is continual domestic crisis. Most often all three elements are present. One commonly finds in such a home a mother with a high and exacting moral standard of behavior and a father who is morally lax. Early in life the child reacts to this by having frequent nightmares, enuresis, and other symptoms that indicate he is operating under severe emotional stress. More important, he shows by reacting this way that he is not communicating well or interrelating well with his parents—usually his father, but often his mother as well.

As he grows older, he shows other signs of emotional immaturity. His school attendance becomes irregular. His grades are poor. Usually his mental ability is much higher than his scholastic achievement. As a youngster he is often involved in sexual misadventures, gambling, and theft. Frequently he is in conflict with authoritarian figures such as police and teachers. Once he leaves school, either by dropping out or barely squeezing through, he follows the same irregular pattern of behavior in job employment and credit instability. He develops a nomadic tendency. Quite often his only aggressive outlet for his hostility and anxiety is through sexual encounters of one sort or another.

If he manages to get into the service the situation is no better. According to Ausubel, the inadequate personality does quite poorly in the service. He shirks duty, is insubordinate, and is frequently hauled before disciplinary boards and/or courts martial. For this sort of person, cannabis seems to have an "adjustive value"; it pulls him into line in his own (but not necessarily others') thinking because it gives him a sense of well-being and helps him "cope with reality," gives him unwarranted feelings of self-confidence, and releases aggressive and erotic tendencies. It also reduces the anxiety he would normally feel when participating in socially unacceptable hedonistic gratifications. In other words, it exaggerates the tendencies he had before he took the drug. The problem is that his pre-drug self was hardly acceptable; when the drug magnifies his problems, the situation becomes intolerable for people around him.

The inadequate personality who uses marijuana habitually, Ausubel says, resembles his opiate-addicted counterpart. There are, however, some striking differences. Most cannabis addicts come from homes that have greater emotional conflict than those of opium addicts, and exhibit a greater difference between the moral standards of the father and mother. The child usually reacts to this by becoming aggressive and/or sexually hedonistic. He may, on the other hand, however, just drop out.

When cannabis comes along, it is suitable for either purpose. He can "turn on" sexually, or he can turn it all off and become asexual and introverted. The heroin addict has no such alternative. If he becomes hooked on opiates he can only turn off and nod out, becoming aggressive only when he is in need of his drug to relieve both physical and psychological withdrawal pain. The cannabis user can swing either way, depending on his intent and goal.

In a technical résumé Ausubel says this of the cannabis versus the heroin user: "The inadequate personality who turns to the opiates . . . must be primarily concerned with attaining the nonspecific psychological aspects of euphoria—the aspects that are realized by inhibition of the self-critical faculty and by elimination of primary drives. The marijuana user, on the other hand, is more actively concerned with experiencing the sensuous and hedonistic components of drug-induced euphoria."

How can you say cannabis is bad when one of the top officials in Washington, Dr. Goddard, said he'd rather have his daughter smoke cannabis than take a drink of liquor.

Did he indeed? What actually happened to Dr. Goddard was that he was misquoted. It happens to all public speakers now and then. This author remembers having given a talk on cannabis at which the question was asked, "If a person smoked two joints a day or two packages of cigarettes a day, which would be more physically harmful to the smoker?" The answer, obviously, was that two packages of cigarettes would cause more physical harm. The following day a reporter blithely wrote the following: "When asked about tobacco and marijuana, Dr. Bloomquist said that tobacco was more harmful than pot." Having had this experience I find it easy to understand what happened to Federal Food and Drug Commissioner Dr. James L. Goddard.

Dr. Goddard was holding an informal press conference following a talk at the University of Minnesota when a question about cannabis was asked. A campus correspondent, probably indulging in wishful thinking, rushed what he thought was the answer to the question to UPI, which released it on October 17, 1967, stating that Dr. Goddard had affirmed he would not object to his daughter's smoking marijuana any more than if she drank a cocktail. The *New York Times* front-paged the story and the *Washington Post* headlined, "FDA HEAD DOUBTS POT IS WORSE THAN ALCOHOL." The newspapers were reporting honestly what their correspondent had told them.

In Washington during the next three weeks, some angry congressmen demanded Goddard resign. Medical authorities across the nation besieged Dr. Goddard's office with calls accusing him of doing "irreparable damage across the college campuses as well as in the high schools." But as the noise began to hit its peak it was discovered that a local radio station had recorded Dr. Goddard's actual remarks and that a transcript of the comments was available. Referring to it, Dr. Goddard remarked dryly, "You will note that I did not advocate free use of marijuana, did not dismiss its possible dangers to health, nor did I fail to recognize the fact that possession of marijuana is illegal."[23]

As for the comment Goddard was supposed to have made about objections to his daughter's smoking marijuana, the FDA head had actually replied: "We've discussed this at home. I would [object] in terms of the law today and any possible long-term effect." Later in amplifying this statement Dr. Goddard said, "I wouldn't want my daughter or any other young woman to use marijuana until we know more about it." Shortly thereafter, UPI, which had been as misled as everyone else, sent Goddard a letter of apology.[24] "UPI erred in attributing to you an unqualified statement which in fact was considerably qualified." But the damage was done, for many who read the first report now would never believe that the retraction was anything but another government plot spurred on by the cannabis-hating Establishment to keep the real truth hidden.

This is the exact exchange from the radio station broadcast transcript:

> Question: "Would you describe it [cannabis] as being more dangerous than alcohol? Marijuana is more serious than alcohol?"
>
> Goddard: "Well, trying to compare two different drugs is a very risky business itself. They have quite different mechanisms of action; alcohol's a depressant, where marijuana's a mild hallucinogen, at best, or maybe a euphoric.
>
> "Now they both share some properties in common, however, they both distort our sense of reality, and therefore it's dangerous to operate heavy equipment or drive a vehicle when we're under the influence of either one of these.
>
> "Alcohol probably lends itself more readily to control on the part of the individual, with respect to the dosage he's receiving than marijuana does, at least to the inexperienced.

"So, there are some similarities, but there are also some differences. And as I've mentioned many times, we don't know what the long term effects of smoking marijuana or using marijuana in other forms might be, and we have to carry out this kind of research before, I for one, would be satisfied to say that the drug is safe under any conditions."[25]

Later, before a House Commerce Committee meeting in which Goddard was asked to explain his erroneously reported statement, the FDA chief made himself quite clear: "I did not, and I do not, condone the use of marijuana. I did not, and I do not, advocate the abolition of controls over marijuana. I did not, and I do not, propose 'legalizing' the drug." While admitting that he does have reservations about current penalties imposed on cannabis use, which he feels "prevent full and effective protection of the public interest in the matter of abused drugs of any kind," he stressed that much is unknown about marijuana and its effects.[26]

"No one in the scientific or medical communities is satisfied with the level of knowledge we have," he said. "Clearly, while the answers to these questions are being formulatd by the scientific community our enforcement efforts in the Food and Drug Administration as well as in the Bureau of Narcotics must continue." The FDA head also reported that marijuana use has been present in nine out of ten investigations of LSD and other hallucinogens of that type. Commenting on the experience of FDA agents and observations made on the effects of using cannabis, Goddard said, "The most common reaction to the use of marijuana is development of a state of mind in which ideas seem disconnected, uncontrolled, and freely flowing. Perception is disturbed, minutes seem to be hours and seconds may be broadened and objects may appear far away." And finally he noted, "With large doses vivid hallucinations may occur and panic with a fear of death may make the experience highly unpleasant."

Does the use of cannabis lead to the abuse of more dangerous drugs?

Maybe. It depends on the person and the circumstances. At one time, more users progressed to heroin after first using cannabis than refrained from it. Today, because an entirely different group of people with different motivations are the major users of cannabis, this is no longer true. Therefore, many youthful users say they have been lied to and that there is no connection whatever between cannabis and more dangerous drugs.

Pro-cannabis author John Rosevear argues that the only connection between marijuana and heroin "is that they are found together in the statutes and quite probably in the pockets of some heroin sellers. But that is, in total, the end of their association."[27] Recently in the *Harvard Alumni Bulletin* an alumnus (of all things, a judge) said, "It is, of course, absurd to argue that because most of the users of heroin first used marijuana, marijuana is proved to be a usual preliminary step to heroin addiction. One might as well say that because most users of heroin once imbibed milk, milk leads to heroin addiction."[28]

This kind of illogic is so frequently heard it is necessary to state the argument clearly. First, suppose all users of cannabis and heroin have used milk; but, although heroin users have all used milk and some 90 percent have used cannabis prior to using heroin, only a small segment of cannabis users have used heroin. Now, although almost all of the population has used milk, let's say that only about 15 percent of the young population (which constitutes about half the present total population) has used cannabis. In other words, some 7½ percent (a rough estimate) of Americans have used cannabis at least once. Of this 7½ percent only 12 percent are currently progressing to heroin. (The 12 percent figure comes from the Attorney General's Office of the State of California and may serve as a pattern sample for major cities across the country.) Now, the 7½ percent of the population that has used cannabis and the 12 percent (of that 7½ percent) that has gone on to heroin have an almost unanimous history of drinking milk. But at least 90 percent of all heroin users share one major characteristic not shared by the remaining 85 percent of Americans (who have almost unanimously drunk milk). That charactertistic is their use of cannabis.

Nine out of ten heroin users—sometimes more, depending on the study quoted, but never less—used cannabis first. They found it was not sufficient to salve their ego-inadequacies and stepped up to something more suited to their emotional needs. In other words, while all heroin users drank milk not all milk-drinkers used heroin. Heroin users are all members of the class milk-drinkers, but so are almost all other people. But virtually all heroin users (90 percent) are members of the much more selective class of cannabis users. Such an enormous overlap can hardly be dismissed as accidental, or equated with an overlap of a much larger and much less highly specified group.

The American Medical Association also has some things to say on this subject, once again through the Committee on Alcoholism and Drug Dependence:

> Smoking marijuana, or pot, produces feeling of well being and also sensory distortions. These effects, though similar in kind to those produced by LSD and other potent hallucinogens, are far less intense. Ironically, this is marijuana's chief danger, because the user may then try stronger substances, including heroin.
>
> Although marijuana does not lead inevitably to heroin abuse, it is a fact that most heroin abusers have experimented first with marijuana. Traditionally, they have been introduced to both drugs through friends or other contacts in the "hard drug" culture. A sizable minority who try cannabis are discontented with what they experience. They expect ever-increasing pleasurable effects, and they don't get them, some will turn to heroin, but more of the discontented will try other drugs, particularly LSD, because they don't want to risk physical dependence. They often will continue on pot while taking other drugs in sequence or at the same time. . . .
> For many, marijuana is most harmful as the teacher of "Drug Abuse A-1," an introductory course in the pleasures and pitfalls of dependence—where the pleasures seem to promise more to come and the pitfalls appear minor and easily avoided.[29]

Citing Charen's and Perlman's paper on the "Personality Studies of Marijuana Addicts"[30] and Merrill's article on "Marihuana, the New Dangerous Drug."[31] Ausubel says, "Prior to the 1950–51 epidemic of marijuana usage it was generally believed that the use of marijuana [did] *not* lead to morphine or heroin or cocaine addiction and no effort [was] made to create a market for these narcotics by stimulating the practice of marijuana smoking. However, the typical sequence of drug use [from marijuana to heroin] during the teenage outbreak of addiction led to the belief that marijuana smoking per se increases the later likelihood of opiate addiction by creating an appetite for even bigger thrills."[32]

Ausubel goes on to note that this sequence of events was not necessarily causal, but was primarily an instance in which reactive drug addicts were exposed to both drugs and, having no personality preference for either, chose the most available, least expensive, and least dangerous drug first. "In the case of addicts with marked personality defects, however," he says, "there is unequivocal evidence of specificity of preference. Opiate addicts invariably prefer opiates and marijuana addicts marijuana when free access to either drug prevails. Marijuana addicts (apart from the reactive variety) will only turn to opiates if their personality structure is such as to give the latter drugs preferential adjustive value. In such cases marijuana use is not the determining factor in opiate addiction but at most a stepping stone which lowers restraints."

Why do you keep talking about bad reactions to cannabis? You know there has never been any proof of this, nothing in the medical literature that can be supported, nothing at all that's happened here in the United States with the mild forms of cannabis used today.

Dr. Martin H. Keeler[33] presented a list of adverse reactions to *Cannabis americana* and *mexicana* in American users at the May, 1967, American Psychiatric Association meeting in Detroit, Michigan. Dr. Keeler saw eleven individuals who reported adverse reactions associated with the use of marijuana. The things they complained about were panic and fear, depersonalization, gross confusion and disorientation, depression, and paranoid phenomena occurring during the drug reaction. There was also a complaint about confusion and hallucinations occurring on and off for several weeks afterwards. In addition, two of the users experienced major changes in behavior and style of life after the use of cannabis. Others became schizophrenic subsequent to the combined use of cannabis, LSD, and amphetamine (obviously, if you are pro-cannabis, you know it was the LSD and amphetamine). Another complained of recurrent depression following her initial use of cannabis.

Let's take a look at a few of these cases:

A twenty-one-year-old man stated that after smoking more than his usual amount he became disoriented to time and place, could not think, and he had difficulty in controlling his limbs. For some weeks thereafter he intermittently experienced hallucinations resembling those he had had during the reaction.

A twenty-year-old woman stated that while smoking marijuana she became convinced that she did not exist in a spatial sense. She thought that she was merged with the universe or, alternatively, a point in space without dimensions. Such ideation, accompanied by anxiety, would persist for some hours after use of the drug.

A twenty-three-year-old woman stated that during the experience and for·some hours afterward she would have the "horrors." She described this as a feeling that indescribably evil things would happen to her because of the kind of person she was.

A twenty-two-year-old man stated that during the drug reaction he would become convinced that his taking the drug was part of some gigantic plot but that he did not know what the plot was.

A twenty-year-old man stated that after taking marijuana he recognized that his previous goals, including what he called conventional ambition, conformity, and fear, were not as important as the need to express himself and achieve independent identity. His interest and achievement in academic areas deteriorated and his dress became nonconventional.

In his discussion Keeler noted he was not alone either in his experience or in his reporting of his observations. The first report he quoted is of sufficient importance to any discussion of cannabis to deserve mention here. It was made by Dr. Samuel Allentuck, the psychiatrist who was in charge of the mayor's committee on marijuana clinical study group (of the La Guardia Report committee). Dr. Allentuck administered the equivalent of between 30 and 320 mgs. of tetrahydrocannabinol orally to 72 subjects. (A joint was considered to contain between 80 and 160 mgs. of marijuana. The subjects thus received an equivalent of from less than one joint to as high as four joints in this study.)

Of these seventy-two subjects, nine had psychotiç episodes— i.e., 12.5 percent or one out of eight. Six of these psychotic episodes, Allentuck says, "are examples of acute marijuana intoxication in susceptible individuals which comes on shortly after the drug has been taken and persists for several hours. The main features of the poisoning are the restlessness and mental excitement of a delirious nature with intermittent periods of euphoria and an overhanging state of anxiety and dread."

The remaining three subjects presented the features of marijuana psychosis, Allentuck reported. Of these one was an epileptic, another a one-time heroin addict, and the third a prepsychotic personality. "The conclusion," Allentuck wrote, "seems warranted that given the potential personality make-up and the right time and environment, marijuana may bring on a true psychotic state."[34]

In 1938 Frances Ames[35] administered between 24 and 45 mgs. of a cannabis extract orally to each of ten subjects. One subject in this study experienced intense anxiety, while five others exhibited some degree of delusional thinking. De Farias,[36] in 1955, gave cannabis to nine subjects, both orally and in smoked form, and found that of the nine, one had delirium and confusion with apprehension of impending death.

We would do well to remember all these studies when charges are made that "no work has been done on cannabis," or that the Bureau of Narcotics and Dangerous Drugs prevents researchers from studying the drug.

Keeler, summarizing his study and the others he referred to, concludes that:

1. Even though all investigators might agree that marijuana can't produce functional psychopathology, but only precipitates it in people who had such tendencies before using the drug, we must recognize that such usage might precipitate trouble that would not otherwise have occurred or, if it did occur, would have happened at a later time.

2. The medical literature definitely *does* indicate that marijuana, depending on dose and subject, can precipitate acute brain syndromes, panic, and delusional thinking during the reaction. He leaves it to authorities in the field to decide whether or not these sorts of reactions constitute psychopathology.

3. The dissolution of one's ordinary defense measures, with which he usually protects himself from stress and anxiety, is particularly potentially dangerous for borderline schizophrenics. He does not indicate, nor do most authorities, how one can separate borderline "split personalities" from stable individuals who might decide to use cannabis.

"The evaluation of the harm a drug does requires some consideration of its benefits. Users of marijuana state," Keeler observes, "that it is a source of positive pleasure, that it enhances creativity, that it provides insight, that it enriches their lives.

These are hardly minor claims." The problem in this area, however, is that individuals who use a drug that destroys one's ability to perceive objectively are not in a proper position to decide if the drug experience is sufficiently positive to override the negative effects it produces

In the study performed by Keeler the cannabis users were, in most instances, unable to reach a conclusion that the negative effects, despite their intensity, were sufficiently harmful to warrant discontinuance of the use of cannabis. In fact, according to Keeler, "All but two of the eleven individuals reporting adverse reactions considered the benefits to far outweigh the unfortunate aspects and planned to continue use of the drug." This conclusion is reminiscent of Timothy Leary's statement that ninety percent of the subjects in four separate studies, one of them his, testified enthusiastically about the effects of consciousness-expanding drugs.[37]

Cannabis is now a sacrament in some new religions, such as Dr. Leary's League of Spiritual Discovery Church. How can the law prohibit use of a sacrament in this country, where religious freedom is guaranteed by the Constitution?

A number of attempts have been made to organize psychedelic drug users into some sort of "church" which would be protected by constitutional law. Timothy Leary recognized this some time ago, when he organized his LSD group into a church, hoping it would find a place among other religions. (His efforts have caused some concern on the part of the LDS—Latter Day Saints, or Mormons—who do not appreciate being linked with Mr. Leary.) Rosevear offers a hopeful note on this approach: ". . . an out is beginning to appear under the gentle wing of the Constitution. That is, drug-taking is becoming recognized as an internal personal emotion, which might qualify as a religious experience. And, under the first article of the Bill of Rights ('Congress shall make no law respecting an establishment of religion, or prohibiting the free exercise thereof. . . .') such practices are certainly justified. . . ."

"Under the image of religion," Rosevear continues, "the public may be able to convince itself that smoking pot or swallowing acid [LSD] is all right for some people." Rosevear is wise enough to recognize that this idea is not without its pitfalls. People who have difficulty accepting the new morality of the psychedelic religion may balk. Then, too, if a church is organized, members will be expected to attend meetings, pay a minister, and all the rest. "Thus far," Rosevear says, "such ritualistic displays have failed to appear in the form of a marijuana religion. One reason is that drug takers often object to many customs. The drug taker's common boundary is their objection. It is doubtful that marijuana users will ever organize in a conventional 'church'."[38]

It may be doubtful, but hippie "priest" Gridley Wright recently appeared in a Los Angeles court to defend his propriety in founding a new religion called "Trust," which used cannabis as its sacrament. He was able to find theologians willing to testify that he might have some valid reasons for his belief.[39] The argument was that forty-five percent of Navajos are members of the Native American Church, and that peyote has been recognized by the government as an official sacrament, or at least a vital part of that religion. With this as a precedent it was argued that any ban on psychedelics constitutes an infringement on personal freedom and a violation of the First Amendment.

It should be recognized, however, that the hallucinations afforded by the peyote, which American Native Church worshippers feel gives them a closer contact with God, are only one facet of the ritual. Peyote also causes violent emesis. This, too, has a place in the ceremony in that it is interpreted as a purging of, or perhaps a penance for, sin. As one wag put it, it is a faith consisting of "Turning on, Tuning in and Throwing up." It takes a faithful worshipper to follow all the requirements of this ritual.

Practical but hopeful, John Rosevear stated the issue in trying to establish a new psychedelic religion: "The problem that now might arise would be to make the higher courts realize that 'getting high' is a religious thing to do."[40] In Wright's case, Deputy District Attorney for the City of Los Angeles, Herbert Jacobowitz, placed the following argument before the bench: "There is no evidence there is such a religion [as Trust]. Second, there is no evidence the defendant is connected with it." Finally, "If he is, there is no evidence showing his use of marijuana on May 18 [when he said on a radio program defending the use of cannabis that he was 'righteously stoned' at the time of the broadcast] was connected with his religion."

Superior Court Judge Mark Brandler agreed. "None of the civil liberties are absolute in themselves," the judge told Wright.

"They must be measured by the public welfare and limited by it." The judge called Wright's claim that he had used marijuana for sacramental purposes "a sham and completely spurious." The jurist said: "Crime is not the less odious because a self-appointed high priest of a subculture suggests that he uses marijuana as a sacrament of his religion."[41]

The story of Gridley Wright will strike numerous divergent chords of response among readers. Once a successful stockbroker, he became involved with cannabis, and the combination of pot and Mr. Wright produced a highly publicized dropout. At his first arraignment he convinced the judge he no longer needed nor was attracted to drugs and was placed on probation. A short time later he returned again before the court, once more using pot, and this time returned to jail until he changed his mind.

In June of 1969, having spent eighteen months behind bars, Mr. Wright again pled with the court for his freedom, this time denouncing pot and drugs and stating he no longer wished to be a symbol for those who use it—if it meant imprisonment.

When asked what he now planned to do the thirty-five-year-old ex-hippie priest stated he planned to move to the Big Sur area, and conduct sensitivity sessions. Asked why he renounced his drug use, he said, "Captivity did it. I got tired of being locked up and my agreeing [to the terms of probation] was the only key to the lock."[42]

Those who espouse incarceration as a "cure" for drug use may well cite the Wright case as an example of how well the law plus heavy penalties works. Those in the counterculture, on the other hand, may express diametrically opposed viewpoints. All must admit that for many, prison has the ability to produce the results desired by the Establishment where drug use is concerned. None, however, is really ready at this point to note how high a price is exacted for this pyrrhic victory, or if the price is either worth or worthy of the results.

The idea of using cannabis as a religious sacrament and affording it the protection of the Constitution, says attorney Gene R. Haislip, is a unique proposal. It is unique because those who propose it seem to wish to deny the availability of the drug to those who are not members of their organization. Instead, they seem to want to make it available only through quasi-religious controls monitored by them. In this instance the right to use drugs under the guise of a religious setting raises questions of law and fact. "The First Amendment to the Constitution," Haislip says, "states that the Congress shall make no law prohibiting the free exercise of a religion. While this is an absolute prohibition in regard to mere religious beliefs or opinions, it is well recognized that the legislature may inhibit acts or practices which tend toward the subversion of the civil government, or which are made criminal by the law of the land."[43]

Haislip refers to three cases in which the courts have ruled in one way or another concerning religious freedom when it came in conflict with the law of the land. One of the more precedent-setting, *the United States vs. Reynolds,* dealt with the question of polygamous marriage within the Mormon Church.[44] The law ruled against the church, decreeing that polygamy must end. The church, although it never changed its official stand on the religious propriety and validity of polygamy, complied with the decision.

In another instance, the *People vs. Woody,*[45] the California Supreme Court held that certain Indian tribes had a constitutional right to use peyote in their religious services in spite of the prohibitions of California law. In this case, the church demonstrated that the law was a substantial infringement on its religious practice, and that the practice was required by a faith that was established to be a bona fide religious organization. The state could not disprove this claim in the case of the Native American Church; thus the decision was in favor of the church.

In the case of the Indian peyote cult, the court found that a history of peyote use, and ceremonial refinements surrounding its use, stretched back to the seventeenth century. Those who tried to have cannabis legalized as a sacrament were not able to provide the court with any historical precedents. Additionally, the court noted there is growing evidence that repetitive use of hallucinogens may be a health hazard. It said if one organization was permitted to use the drug or drugs on such a flimsy basis, large numbers of persons would be likely to advance spurious claims of faith in order to avail themselves of such privileges.

The state used the spurious-claims argument in arguing the third case cited by Haislip, *Sherbert vs. Verner.*[46] In this case, the claimant felt she should receive unemployment benefits even though she had refused to accept employment, because the jobs offered her would require her to work on Saturdays, contrary to the teachings of her faith. The court held that in this case, the state's fear of spurious claims was founded on nothing but conjecture, and decided in favor of the defendant.

Haislip argues that in our society, "it is notorious that tens of thousands of persons abuse drugs for hedonistic, or at least nonreligious purposes." Therefore, he calls justified the state's fear of spurious claims that an individual's use of cannabis is "religious." Because of the intensive use of drugs in this country, he says, "it cannot be said that such a fear would be based on mere conjecture. Accordingly, the constitutional claim for privileged drug abuse seems to be without merit."

And that, apparently, is where the "sacrament" controversy stands at the moment.

Many scientists feel cannabis may have value in medical use. The government won't permit the drug to be adequately studied, however, so this use can't be found. Why is it that the government refuses to let investigators experiment with cannabis and study its effects?

This is another of the marijuana myths, this one propagated by pro-cannabis forces. Federal law has never prohibited valid research by competent men; in fact, the government encourages it, with the assurance that any new, safe, tested medicines will be made available to doctors under any appropriate controls necessary.

The problem that arises is that authorities have been overwhelmed by pro-cannabis individuals who do not have the experience, equipment, or proper motivation to be safely granted permission to experiment with a dangerous drug. The author knows of a pro-cannabis psychiatrist who repeatedly petitioned the Bureau of Narcotics and Dangerous Drugs for permission to possess legally a kilogram of cannabis for "experimental purposes." Since he was aligned with no recognized research program and was an admitted user of the drug, permission was denied. He constantly complained that proper investigation was being hampered by the Bureau and many uninformed individuals agreed with him. Moreover, other pro-cannabis advocates have made a similar charge.

"There are few experimenters who would be prepared to

risk working in such a controversial field," Oxford postgraduate student Stephen Abrams insists. "Furthermore, the drug has been removed from the Pharmacopoeia, and is virtually unavailable for research purposes. To be in possession of cannabis or to import it, one must hold a license issued by the Home Secretary." (In the United States such a license is issued by the Department of Justice.) "Those who have a legitimate right and a scientific reason to possess cannabis find that they cannot obtain it, but their students have no difficulty in purchasing it for the purpose of 'getting stoned.' One could, of course, take the risk of performing research with illegally bought supplies. . . ."[47]

Although Abrams apparently did not involve himself in officially approved experiments, he did offer suggestions as to how such experiments ought to be conducted, or at least on whom. His choice: "cannabis users within a university community," because these people are closest to representing the country as a whole. Among such users Abrams has noted a generally uncertain academic record, which, however, he does not believe is ground for "serious concern." He has also noted among this group the absence of athletes and politicians and the frequent incidence of "a certain number of malcontents and weak or disturbed individuals of the kind who would be expected to join whatever protest movement was most popular at the moment."

Abrams weakens his own case for confining research to college users, especially when he emphasizes that these users generally do not get into trouble. He appears to want to stack the research so that the most favorable conclusion possible for cannabis will emerge. This is hardly the attitude of the objective researcher who simply wants to find the truth. It is not surprising that governments screen carefully those who apply to engage in research on cannabis.

It is true that some state laws have inhibited investigations by private individuals. An addition to the Health and Safety Code (11655) of the State of California,[48] for instance, served to inhibit research by individuals not associated with universities. A private laboratory, for example, was forbidden under this law to conduct investigation under a large annual grant. In this instance, which has now been corrected, it may have been true that proper investigation was impeded and that the state was over-zealous in controlling cannabis for experimental purposes because of its concern over the widespread use of cannabis. But these restrictions are far from constituting a ban on legitimate research.

By contrast with the extreme caution of some states, the National Institute of Mental Health sponsored $625,000 worth of research on cannabis in the United States in 1967 and increased the amount allotted for such purposes for 1968. Regarding premature conclusions concerning cannabis, NIMH Director Stanley Yolles says: "Advocates of legalized pot are going a little too fast without any real fundamental information about its pharmacological effects." To such persons the door to research may be indeed difficult to open. But, then, society may be better off if they do not have too ready access to the keys.

In 1969, however, the withholding of the keys seemed to bug even Dr. Yolles. "How long, oh, Lord, how long are we going to suggest new committees, new commissions and new task forces in lieu of doing something?"[49] Apparently the wait is over, although progress is not fast enough to suit some. Several congressmen have asked the NIMH for a report on pot smoking similar to the 1964 Surgeon General's report on tobacco (which the tobacco companies say proves very little about the adverse effects of tobacco). By the end of 1969, several studies were in progress. These studies, far from proving pot was "cool," made it apparent that problems connected with pot use not only existed, but could reasonably be expected to increase.

In late 1969 the NIMH funded some seventeen basic research projects and was growing its own grass to distribute to investigators. At the Worcester (Mass.) Foundation for Experimental Biology, Dr. Sumner H. Burstein discovered that THC was metabolized in the liver. Dr. Louis S. Harris, working under another NIMH grant, noted that THC inhibited microsomal (liver) enzymes that play a role in the metabolism of a number of drugs. This discovery made it possible to predict several lethal situations which might arise if pot was used with, say, barbiturates. The action of THC seems to delay liver metabolism of drugs. Thus, barbiturates and pot could accumulate in the bloodstream at possibly fatal levels, if they were used together.[50]

Another investigator, Dr. Henry Pace of the University of Mississippi, noted that evidence in animal experimentation raised again the specter that cannabis might cause teratogenesis, i.e., damage to unborn children. Pot, he said, "may cause chromosome breaks with true [unrepairable] damage."[51] Referring to another, as yet unpublished, work, Dr. Pace noted that there was already some information indicating that THC readily crosses the placenta and enters the fetus. How important this is remains to be seen.

By the beginning of 1970, several members of the Senate had introduced bills requiring an annual report to Congress on the current knowledge, including recommended legislation. The first response was submitted on January 31, 1971. To evaluate current knowledge the Senate recommended that a special committee be set up by the President and the Senate and House of Representatives to study cannabis and come up with some valid conclusions. (Such a committee has now been appointed.)

Dr. Stanley Yolles, director of the National Institute of Mental Health promised in 1970 that this information and reasonable answers should be available within two years. (Interestingly, the pro-pot forces, about this time, began an all-out effort to legalize pot . . . NOW.) To this end, the NIMH had invested, by early 1970, some 10 million dollars for projects in the biological, social and psychological sciences.[52]

Interestingly, grass is now being investigated because some feel it might have medicinal value. Supported by NIMH contracts, the Arthur D. Little Company plans to produce about 2.5 kilograms each of delta 8 THC and delta 9 THC. (Readers being offered "THC" on the street are advised to hang on to it because, *if it's real*, it's pure gold. The 5.0 grams being made for the government will cost taxpayers about $150,000.)[53]

According to Dr. Harry Pars, current investigation centers on three prime possible medicinal uses for marijuana: as an analgesic for relieving pain, to help reduce blood pressure, and as a psychotherapeutic agent, because it has been shown that under certain circumstances, pot can serve as an antidepressent and anti-anxiety drug.[54]

Thus, in two years we may have the answer. Perhaps the pro-pot people will be able to say, "We told you so," and Professor of Law John Kaplan may be found justified in advocating the immediate legalization of pot. If so, researchers will have had to establish that adverse reactions to pot are truly minimal, that there are no long-term effects, and that we have finally found a safe euphoriant. Such a finding would dispel our current fear that youths are being hurt by marijuana. From this author's standpoint, no answer could be more welcome.

Name one, just one, activity where the use of cannabis can really be proved to cause a problem.

Just one? Let's talk about driving a car. A number of very interesting people have discussed the cannabis-car accident problem. For instance, Timothy Leary, discussing the subject of consciousness expansion with Richard Alpert, said that of course the danger "is not physical. A recent editorial in the *Medical Tribune* clearly recognizes the physical safety of consciousness-expanding drugs. Nor is the danger psychological. In studies reported by Ditman, McGlothlin, Leary, Savage, up to 90 percent of subjects taking these drugs in supportive environments testify enthusiastically. The danger is not physical or psychological but social-political, for the effect of consciousness-expanding drugs will be to transform our concepts of human nature, of human potentialities, of existence. . . . The political issue involves control: 'automobile' means that the free citizen moves *his* own car in external space. Internal automobile. Auto-administration. The freedom and control of one's experiential machinery. Licensing will be necessary. You must be trained to operate. You must demonstrate your proficiency to handle consciousness-expanding drugs without danger to yourself or the public. The Fifth Freedom—the freedom to expand your own consciousness—cannot be denied without due cause."[55]

The automobile is recognized as being a dangerous, complicated piece of machinery. It is further recognized that people who are up on drugs, any drugs which distort the mind, are far from capable of operating a vehicle. License or no license, training or no training, freedom or no freedom, a man who cannot operate his thinking processes cannot be trusted to operate a complicated vehicle, particularly when the driver may endanger the rights and lives of others.

Let's take a look at the comments of another pro-cannabis leader and see what he has to say in this respect. Rosevear, in this context, is discussing crime and pointing out that people become so relaxed and happy on cannabis that, according to his observations, "it is difficult to see how the intoxicated could motivate himself adequately to go through the motions of any crime.

"Many who are under the drug's spell," he says, "find that simple acts, such as getting a glass of water, are laborious. . . .

It is difficult, if not impossible, to imagine how this type of intoxication could allow a person to write a bad check. And to suggest that this kind of intoxication could allow anyone to fulfill the complications of a murder is absurd."[56]

These observations by Rosevear are interesting. Do cannabis users drive when they are using the drug?

"In areas where police are especially diligent about arresting marijuana smokers," Rosevear says (although not in direct reply to the question stated above), "the 'pot parties' become infrequent, and the practice of clandestine smoking is considered fairly dangerous. When that happens, the occasion of smoking takes on other qualities. For instance, smoking in an automobile is considered especially safe, for if the police stop the car, the possessors merely sprinkle their pot to the wind. The driver of the car smokes if he feels he can 'handle' the situation—if his judgment will not be seriously impaired."[57]

Elsewhere Rosevear asks: "Will it be transported in cars? Will it be smoked in cars? One might be justifiably alarmed if he saw an obviously intoxicated group of people climb into an auto and head for the expressway. Whether the intoxication was due to pot, whiskey or pills makes little difference. What can be done about preventing people from driving an auto under pot's influence? The answer is maddeningly clear: absolutely nothing. Just like alcohol. Further, if a person is high and chooses to drive, and is stopped by the police, he can deny knowledge of marijuana and there is no way to prove otherwise.

"Some people say that if they're high and have to drive, they must concentrate hard on the driving, and all the fun part of the high is used up. Others," Rosevear continues, "who have smoked pot for a long time, drive as carefully high as not. Further, if the drug's use is as widespread as opinions often indicate, then the lack of auto accidents attributable to it might point out that the smokers are using unusually sound judgment."

"However," Rosevear continues, "unlike alcohol drinkers, most pot smokers studiously avoid driving while high. Nevertheless, he who is compelled to try and transcend his reality by some other spirit than alcohol is certainly not 'one of the boys.' A primitive, subtle taboo acts as a definite segregator."[58]

The matter of driving while on cannabis is getting to be an international problem. According to Drs. Dana Farnsworth and

Curtis Pound of the Harvard University Health Service, "A dangerous effect from marijuana is the slowing of reflexes. Since marijuana also causes distortion of reality, particularly of the sense of time, the drug is frequently a cause of automobile accidents."[59] There's more to it than that. Check the remarks previously made concerning the effects of even mild cannabis use on vision, the reference to the flashback phenomena, and the production of visual and auditory hallucinations, and the picture begins to take form.

The fallacies in Rosevear's arguments are clear: on the one hand, he acknowledges that marijuana incapacitates the user for many normal and simple activities; on the other, he ignores the obvious dangers of driving while under the influence of the drug. The testimony of the doctors of the Harvard Health Service suggests, moreover, that there is a record of cannabis-associated automobile accidents. And there is other testimony of the same kind.

In Mexico and in Cuba, says Dr. Pablo Wolff, "numerous traffic accidents . . . are attributed to the use made of the herb by some drivers, especially of buses! This is possible due to its influence on the perception both of time and space, which prevents the correct localization of objects."[60] In France, according to a statement made by the French delegation before the United Nations Commission on Narcotic Drugs in 1963,[61] concern was expressed over the high rate of road accidents that appeared to be attributable to the abuse of drugs and "particularly cannabis." In a report to the same Commission in 1965, on this general question, it was noted that persons using heroin, morphine, and similar drugs are not likely to be using motor vehicles for a variety of reasons but that:

> An exception may lie in the case of cannabis, which is more readily available and more widely used in several parts of the world. Light indulgence in cannabis may create euphoria without a desire to curtail all physical activity as mentioned in the case of more potent drugs.[62]

Agreeing, though he has for years advocated a repeal of the current marijuana laws, Sociologist Alfred Lindesmith makes this observation:

"No one, of course, recommends the use of marijuana nor does anyone deny that there are evil effects and consequences associated with using it. The fact that the use of marijuana is outlawed, for example, means that it is often obtained through association with unsavory types, often used in an underworld environment, and the user takes the risk of criminal prosecution. *It is also undeniable that marijuana intoxication may sometimes lead to automobile accidents and to irresponsible or criminal acts*" [italics added].[63]

In his 387-page attempt to seemingly discredit much if not most of what has been thus far observed negatively about cannabis, Professor of Law John Kaplan makes a number of interesting observations concerning the drug and driving. He attacks available material, raising a question of doubt and indicating that if there is not incontrovertable evidence that the drug is bad, there seems to be justification for legalization. He implies that if we don't legalize marijuana and treat the marijuana-using driver as we do the alcohol-using driver, we are not being consistent.[64]

Professor Kaplan, seemingly in an attempt to be fair, implies that if alcohol is legal, then pot should be legal too. He does not adequately pursue the alternative course, namely that since both are bad, neither should be legal. The Professor uses some interesting logic in attempting to prove his point. His implication is that if the driver were stable then a given drug would not be a problem. He seems to ignore the question of *abusive* use of either alcohol or pot, which is really the only major point of concern (along with unexpected adverse reactions to either drug, but particularly to cannabis—i.e., flashbacks, bummers, uncontrollable paranoia, psychotomimetic reactions) by noting that, "contrary to common belief, their primary cause [accidents] is not simple social drinking."[65] This is hardly revelatory. An alcoholic drink or two, unless one is unusually susceptible or it is an unusually potent drink, will probably have little significant effect on the driver, particularly if he has the common sense to give it a chance to wear off before driving. The same can be said of a toke on a joint, although many simply refuse to consider this possibility.

Kaplan makes another observation: "It has been shown dramatically that, to an extent not previously realized, it is the alcoholic who becomes involved in the serious accidents."[66] This comment is significant because it shows the difference in reasoning between attorneys and physicians. Doctors, who have treated alcoholics and have tried to repair the carnage caused by their out-of-control activities, have known for years that it is the alcoholic (specifically the alcoholic who gets drunk) that is primarily involved in accidents where the use of alcohol and its resultant automobile accident rate is concerned. They may have had no double blind studies, they may have had no "proof" in the sense that an attorney would accept. But they were certain this was so.

Mr. Kaplan does a much better job of casting doubt on alcohol's safety. He notes the work of Dr. Julian Waller of the University of Vermont Medical School, who estimates that while alcoholics in the State of California account for 6.5 percent of the driver population and for ten percent of the total mileage, various studies estimate that they are involved in between forty-one and sixty-two percent of the known traffic crashes.[67] Another study of Michigan drivers is cited: of seventy-two fatal collisions, forty percent of the drivers were chronic alcoholics, and ten percent more were problem drinkers.[68] He cites a third study of ninety-six drivers showing that thirty-seven percent of those responsible for fatal crashes were alcoholics who had been imbibing at the time of the crash.[69]

(One could argue, since the above represents material impressive to Mr. Kaplan, that Dr. Waller's statistics are only estimates and thus invalid, that the drivers were not at fault because they were not in control of their senses due to the effects of the alcohol, and that the drug was not at fault because it was the personality of the driver and not the drug per se that was the primary causative factor, and thus neither was at fault since one was interdependent on the other.)

Mr. Kaplan now introduces another deviation from the point. "Moving on," he says, "to the laboratory data on marijuana, we can say that if driving is a complex task, the chances are it will be adversely affected by marijuana use."[70] Choosing not to attack the drug, he directs the heat toward its associated item—in this case driving. "The problem is that it is not at all clear that the vast majority of driving situations—even emergencies—are, in this sense, complex tasks." Apparently, driving under the influence of marijuana can be considered very dangerous, or not at all dangerous, depending on how complex one feels the task of driving ("even in emergencies") is.

Mr. Kaplan further notes the comment of Irvin Lang (who has served as chief counsel for the New York State Narcotic Addiction Control Commission), who argues that society has the right to ban marijuana in contrast to alcohol, since we can test the alcoholic and "prove" his drug involvement, whereas a similar test is not available for marijuana. Mr. Kaplan calls Mr. Lang's comments merely an afterthought, since the marijuana laws were passed with things other than driving in mind, and "the very penalties we attach to marijuana offenses show that the driving problem is not the real reason for marijuana criminalization."[71] Mr. Kaplan is correct in this. The reason society took its rigid stand against marijuana was that the ruling majority decided the drug did not belong in our culture. Having reached that decision, the society established laws that remained effective until a younger generation with drug interests of its own revolted against the laws.

Mr. Kaplan then refers to a recent study performed by Crancer et al,[72] allying himself with the study's tentative conclusions that subjects high on pot perform better behind the wheel than do those on alcohol. Many aspects of the Crancer study are open to serious debate, but the researchers should be commended for attempting to investigate the question, and for publishing all of their findings, pro and con. But less praise is due those who have tried to extrapolate from the findings conclusions never intended by the researchers. Crancer et al did *not* conclude that marijuana use does not impair driving, or that it is safer than alcohol for those behind the wheel. Unfortunately, others have not hesitated to use the study to "back up" those conclusions.

Here is what happened: Crancer et al set out to measure the effects of a "normal social marijuana high" on driving. From earlier experiments, Crancer had concluded that a driving simulator test is more valid in measuring a driver's ability than is an actual behind-the-wheel road test. Accordingly, he seated each of his volunteer subjects at a console mockup of a recent-model car, and projected on a screen in front of them films simulating varying road conditions. Theoretically, the test can evaluate a subject's driving performance in terms of accident rates.

Comparing the performance of drivers intoxicated on marijuana and alcohol, the authors concluded that: "Marijuana-wise subjects experiencing a social marijuana high accumulated significantly more speedometer errors on the simulator than under control conditions, while there was no significant difference in accelerator, brake, signal, steering and total errors. The same subject, intoxicated from alcohol, accumulated significantly more accelerator, brake, signal, speedometer and total errors than under control conditions, while there was no significant difference in steering errors." This is how the press reported the conclusions: "Marijuana fails to mar driving in simulator."[73] Let's see what really happened.

Seven girls and twenty-nine men with a mean age of twenty-three years were tested after first being cleared for reasonable mental and physical health. They were examined in the simulator for approximately a half hour under three sets of conditions. First, they were given two joints and permitted to determine when they were high. *It was the subjects' evaluation that set the endpoint.* All youths were experienced marijuana smokers with a high preference for pot over alcohol, and all had been smoking pot on a minimum basis for at least twice a month for the past six months. Considering Axelrod's study showing the buildup of cannabinol in the body for a period of seven to eight days following the last smoking or ingestion, it may not be unreasonable to question if some residual effects from previous smoking might have been present when the test began. The subjects tested at a given time for driving under the influence of marijuana were allowed to smoke the pot for a half hour, then given the simulator test a half hour later as they were really beginning to get the first glow of the trip.

When the subjects were tested for alcohol, they were given approximately 112 cc. of 95 percent alcohol (equivalent to eight ounces of 86 proof liquor). As pharmacologist H. Kalant has noted,[74] "This is far more than the amount required for a normal social alcohol "high" and would probably produce a peak blood alcohol concentration of about 0.15 percent." Crancer, however, was hitting at a peak of 0.1 percent alcohol *and used standard breathalyzer readings to be certain his subjects were adequately bombed on booze; he did not let them set their own levels as he did with pot users.* Further, no allowance was made for the fact that alcohol and pot seem to be synergistic, and if residual cannabinol was in the system of the subject now taking alcohol, the effects would be augmentive.

The third trip was a control, during which the subjects were allowed to determine when they felt normal physiologically and psychologically. No drugs were used during this time of the experiment. Interestingly, as Kalant has noted, the total group was favorably disposed toward pot over alcohol. If they determined not to perform well on booze they could have bombed the test by doing poorly on the alcohol section. This could have been unconsciously accomplished out of bias as well as directly due to intent.

Another and perhaps the most critical point was apparently never considered: the ability to crash and/or to maintain when up on pot. If one is under stress and high, he can crash (come down) and act quite normal during the time he is under duress. Later, he may go up again or not, depending on circumstances. Additionally, a person who has taken pot and is under stress may maintain (ride out the effects) while he needs to, then relax later and trip. This means that under driving simulator conditions where he had to maintain, he could. It says nothing about how he would do when the pressure was off and he was driving along under usual road conditions.

This author has no question that this ability to crash and/or maintain at will is real and can be performed by most pot smokers if they are not too high or not having adverse reactions. The same does not seem to be so with alcohol. This point has been laboratory tested, for those requiring "proof", by Caldwell et al, and reported in the December 1969 issue of *Perceptual and Motor Skills.* "The researchers," said *Science News,* "noted that some of the marijuana smokers claimed an ability to turn off the drug high when taking the tests." In this instance the users were being given tests of auditory and visual acuity. "This ability," say the researchers, "if it is a real one, raises the issue whether such tests (which comprise the majority of those used in studies reported to date) are valid indicants of the marijuana experience or simply measures of an interesting concomitant of the drug's effect, namely, the ability to respond normally at will."[75]

Kaplan,[76] referring to the fact that pot-prejudiced subjects could well bomb the alcohol section of the experiment, noted that Crancer failed to use a control group of alcohol-prejudiced people in a concomittant experiment. He further notes that it does not necessarily follow that, just because a drug has no apparent effect on performance in a simulated task, it will have no effect on performance of the actual task. Crancer agrees. His final conclusion is that "Further study is needed to determine the applicability of these results to actual driving."[77]

Interestingly, the HEW report to Congress also has some observations to make on the Crancer study. On pages 11 and 12 of the report we find this: "One widely reported finding using a driver simulator was that the performance of marijuana using drivers was equal on the average to that of a non-intoxicated control group. It is, however, important to note that this was based on a single study of intoxicated drivers under test conditions that might be expected to be highly motivating. In addition, half the drivers in the experimental group did more poorly than did the control group. This suggests that the ability to compensate for the effects of marijuana—to suppress the 'high'— may differ markedly from individual to individual. The relevance of this work to more typical driving conditions is not known."

"It is noteworthy," HEW continues, "that in another series of studies not directly concerned with driving, marijuana intoxicated subjects consistently answered, 'No!' when asked, 'Do you think you could drive a car now?' Preliminary results of a study of attention skills believed to be among the best predictors of actual driving performance have shown performance decrements under marijuana use similar to those found when drivers have consumed moderate amounts of alcohol."

Although no other reports were noted in Kaplan's evaluation, Crancer's study is not the only one to investigate the effects of cannabis on driving. In May, 1969, Dr. Theodore James of South Africa also noted the numerous problems of altered perception, judgment, coordination, and memory which may endanger the cannabis-using driver. "I know of no conviction for dangerous driving while 'under the influence of dagga [cannabis], but the reasons for this are pretty obvious. It is difficult enough to bring in a verdict of dangerous driving while under the influence of alcohol, without thrusting this infinitely more difficult proof upon the shoulders of the public prosecutor."[78]

James then proceeds to discuss the many facets of cannabis effects known to students of the drug, noting, "It is not uncommon for the effects of alcohol and [cannabis] to be compared, but this comparison can be faulted. The likeness is superficial only. Alcohol induces a contraction of the personality and is essentially a depressant and not a stimulant, whereas dagga is curiously enough both stimulant and depressant but in different areas. Dagga does produce drowsiness and even sleep if the smoker be left undisturbed but it is also capable of an astonishing augmentation of physical strength. What is known about the time of onset and the duration of these pleasurable sensations is significant where driving a car is concerned. To drink alcohol to the blood level of carelessness is not necessarily a long undertaking and if this is followed by the drinker driving a car, then he does so with all his senses blunted as well as with a degree of defective muscular coordination. Alcohol per se does not stimulate agreeable sensory perception, which dagga does, but by removing inhibitions it apparently expands the drinker's personality. Dagga in moderation need not incoordinate the neuromuscular system but it does falsify impressions to render them enjoyable: and this is where dagga and the driver become a dangerous combination. But dagga plus alcohol in the driver is even worse."[79]

James' comments so adequately fill the gaps in the Crancer report that further comparison should not be necessary. Even Kaplan, after reviewing the Crancer report, seems to have misgivings about the situation, and comments about three other studies also done on marijuana-using drivers.[80] In each of the cases involved in these studies, the marijuana-using subjects seemed to have a significantly higher number of traffic violations, but not a greater number of actual accidents. Kaplan explains these increased violations on the theory that marijuana users, by the very nature of their drug use, reveal themselves to be less law-abiding people. Perhaps, he muses, they would be more likely to violate the traffic laws in situations where safety was not really at stake. Kaplan does not indicate how he obtained the impression that such users could validly distinguish between safe and unsafe conditions.

"The fact that the number of accidents was no greater takes on added significance because of the many studies showing that comparably heavy drinkers are involved in considerably more accidents than is the population at large." Then he notes, ". . . we can reach no firm conclusion from this because it is possible that the marijuana users did not use their drug so heavily or else did not drive under its influence sufficiently often so that a statistical difference would be noted. Such studies on driving records are, after all," Kaplan concludes, "very crude indications of a likelihood of serious accidents."[81]

People will use cannabis anyway, so shouldn't it be legal?

This argument could be applied to many things, from heroin to prostitution, to anything that human beings have found a use or abuse for. We might as well argue for the legalization of murder, since people have always done it. The only consistent philosophic position that could condone cannabis on these grounds is anarchy.

It doesn't hurt anybody, does it?

This we know is false. What about "bummers," "bad trips," and "flipouts"? What about the amotivational syndrome and the cannabis dropout? The fact is that cannabis does hurt some people. Until we know a great deal more about it and about how to control it, it is rather callous to allow its indiscriminate use by persons who may indeed be hurt by it.

Isn't cannabis lauded in literature?

So is a great deal else that may not be very good—incest, sadism, or lying on beds of spikes. Besides it is necessary to pick and choose one's literature. Especially today, with the cult of the grotesque, the sadistic, the perverse, it is possible to find literary enthusiasm for almost anything. Literary praise, like most other kinds, must still be measured against the standards and beliefs which shape the literature. A cannabis enthusiast may also be a writer, and may write glowingly of the drug, but it is extremely doubtful that his drug enthusiasm came from literature itself. Rather the drug insinuated itself into his writing. The whole weight of Western literature in any case can hardly be said to fall on the pro-cannabis side.

Can't people be addicted to milk?

To speak conversationally, yes; to speak scientifically, no. People can be inordinately fond of a great many things, and careless usage in speech will often lead them to speak of being "addicted" to some of these things. As addiction is defined scientifically in regard to narcotics, mere extreme fondness is not sufficient. Even "dependence," as it is used in regard to cannabis and other drugs, is too strong a word to apply to a strong liking for something. You deceive yourself if you imagine that casually expressed "addiction" to milk, or chocolate, or cherry tomatoes is the same thing as addiction to a drug.

Smoking pot doesn't cause cancer . . .?

That's a relief! But how do you know? Smoking tobacco doesn't cause cancer according to the American tobacco manufacturing companies. Are you sure when you inhale all that steaming hot smoke into the tender alveoli of your lungs—smoke that is loaded with contaminants that may make smog look like steam—that your tissue will blandly cough it back with a smile, saying, "It's only pot; it can't harm you!" Ever hold a reefer to your lips? Hot! Particularly the "roach." Do you know why so many cigar and pipe smokers get cancer of the lips? Heat and pressure. You don't get much pressure from a joint. But you surely get heat.

Isn't it true that Weil et al recently stated that marijuana failed to produce adverse effects on human subjects? How do you explain this?

The best explanation lies in reading the original report, rather than accepting loose interpretations of incomplete journalistic accounts. In its proper perspective this report is quite important; distorted, it can be very misleading.

Critically, the study was very brief. Nine cannabis-naive subjects (including one who openly stated his desire to "prove" pot was harmless) and eight chronic smokers were tested in four three-hour sessions. This sort of short-run, small sample study cannot, of course, be expected to produce any conclusions concerning the possibility of ultimate deleterious effects. Recognizing the limited time involved with the experiment, one would expect, and the investigators did find, that the use of marijuana in this setting produced few if any adverse reactions in the subjects.

The study did show that marijuana consumption is safe enough to be used on human subjects in the laboratory, in studying the effects of the drugs contained in cannabis. It demonstrated that not only did drug naive (inexperienced) subjects often lack strong subjective reactions to the drug, but that they also differed in other responses, compared to those observed in chronic smokers. Superficial and pro-marijuana accounts tended to ignore or minimize the report's finding that pot-naive smokers in the study did show impaired intellectual and psychomotor responses, although chronic pot smokers did not. The study also demonstrated that certain generally known physical effects do occur, and that the trip in this setting could be expected to last about three hours.[82]

Needless to say, the most often quoted part of the report was the statement that there were no adverse reactions among the subjects in the study. The authors later attempted to qualify this statement for the press by noting the limitations of the study, but their attempt lacked the news value of the original report, and thus received little publicity.

notes

Notes for pages 1–16

1. from cannabis to marijuana

1. H. Maclagan, "Extract of Cannabis Indica," *American Druggist,* July 18, 1884, pp. 121–122.
2. *Marijuana and Health,* A Report to the Congress from the Secretary, Department of Health, Education and Welfare, January 31, 1971, p. 21.
3. Raphael Mechoulam, "Marijuana Chemistry," *Science,* June 5, 1970, pp. 1159–1166.
4. *Marijuana and Health, op. cit.,* pp. 105–106.
5. Jared Tinklenberg, personal communication.
6. *Marijuana and Health, op. cit.,* p. 107.
7. *Ibid.,* p. 21.
8. *Marijuana Newsletter,* quoted in John Rosevear, *Pot: A Handbook of Marijuana* (New York: University Books, 1967), p. 42.
9. *Ibid.,* p. 44.
10. Vincent DePaul Lynch, personal communication.
11. "WPA Workers Assigned to Marijuana Eradication," *J.A.M.A.,* August 8, 1936, p. 437.
12. "Marijuana Grown on Vacant Lots," *J.A.M.A.,* September 14, 1935, p. 891.
13. "Sawtoothed," *The New Yorker,* August 11, 1951, pp. 18–19.
14. Rosevear, *op. cit.,* p. 46.
15. H. J. Wollner et al, "Isolation of a Physiologically Active Tetrahydrocannabinol from Cannabis Sativa Resin," *J. Amer. Chem. Soc.,* January 1942, pp. 26–29.

2. the history of the weed

1. Shen Nung, quoted in Norman Taylor, *Narcotics: Nature's Dangerous Drugs* (New York: Dell Publishing Co., 1963), p. 11.
2. E. Bretschneider, "Botanicum Sinicum: Mareria Medica of the Ancient Chinese," *J. North China Branch Shanghai Roy. Asiatic Soc.,* 1890–1891, p. 66, and 1894–1895, p. 378, quoted in Robert P. Walton, *Marijuana: America's New Drug Problem* (Philadelphia: J. B. Lippincott, 1938), p. 2.
3. S. Julian, "Substance Anesthétique Employée en Chine, dans le Commencement du III Siècle de Notre Ere, pour Paralyser Momentanément la Sensibilité," *Compt. Rend. Acad. Sci. Paris,* 1894, pp. 195–198, quoted in Walton, *op. cit.,* p. 2.
4. *Indian Hemp Drugs Com-*

mission Report, Government Printing Office, 1893–1894, p. 250, quoted in Walton, *op. cit.,* p. 5.

5. J. Campbell Oman, *The Mystics: Ascetics and Saints of India* (London: T. F. Unwin, 1903), quoted in Walton, *op. cit.,* p. 5.

6. R. N. Chopra, *Indigenous Drugs of India* (Calcutta: Art Press, 1933), quoted in Walton, *op. cit.,* p. 3.

7. *Indian Hemp Drugs Commission Report, op. cit.,* quoted in Walton, *op. cit.,* p. 3.

8. *Ibid.,* p. 250.

9. League of Nations, Geneva, 1928–30, Advisory Committee on Traffic in Opium and Dangerous Drugs, p. 12, quoted in Walton, *op. cit.,* p. 4.

10. Homer, *The Odyssey,* Book IV (Chicago: Great Books of the Western World, Encyclopedia Britannica, Inc., 1952), p. 220.

11. Herodotus (English translation by Carey, 1848), IV, Chapters 74–75, and I, Chapter 202, quoted in Walton, *op. cit.,* p. 8.

12. R. F. Burton, trans., *The Book of the Thousand Nights and a Night* (Benares: Kamashastra Society, 1885), X, p. 91, quoted in Walton, *op. cit.,* p. 8.

13. Pliny, quoted in Walton, *op. cit.,* p. 8.

14. Dioscorides, quoted in Walton, *op. cit.,* p. 8.

15. Caludius Galen, *Galeni Librorum* (Venice, 1597), De Alimentorum Facultatibus, Cap. 34, 15 F. Secunda Classis, quoted in Walton, *op. cit.,* p. 8.

16. Walton, *op. cit.,* p. 10.

17. *Ibid.*

18. Sylvester DeSacy, *Chrestomathie Arabe* (1826), II, pp. 138–143, quoted in Walton, *op. cit.,* p. 12.

19. Philip K. Hitti, "The Assassins," in *The Book of Grass,* edited by George Andrews (New York:

Grove Press, Inc., 1967), pp. 23–25.

20. *Ibid.,* p. 24.

21. Joel Fort, *The Pleasure Seekers* (Indianapolis: Bobbs-Merrill Co., 1969), p. 103.

22. Jerry Mandel, "Hashish, Assassins, and the Love of God," *Issues in Criminology,* 1966, pp. 149–156.

23. John Kaplin, *Marijuana, The New Prohibition* (New York: The World Publishing Co., 1970).

24. Don M. Casto, III, "Marijuana and the Assassins—An Etymological Investigation," *Int. J. of the Addictions,* December 1970, pp. 747–755.

25. Gelett Burgess, *The Oxford Dictionary of Quotations,* 2d ed. (London: Oxford University Press, 1955), p. 100.

26. Akin Davies, "Nigeria Whispers," in George Andrews (Ed.), *The Book of Grass* (New York: Grove Press, 1967), p. 153.

27. John Rosevear, *Pot: A Handbook of Marijuana* (New York: University Books, 1967), p. 73.

28. Louis S. Goodman and Alfred Gilman, *The Pharmacological Basis of Therapeutics,* 2d ed. (New York: The Macmillan Co., 1955), p. 174.

29. R. E. L. Masters and J. Houston, *Varieties of Psychedelic Experience* (New York: Holt, Rinehart, and Winston, 1966), p. 37.

30. Rosevear, *op. cit.,* p. 146.

31. Jacques J. Moreau, "Du Hachich et de l'Alienation Mentale," quoted in *The Drug Experience,* edited by David Ebin (New York: The Orion Press, 1961), p. 4.

32. David Ebin (Ed.), *The Drug Experience, ibid.,* pp. 4–5.

33. Ritz-Hugh Ludlow, quoted in Allen Geller and Maxwell Boas, *The Drug Beat* (New York: Cowles Book Co., Inc., 1969), p. 17.

34. *Ibid.,* pp. 19–20.

35. Rosevear, *op. cit.,* p. 24.

3. the world of marijuana

1. Louis S. Goodman and Alfred Gilman, *The Pharmacological Basis of Therapeutics*, 2d ed. (New York: The Macmillan Co., 1955), p. 174.

2. Jerry Cohen, "Marijuana: Views Collide," *Los Angeles Times*, December 4, 1967.

3. David Smith, "Testimony before Assemblyman Pete Wilson," Los Angeles, California, March 1, 1968.

4. Nathan B. Eddy, quoted in "Marijuana Controls," *Los Angeles Times*, January 19, 1968.

5. Joel Fort, quoted in "When Patients Ask Your Views on Marijuana," *Patient Care*, December 1967, p. 12.

6. "The Marijuana Problem," *Newsweek*, July 24, 1967.

7. "Marijuana: Millions of Turned on Users," *Life*, July 7, 1967.

8. David Popoff, "Feedback on Drugs," *Psychology Today*, April 1970, p. 52.

9. J. Fred Shick et al, "Use of Marijuana in the Haight-Ashbury Subculture," *J. of Psychedelic Drugs*, Fall 1968, p. 58.

10. J. Fred Shick et al, *op. cit.*, quoted in David E. Smith, *The New Social Drug* (Englewood Cliffs, N.J.: Prentice-Hall, 1970), p. 44.

11. Shick et al, *op. cit.*, p. 57.

12. Popoff, *op. cit.*, p. 51.

13. Popoff, *op. cit.*, p. 52.

14. Sidney V. Cohen, *Uncanny Power of the Hallucinogens: The Drug Takers* (New York: Time-Life Books, 1965), p. 102.

15. "Hippies' Dream Farm," *Time*, September 8, 1967, p. 17.

16. "Parents Admit to Giving 5 Children LSD, Marijuana," *Los Angeles Times*, January 30, 1967.

17. "Teen Party Raided and Dope Seized," *Los Angeles Times*, November 13, 1967.

18. *Marijuana and Health*, A Report to the Congress from the Secretary, Department of Health, Education and Welfare, January 31, 1971, p. 5.

19. "A Joint/or Isn't It?" ad in the *Los Angeles Free Press*, January 26, 1968, p. 25.

20. "Girl 15, Arrested for Marijuana Sale," *Los Angeles Times*, September 23, 1967.

21. "Fake Marijuana Sales Jail Youth," *Los Angeles Times*, September 29, 1967.

22. Norman Vincent Peale, *Look*, November 7, 1958.

23. George Reasons, "Johnny, 16, Tells His Success Story as a Marijuana Salesman," *Los Angeles Times*, February 24, 1963.

24. John Rosevear, *Pot: A Handbook of Marijuana* (New York: University Books, 1967), pp. 66–67.

4. the pleasant effects

1. "Pop Drugs: The High as a Way of Life," *Time*, September 26, 1969, p. 68.

2. *Ibid.*, p. 69.

3. Andrew T. Weil, Norman E. Zinberg and Judith M. Nelsen, "Clinical and Psychological Effects of Marijuana in Man," *Science*, December 13, 1968, p. 1237.

4. *Ibid.*, p. 1236.

5. "Correspondence: The Grass and the Fuzz," *Playboy*, February 1968, p. 42.

6. "Letters to the Editor," *U.S. News & World Report*, August 7, 1967.

7. *Marijuana and Health*, A Report to the Congress from the Secretary, Department of Health, Education and Welfare, January 31, 1971, p. 9.

8. *Ibid.*, p. 42.

9. P. A. L. Chapple, "Cannabis, A Toxic and Dangerous Substance—A Study of Eighty Takers," *Br. J. Addiction*, August 1966, p. 269.

10. "Suicide's Tape Tells Why He Chose Death," *Los Angeles Times*, February 22, 1970, p. 2.

11. C. W. M. Wilson, *Adolescent Drug Dependence* (London: Pergamon Press, 1968), p. 119.

12. *Ibid.*

13. Jared Tinklenberg, personal communication.

14. Wilson, *op. cit.*, p. 119.

15. John Kaplan, *Marijuana—The New Prohibition* (New York: World Publishing Co., 1970), p. 68.

16. Letter from Jared Tinklenberg, December 29, 1969, quoted in Kaplan, *op. cit.*, p. 68.

17. Norman Zinberg and Andrew Weil, "The Effects of Marijuana on Human Beings," *New York Times Magazine*, May 18, 1969, p. 28, quoted in Kaplan, *op. cit.*, p. 56.

18. L. E. Hollister, "Marijuana in Man: 3 Years Later," *Science*, April 2, 1971, pp. 21–29.

19. R. Adams et al, "Structure of Cannabinol. III Synthesis of Cannabinol," *J. of the Amer. Chem. Soc.*, 1940, pp. 2204–2207.

20. *Marijuana and Health, op. cit.*, p. 22.

21. *Ibid.*, p. 23.

22. *Ibid.*, p. 2.

23. *Ibid.*, p. 27.

24. Marshman and Gibbons, quoted in *Marijuana and Health, op. cit.*, p. 28.

25. *Marijuana and Health, op. cit.*, p. 28.

26. Sidney Cohen, quoted in *Time, op. cit.*, p. 69.

27. *Time, op. cit.*, p. 69.

28. Howard Becker, "Becoming a Marijuana User," *American Journal of Sociology*, November 1953, p. 235.

29. John Kaplan, *op. cit.*, p. 69.

30. Frederick T. Melges et al, "Marijuana and Temporal Disintegration," *Science*, May 29, 1970, p. 1118.

31. Charles Baudelaire, *The Essence of Laughter and Other Essays* and *Journals and Letters*, quoted in *The Drug Experience*, edited by David Ebin (New York: The Orion Press, 1961), p. 19.

32. *Ibid.*, p. 20.

33. *Ibid.*, p. 20.

34. *Ibid.*, p. 21.

35. *Ibid.*, p. 21.

36. *Ibid.*, p. 22.

37. *Ibid.*, p. 27.

38. *Ibid.*, p. 28.

39. Jack S. Margolis and Richard Clorfene, *A Child's Garden of Grass* (North Hollywood, Calif.: Contact Books, 1969), p. 146.

40. *Ibid.*

41. *Ibid.*, p. 32.

42. *Ibid.*, p. 33.

43. *Ibid.*, p. 34.

44. *Ibid.*, p. 34.

45. Sheldon Cholst, "Notes on the Use of Hashish," in *The Marihuana Papers*, edited by David Solomon (Indianapolis: Bobbs-Merrill, 1966), p. 221.

46. *Ibid.*, p. 217.

47. *Ibid.*, p. 217.

48. *Ibid.*, p. 218.

49. *Ibid.*, p. 219.

50. *Ibid.*, p. 219.

51. Baudelaire, *op. cit.*, p. 22.

52. Coles Phinizy, "Bora-Bora: A Paradise on a Precipice," *Sports Illustrated*, January 15, 1968, p. 25.

53. *Marijuana and Health, op. cit.*, p. 8.

54. John Rosevear, *Pot: A*

Handbook of Marijuana (New York: University Books, 1967), p. 97.

55. *Ibid.*, pp. 86–87.

56. Edward R. Bloomquist, "Marijuana: Social Benefit or Social Detriment?" *Calif. Med.*, May 1967, pp. 346–353.

5. physical effects

1. John Rosevear, *Pot: A Handbook of Marijuana* (New York: University Books, 1967), pp. 81–82.

2. Erich Goode, "Marijuana and the Politics of Reality," *Journal of Health and Social Behaviour*, June 1969, pp. 83–94.

3. "Change, Yes — Upheaval, No," *Life*, January 8, 1971, pp. 21–30.

4. Goode, *op. cit.*, p. 86.

5. *Ibid.*

6. John Kaplan, *Marijuana— The New Prohibition* (New York: World Publishing Co., 1970).

7. David E. Smith and Carter Mehl, "An Analysis of Marijuana Toxicity," in David E. Smith, *The New Social Drug* (Englewood Cliffs, N.J.: Prentice-Hall, Inc., 1970), pp. 63–64.

8. *Ibid.*, p. 64.

9. C. W. M. Wilson, *Adolescent Drug Dependence* (London: Pergamon Press, 1968), p. 118.

10. Norman Zinberg and Andrew Weil, "The Effects of Marijuana on Human Beings," quoted in Kaplan, *op. cit.*, p. 57.

11. Howard Becker, "Becoming a Marijuana User," *American Journal of Sociology*, November 1953, pp. 235–242.

12. Dan MacLean, personal communication.

13. H. S. Gaskill, "Marijuana, an Intoxicant," *Am. J. Psychiatry*, September 1945, pp. 202–204.

14. S. Allentuck and K. M. Bowman, "The Psychiatric Aspects of Marijuana Intoxication," *Am. J.*

Psychiatry, September 1962, pp. 248–251.

15. R. Adams, "Marijuana," *N. Y. Acad. Med.*, November 1942, pp. 705–730.

16. L. E. Hollister, R. K. Richards and B. A. Gillespie, "Comparison of Tetrahydrocannabinol and Synhexyl in Man," *Clin. Pharmac. Ther.*, November-December 1968, pp. 783–791.

17. Andrew T. Weil, Norman E. Zinberg and Judith Nelsen, "Clinical and Psychological Effects of Marihuana in Man," *Science*, December 13, 1968, pp. 1234–1242.

18. H. Mohan and G. C. Sood, "Conjugate Deviation of the Eyes Following Cannabis Indica Intoxication," *Brit. J. of Opth.*, March 1964, pp. 160–161.

19. David Smith, *op. cit.*, p. 65.

20. A. Bouhuys et al, "Byssinosis in Hemp Workers," *Arch. Environ. Health*, April 1967, pp. 533–544.

21. A. Barbero and R. Flores, "Dust Disease in Hemp Workers," *Arch. Environ. Health*, April 1967, pp. 529–532.

22. Weil et al, *op. cit.*, p. 1237.

23. F. Ames, "A Clinical and Metabolic Study of Acute Intoxication with Cannabis Sativa and Its Role in the Model Psychosis," *J. Ment. Sci.*, October 1958, pp. 972–999.

24. H. Isbell et al, "Effects of (–)-Delta-9-Transtetrahydrocannabinol in Man," *Psychopharmacologia* (Berlin), pp. 184–188.

25. Gaskill, *op. cit.*, pp. 202–204.

26. Ames, *op. cit.*, pp. 972–999.

27. Jared Tinklenberg, personal communication.

28. Ames, *op. cit.*, pp. 972–999.

29. Jack Margolis and Richard Clorfene, *A Child's Garden of Grass* (North Hollywood, Calif.: Contact Books, 1969), p. 146.

30. C. J. Miras, "Experience with Chronic Hashish Smokers," quoted in J. R. Wittenborn, *Drugs and Youth* (Springfield, Ill.: C. C. Thomas, 1969), p. 193.

31. M. C. Kew, "Possible Hepatotoxicity of Cannabis," *Lancet,* March 15, 1969, p. 578.

32. A. H. Henderson and David J. Pugsley, "Collapse after Intravenous Injection of Hashish," *Brit. Med. J.,* July 27, 1968, pp. 229–230.

33. Allen B. King and David L. Cowen, "Effects of Intravenous Injection of Marijuana," *J.A.M.A.,* October 27, 1969, pp. 724–725.

34. Nancy E. Gary and Victor Keylon, "Intravenous Administration of Marihuana," *J.A.M.A.,* January 19, 1970.

35. Jerome H. Jaffe, quoted in Louis S. Goodman and Alfred Gilman, *The Pharmacological Basis of Therapeutics* (New York: The Macmillan Co., 1970), p. 299.

36. S. Deakin, "Death from Taking of Indian Hemp," *Indian Medical Gaz.,* 1880, p. 71.

37. R. P. Walton, *Marijuana: America's New Drug Problem* (Philadelphia: J. B. Lippincott, 1938), p. 126.

38. A. Heyndrickx, Ch. Scheiris and P. Schepens, "Toxicological Study of a Fatal Intoxication by Man Due to Cannabis Smoking," *J. Pharmacie. Belique.,* July-August 1969, pp. 371–376.

39. *Marijuana and Health,* A Report to the Congress from the Secretary, Department of Health, Education and Welfare, January 31, 1971, p. 60.

40. P. A. Martin, "Cannabis and Chromosomes," *Lancet,* February 15, 1969, p. 370.

41. R. L. Neu et al, "Cannabis and Chromosomes," *Lancet,* March 29, 1969, p. 675.

42. T. V. N. Persaud and A. C. Ellington, "Cannabis in Early Pregnancy," *Lancet,* December 16, 1967, p. 1306.

43. T. V. N. Persaud and A. C. Ellington, "Teratogenic Activity of Cannabis Resin," *Lancet,* August 17, 1968, pp. 406–407.

44. W. F. Geber and L. C. Schramm, "Effect of Marijuana Extract on Fetal Hamsters and Rabbits," *Toxic. Appl. Pharmacol.,* March 1969, pp. 276–282.

45. Harris Isbell, "Effects on Infant Breastfed by Marijuana-smoking Mother," *J.A.M.A.,* July 6, 1970.

46. C. J. Miras, quoted in *Hashish: Its Chemistry and Pharmacology,* Ciba Foundation Study Group, No. 21 (London: Churchill, 1965), pp. 37–47.

47. G. Joachimoglu and C. J. Miras, "Study of the Pharmacology of Hashish," *Bull. Narcotics,* July-December 1963, p. 97.

48. Isbell et al, *op. cit.,* pp. 184–187.

49. "Marijuana Persistence in the Body," quoting the work of Louis Lemberger, Stephen Silberstein, Julius Alexrod and Irwin Kopin, *Science News,* December 26, 1970.

50. Jaffe, *op. cit.,* p. 299.

51. Miras, *op. cit.,* pp. 37–47.

52. Jaffe, *op. cit.,* p. 299.

53. E. S. Boyd and D. A. Merritt, "Effects of Barbiturates and a Tetrahydrocannabinol Derivative on Recovery Cycles of Medial Lemniscus, Thalmus and Reticular Formation in the Cat," *J. Pharmacol. Exp. Ther.,* 1966, pp. 376–384.

54. A. J. Lapa et al, "Blocking Action of Tetrahydrocannabinol upon Transmission in the Trigeminal System of the Cat," *J. Pharmacol.*, 1968, pp. 373–376.

55. R. Dagirmanjian and E. S. Boyd, "Peripheral Effects of a Tetrahydrocannabinol," *Fed. Proc.*, 1960, p. 267.

56. E. S. Boyd and D. A. Merritt, "Effects of a Tetrahydrocannabinol Derivative on Some Motor Systems in the Cat," *Arch. Int. Pharmacodyn.*, 1965, pp. 1–12.

57. B. C. Bose, A. Q. Saifi and A. W. Bhagwat, "Observations on the Pharmacological Actions of Cannabis Indica," Part II, *Arch. Int. Pharmacodyn.*, January 1, 1964, pp. 285–290.

58. Wilson, *op. cit.*, p. 132.

59. Council on Mental Health and Committee on Alcoholism and Drug Dependence, "Dependence on Cannabis (Marijuana)," *J.A.-M.A.*, August 7, 1967, pp. 368–371.

60. Weil et al, *op. cit.*, p. 1242.

6. bummers

1. Jack S. Margolis and Richard Clorfene, *A Child's Garden of Grass* (North Hollywood, Calif.: Contact Books, 1969), p. xii.

2. *Ibid.*, p. 45.

3. Howard S. Becker, "Becoming a Marijuana User," *American Journal of Sociology*, November 1953, pp. 235–243.

4. "The La Guardia Report," quoted in Donald B. Louria, *The Drug Scene* (New York: McGraw-Hill, 1968), p. 102.

5. Earl Wilson, "The Crazy Dreamers," *Colliers*, July 4, 1949.

6. Charles W. Wahl, "The Diagnosis and Treatment of Status Medicamentosus," Drug Takers' Symposium, University of California, Los Angeles, 1967.

7. "Pop Drugs: The High as a Way of Life," *Time*, September 26, 1969, pp. 68–78.

8. I. C. Chopra and R. N. Chopra, "The Use of the Cannabis Drug in India," *Bull. Narcotics*, January-March 1957, p. 23.

9. Dana L. Farnsworth, "The Drug Problem among Young People," *Oklahoma State Medical Association Journal*, September 1968, p. 461.

10. *Ibid.*, p. 463.

11. *Ibid.*

12. *Ibid.*

13. P. A. L. Chapple, "Cannabis: A Toxic and Dangerous Substance—A Study of Eighty Takers," *British Journal of Addiction*, August 1966, p. 271.

14. R. H. Berg, "Why Americans Hide Behind a Chemical Curtain," *Look*, August 8, 1967, pp. 12–13.

15. Becker, *op. cit.*, pp. 235–243.

16. R. L. Blum, "Drugs and Personal Values," paper presented at the National Association of Student Personnel Administrators' Drug Conference, Washington, D.C., November 7–8, 1966.

17. David E. Smith and Carter Mehl, "An Analysis of Marijuana Toxicity," in David E. Smith, *The New Social Drug* (Englewood Cliffs, N.J.: Prentice-Hall, Inc., 1970), p. 76.

18. C. W. M. Wilson, *Adolescent Drug Dependence* (London: Pergamon Press, 1968), p. 123.

19. "Shrinks Differ on Pot Users," *Drugs and Drug Abuse Education Newsletter*, Scope Pub-

lications, Washington, D.C., December 1970, p. 2.

20. "Pot Question Still Simmering," *Drugs and Drug Abuse Education Newsletter*, Scope Publications, Washington, D.C., February 1970, p. 11.

21. Eugene I. Falstein, quoted in *Drugs and Drug Abuse Education Newsletter*, Scope Publications, Washington, D.C., August 1970, p. 7.

22. James L. Mathis, quoted in *Drugs and Drug Abuse Education Newsletter*, Scope Publications, Washington, D.C., December 1970, p. 5.

23. "Correspondence," *Science*, August 2, 1968.

24. *Time, op. cit.*, p. 72.

25. Lincoln Clark, quoted in "Marijuana: Inconsistent Performance," *Science News Letter*, October 31, 1970.

26. *Time, op. cit.*, p. 73.

27. *Ibid.*

28. Wilson, *op. cit.*, p. 130.

29. World Health Organization Expert Committee, quoted in *ibid.*

30. D. E. McMillan et al, quoted in "Pigeon Experiment Suggests MJ May Develop Tolerance," *Drugs and Drug Abuse Education Newsletter*, Scope Publications, Washington, D.C., August 1970, p. 5.

31. J. D. Fraser, "Withdrawal Symptoms in Cannabis Indica Patients," *Lancet*, October 22, 1949, pp. 747–748.

32. Chapple, *op. cit.*, p. 279.

33. *Indian Hemp Drugs Commission Report* (Washington, D.C.: Government Printing Office, 1893–94), quoted in Robert P. Walton, *Marijuana: America's New Drug Problem* (Philadelphia: J. B. Lippincott, 1938), p. 2.

34. Chapple, *op. cit.*, p. 279.

35. Donald B. Louria, *The Drug Scene* (New York: McGraw-Hill, 1968), p. 108.

36. Stanley Yolles, quoted in *Time, op. cit.*, p. 69.

37. Maitland Zane, "Getting High in Society," *San Francisco Chronicle*, October 27, 1970, p. 8.

38. Alfred Lindesmith, quoted in "Pop Drugs: The High as a Way of Life," *Time*, September 26, 1969, p. 69.

39. " 'Casual,' 'Heavy' MJ Users Differ," *Drugs and Drug Abuse Education Newsletter*, Scope Publications, Washington, D.C., August 1970, p. 8.

40. Harry Nelson, "Common Motion Upset. User's Personality Changed by Marijuana, Scientist Says," *Los Angeles Times*, September 13, 1967.

41. C. J. Miras, quoted in *ibid.*

42. "U. C. Psychiatrist Sees Some Lasting Harm in Using Pot," *University of California News Clip Sheet 45*, Berkeley, May 12, 1970.

43. David Perlman, "Marijuana and the Mind, the Findings at Palo Alto," *San Francisco Chronicle*, May 30, 1970.

44. *University of California News Clip Sheet, op. cit.*

45. "Pot Induces Brain Damage, Concludes California Psychiatrist; But Multiple Drugs Involved," *Drugs and Drug Abuse Education Newsletter*, Scope Publications, Washington, D.C., June 1970, p. 13.

46. Andrew T. Weil, quoted in *ibid.*, p. 14.

47. Louis J. West, quoted in *Modern Medicine*, December 16, 1968, p. 46.

48. "W-H-A-A-A-A-A-T??!!" *The Berkeley Barb*, April 22, 1971.

49. Doris Milman, quoted in *Health Bulletin*, February 22, 1969, and in "Pot Dangerous for Unstable Youth," *Science News Letter*, February 15, 1969.

50. Harry Nelson, "Doctor Fears Possible Harm of Marijuana," *Los Angeles Times*, February 5, 1970.

51. C. J. Miras, "Metabolic Problems Among Chronic Hashish Smokers," Report T O, 1953, p. 53.

52. Chapple, *op. cit.*, p. 272.

53. Wilson, *op. cit.*, p. 127.

54. David Smith, "Acute and Chronic Toxicity of Marijuana," *Journal of Psychedelic Drugs*, Fall 1968, p. 44.

55. Chapple, *op. cit.*, p. 269.

56. Jared Tinklenberg, personal communication.

57. Wilson, *op. cit.*, p. 126.

58. P. J. Dally, "Undesirable Effects of Marijuana," *British Medical Journal*, August 5, 1967, p. 367.

59. Doris Milman, letter to *Saturday Review*, December 2, 1970.

60. "Drug Menace: How Serious," interview with John E. Ingersoll, *U.S. News & World Report*, May 25, 1970, p. 41.

61. Jim Brewer, "S. F. Kids on Heroin," *San Francisco Chronicle*, March 9, 1970, p. 24.

62. Harvey Powelson, quoted in *University of California News Clip Sheet, op. cit.*

63. Margolis and Clorfene, *op. cit.*, p. 46.

64. *Ibid.*

65. *Ibid.*, p. 47.

66. *Ibid.*, p. 48.

67. *Ibid.*, p. 54.

68. *Ibid.*, p. 55.

69. Jared Tinklenberg, personal communication.

70. Margolis and Clorfene, *op. cit.*, pp. 54–55.

71. *Ibid.*, p. 55.

72. Andrew T. Weil, quoted from *New England Journal of Med-*icine, April 30, 1970, in *Drugs and Drug Abuse Education Newsletter*, Scope Publications, Washington, D.C., May 1970, p. 9.

73. Erich Goode, "Marijuana and the Politics of Reality," in David E. Smith, *The New Social Drug* (Englewood Cliffs, N.J.: Prentice-Hall, 1970), p. 172.

74. *Ibid.*, p. 173.

75. Smith, "Acute and Chronic Toxicity of Marijuana," *op. cit.*, p. 42.

76. Martin H. Keeler, Clifford B. Reifler and Myron B. Liptzin, "Spontaneous Recurrence of Marijuana Effects," *American Journal of Psychiatry*, September 1968, pp. 344–346.

77. "Tests Show Marijuana Action in Human Body," *Los Angeles Times*, December 18, 1970.

78. Jared Tinklenberg, personal communication.

79. Keeler et al, *op. cit.*, p. 386.

80. Smith, "Acute and Chronic Toxicity of Marijuana," *op. cit.*, p. 42.

81. Armando R. Favazza and Edward R. Domino, "Recurrent LSD Experience (Flashbacks) Triggered by Marijuana," *University of Michigan Medical Center Journal*, 1969, pp. 214–216.

82. Johann Rush, personal communication.

83. Margolis and Clorfene, *op. cit.*, p. 52.

84. Erich Goode, quoted in David E. Smith, *The New Social Drug* (Englewood Cliffs, N.J.; Prentice-Hall, Inc., 1970), p. 172.

7. bad trips

1. Joel Fort, testimony in the People of the State of Michigan *vs.* Eric Lorentzen, Case 69–6119.

2. *Ibid.*

3. John A. Talbott and James W. Teague, "Marijuana Psychosis," *J.A.M.A.* October 13, 1969, p. 299.

4. John Kaplan, *Marijuana —*

The New Prohibition (New York: World Publishing Co., 1970), p. 132.

5. Andrew T. Weil, Norman E. Zinberg and Judith M. Nelsen, "Clinical and Psychological Effects of Marijuana in Man," *Science*, December 13, 1968, p. 1234.

6. *Ibid.*, p. 1238.

7. Frederick T. Melges et al, "Temporal disintegration during Marijuana Intoxication," *Arch. Gen. Psychiat.*, September 1970, pp. 204–210.

8. J. R. Tinklenberg et al, "Marijuana and Immediate Memory," *Nature*, June 20, 1970, pp. 1171–1172.

9. Frederick T. Melges et al, "Marijuana and Temporal Disintegration," *Science*, May 29, 1970, pp. 1118–1120.

10. Earl Wilson, "The Crazy Dreamers," *Colliers*, July 4, 1949.

11. Melges et al, "Temporal Disintegration during Marijuana Intoxication," *op. cit.*, p. 206.

12. Melges et al, "Marijuana and Temporal Disintegration," *op. cit.*, p. 1118.

13. Melges et al, "Temporal Disintegration during Marijuana Intoxication," *op. cit.*, p. 207.

14. Jack S. Margolis and Richard Clorfene, *A Child's Garden of Grass* (North Hollywood, Calif.: Contact Books, 1969), p. 32.

15. Melges et al, "Marijuana and Temporal Disintegration," *op. cit.*, p. 1119.

16. L. D. Clark and E. N. Nakashima, "Experimental Studies of Marijuana," *Amer. J. Psychiat.*, September 1968, pp. 379–384.

17. Tinklenberg et al, *op. cit.*, p. 1172.

18. Frank Johnson, "The Teenager and Drug Abuse," *J. School Health*, December 1968, p. 10.

19. Dana L. Farnsworth, "The Drug Problem among Young People," *Oklahoma State Medical Journal*, September 1968, pp. 461–464.

20. J. C. Toohey, "Marijuana—The Evidence Begins to Grow," *J. School Health*, December 1968, pp. 302–303.

21. Tinklenberg et al, *op. cit.*, p. 1172.

22. Melges et al, "Temporal Disintegration during Marijuana Intoxication," *op. cit.*, p. 208.

23. "People," *Time*, November 16, 1970, p. 46.

24. Melges et al, "Temporal Disintegration during Marijuana Intoxication," *op. cit.*, p. 209.

25. Johann Rush, personal communication.

26. Kaplan, *op. cit.*, p. 184.

27. *Ibid.*, p. 185.

28. *Ibid.*

29. "Letters to the Editor," *Los Angeles Times*, March 20, 1968.

30. Kaplan, *op. cit.*, p. 186.

31. David E. Smith, "Acute and Chronic Toxicity of Marijuana," *Journal of Psychedelic Drugs*, Fall 1968, p. 43.

32. *Ibid.*

33. *Ibid.*

34. *Marijuana and Health*, A Report to the Congress from the Secretary, Department of Health, Education and Welfare, January 31, 1971, p. 15.

35. C. W. M. Wilson, *Adolescent Drug Dependence* (London: Pergamon Press, 1968), p. 124.

36. E. Marcovitz and H. J. Meyers, "The Marijuana Addict in the Army," *War Medicine*, December 1944, pp. 382–391.

37. David E. Smith and Carter Mehl, "An Analysis of Marijuana Toxicity," in David E. Smith, *The New Social Drug* (Englewood Cliffs, N.J.: Prentice-Hall, 1970), p. 63.

38. Andrew T. Weil, "Adverse Reactions to Marijuana," *N. E. J. Med.*, April 30, 1970, p. 1000.

39. Martin H. Keller, "What Are the Questions Concerning Mar-

ijuana?" *North Carolina Medical Journal*, February 1969, pp. 42–43.

40. Weil, "Adverse Reactions to Marijuana," *op. cit.*, p. 1000.

41. "Pop Drugs: The High As a Way of Life," *Time*, September 26, 1969, pp. 68–78.

42. D. E. Smith and C. Mehl, "An Analysis of Marijuana Toxicity," *J. Clin. Toxicology*, quoted by A. Weil, April 30, 1970, *op. cit.*, p. 1000.

43. "Student Use of Drug Rising, Gallup Finds," *Los Angeles Times*, January 17, 1971, p. 5.

44. H. Isbell et al, "Effects of $(-)$ $\triangle^9$ Transtetrahydracannabinol in Man," *Psychopharmacologia*, Berlin, 1967, pp. 184–188.

45. S. Allentuck and K. M. Bowman, "The Psychiatric Aspects of Marihuana Intoxication," *Amer. J. of Psychiat.*, September 1942, pp. 248–251.

46. H. S. Gaskill, "Marijuana, an Intoxicant," *Amer. J. of Psychiat.*, September 1945, pp. 202–204.

47. W. Bromberg, "Marijuana, a Psychiatric Study," *J.A.M.A.*, July 1, 1939, pp. 4–12.

48. Donald Louria, *The Drug Scene* (New York: McGraw Hill, 1968), p. 106.

49. *Ibid.*

50. G. Bartolucci et al, "Marijuana Psychosis," *Canad. Psychiat. Assn. J.*, February 1, 1969, pp. 77–79.

51. *Ibid.*, p. 79.

52. Talbott and Teague, *op. cit.*, pp. 299–302.

53. Lester Grinspoon, "Pot: Hyperemotional Bias Says Harvard Psychiatrist," *Drugs and Drug Abuse Education Newsletter*, Scope Publications, Washington, D.C., January 1970, p. 7.

54. Talbott and Teague, *op. cit.*, p. 300.

55. R. A. Fidaleo, "Marijuana: Social and Clinical Observations,"

USARV Med. Bull., March-April 1968, pp. 58–59.

56. E. M. Heiman, "Marijuana Precipitated Psychosis in Patients Evacuated to CONUS," *USARV Med. Bull.*, May-June 1968, pp. 75–77.

57. W. B. Poste, "Marijuana Use in Vietnam," *USARV Med. Bull.*, September-October 1968, pp. 56–59.

58. E. Casper et al, "Marijuana in Vietnam," *USARV Med. Bull.*, September-October 1968, pp. 60–72.

59. Talbott and Teague, *op. cit.*, p. 299.

60. *Ibid.*, p. 301.

61. *Ibid.*, p. 299.

62. *Ibid.*, p. 299.

63. *Ibid.*, p. 302.

64. Gerald D. Klee, "Marijuana Psychosis," *Psychiatric Quarterly*, Vol. 43, 1969, pp. 719–733.

65. *Ibid.*, p. 730.

66. *Ibid.*, p. 731.

67. William Grossman, "Adverse Reactions Associated with Cannabis Products in India," *Ann. Int. Med.*, March 1969, pp. 529–533.

68. *Ibid.*, p. 529.

69. Johnson, *op. cit.*, p. 10.

70. Doris Perna, "Psychotogenic Effect of Marijuana," *J.A.M.A.*, August 18, 1969, pp. 1085–1086.

71. Martin H. Keeler, "Adverse Reaction to Marijuana," *A. Mourn. of Psychiat.*, November 1967, p. 128.

72. Farnsworth, *op. cit.*, pp. 462–463.

73. "Child Suicide," *The Sciences*, New York Academy of Sciences, September 1970, pp. 28–31.

74. *Ibid.*, p. 29.

75. *Ibid.*, p. 29.

76. *Ibid.*, pp. 28–29.

77. Charles Baudelaire, *The Essence of Laughter and Other Essays* and *Journals and Letters,*

quoted in *The Drug Experience,*
edited by David Ebin (New York:
The Orion Press, 1961), pp. 19–20.

78. "Child Suicide," *op. cit.,*
p. 29.

79. Weil, "Adverse Reactions
to Marijuana," *op. cit.*

80. Robert L. Taylor, John I.
Maurer and Jared R. Tinklenberg,
"Management of Bad Trips in an
Evolving Drug Scene," *J.A.M.A.,*
July 20, 1970, pp. 422–425.

81. Margolis and Clorfene, *op.
cit.,* pp. 50–53.

8. the major controversies

1. Samuel Grafton, "What You
Can Do About the Drug Problem,"
Parents Magazine, November 1970,
p. 73.

2. "Pop Drugs: The High As a
Way of Life," *Time,* September 2,
1969, p. 73.

3. C. W. M. Wilson, *Adolescent
Drug Dependence* (London: Pergamon Press, 1968), p. 134.

4. Lester Grinspoon, quoted in
"Pot Hyperemotional Bias, Says
Harvard Psychiatrist," *Drugs and
Drug Abuse Education Newsletter,*
January 1970, p. 7.

5. *Ibid.,* p. 6.

6. J. Fred. Shick et al, "Use of
Marijuana in the Haight-Ashbury
Subculture," *J. of Psychedelic
Drugs,* Fall 1968, p. 55.

7. *The Facts, Questions and
Answers,* published by The Li-
censed Beverage Industries, Inc.,
New York, 1968.

8. *Ibid.,* p. 4.

9. *Ibid.,* p. 2.

10. *Ibid.,* p. 2.

11. *Ibid.,* p. 3.

12. David Smith, M.D., testi-
mony given before California
Assemblyman Pete Wilson, Los
Angeles, California, March 1, 1968.

13. "Drug Use, Parents Alcohol
Related," *Drugs and Drug Abuse
Education Newsletter,* May 1970,
p. 6.

14. Max Hayman, "The Myth
of Social Drinking," *Am. J. Psychiatry,* November 1967, p. 39.

15. "A Little Family Cheer,"
Newsweek, October 23, 1967.

16. H. B. Murphy, "The Cannabis Habit: A Review of Recent
Psychiatric Literature," *Bull. Narc.,*
1963, p. 1.

17. Antoni Gollan, "The Great
Marijuana Problem," *National Review,* January 20, 1968, p. 75.

18. Dr. William H. Stewart,
quoted in *Ibid.*

19. Robert F. Kennedy, remarks before the World Conference
on Smoking and Health, New York
City, September 11, 1967.

20. Jared Tinklenberg, personal
communication.

21. Max Miller, *Marijuana,* produced by Avanti Films, Los Angeles, 1968.

22. "Will Cigarettes Take to
Pot?" *Business Week,* September 6,
1969, p. 28.

23. "New U.S. Blast at Cigarettes," *San Francisco Examiner,*
September 11, 1970.

24. Gene R. Haislip, "Current
Issues in the Prevention and Control of Marijuana Abuse," paper
presented to the First National Conference on Student Drug Involvement, University of Maryland,
August 16, 1967.

25. H. B. M. Murphy, "The
Cannabis Habit. A Review of Recent Psychiatric Literature," *Bull.
Narc.,* January-March 1963, pp.
15–23.

26. Burnell Blanchard, personal
communication.

27. Erich Goode, *The Marijuana Smokers* (New York: Basic
Books, 1971), p. IX.

28. *Ibid.*, p. 212.

29. *Ibid.*, p. 213.

30. David P. Ausubel, *Drug Addiction: Physiological, Psychological and Sociological Aspects* (New York: Random House, 1964), p. 103.

31. H. S. Gaskill, "Marijuana, an Intoxicant," *Amer. J. Psychiat.*, 1945, p. 202.

32. Ausubel, *op. cit.*, p. 104.

33. *Facts About Marijuana*, Los Angeles Police Department Private Printing, 1966.

34. Haislip, *op. cit.*

35. William F. Quinn, personal communication.

36. Abrams, *op. cit.*, p. 240.

37. "Dependence on Cannabis (Marijuana)," *J.A.M.A.*, August 7, 1967, p. 369.

38. "W-H-A-A-A-A-A-T?!!" *The Berkeley Barb*, April 22, 1971.

39. Merikay, "If You Don't Understand," *Insight*, May 4, 1971, p. 14.

40. U.S. *vs.* Watson: Army SPCM, 7th Jud. Cir., February 13, 1970.

41. J. F. Siler et al, "Marijuana Smoking in Panama," *Mil. Surg.*, November 1933, pp. 269–280.

42. James M. Phalen, "The Marijuana Bugaboo," *Mil. Surg.*, 1943, pp. 94–95.

43. Eli Marcovitz and Henry J. Meyers, "The Marijuana Addict in the Army," *War Med.*, December 1944, pp. 382–394.

44. "Use of Marijuana by GIs in Vietnam Held Not Serious," *Hospital Tribune*, November 20, 1967.

45. Jerry Cohen, "Marijuana: Views Collide," *Los Angeles Times*, December 4, 1967.

46. "Marijuana: 'Nuisance' or Problem in Vietnam?" *U.S. News & World Report*, November 13, 1967.

47. "My Lai: Pot or Not?" *Drugs and Drug Abuse Education Newsletter*, March 1970, p. 4.

48. "Mary Jane in Action," *Newsweek*, November 6, 1967.

49. *Ibid.*

50. *Ibid.*

51. *Ibid.*

52. *Hospital Tribune, op. cit.*

53. *Ibid.*

54. *Ibid.*

55. "Fresh Disclosures on Drugs and GIs," *U.S. News & World Report*, April 6, 1970, p. 32.

56. "What Army Is Doing About GIs on Drugs," *U.S. News & World Report*, January 18, 1971, p. 37.

57. "Who's Pushing Heroin to GIs in Vietnam?" *U.S. News & World Report*, May 10, 1971, p. 30.

58. *Ibid.*

59. *Ibid.*

60. "Trying to Reach Vietnam Veterans," *Behaviour Today*, October 5, 1970.

61. "Washington Whispers," *U.S. News & World Report*, January 12, 1970.

62. "Educational Television Turns on with Partly Manicured Grass Series," *Los Angeles Free Press*, March 15, 1968.

63. "AWOLs Triple," *Los Angeles Free Press*, January 2, 1970.

64. "3800 Discharged by Navy for Drug Offenses," *Los Angeles Times*, April 21, 1970.

65. "Washington Whispers," *U.S. News & World Report*, January 25, 1971.

66. "Discontent, Drug Use, Spiraling in Military," *Drugs and Drug Abuse Education Newsletter*, December 1970, p. 1.

67. "Army Amnesty on Drugs Failing," *Los Angeles Examiner*, April 20, 1971.

68. John A. Talbott and James W. Teague, "Marijuana Psychosis," *J.A.M.A.*, October 13, 1969, p. 301.

69. "Vietnam GIs Take Grass to the Field," *Medical World News*, August 29, 1969, p. 16.

70. *Ibid.*

71. "Cent a Plant. Viet Drive against Plant Launched," *Los Angeles Times*, January 7, 1971, p. 8.

72. Joel Kaplan as told to Christopher S. Wren, "Does Our Army Fight on Drugs?" *Look,* June 16, 1970, p. 76.

73. "U.S. Studying Marijuana, Makes Synthetic Drug," *Boston Sunday Globe,* August 3, 1970.

74. *Ibid.*

75. Correspondence, *Playboy,* September 1968, p. 224.

76. "Vietnam Blues," correspondence, *Playboy,* June 1968, p. 163.

77. "Another Checkup on Drug Use by GIs," *U.S. News & World Report,* August 31, 1970, p. 33.

78. "Mansfield Tells of Viet Fragging," *Los Angeles Examiner,* April 20, 1971.

79. "The Brass and the Grass," correspondence, *Playboy,* October 1970, p. 66.

80. "Pot in Vietnam," correspondence, *Playboy,* December 1969, p. 74.

81. "Pot on Patrol," correspondence, *Playboy,* October 1970, p. 66.

82. "Pot Yes, Pacifism No," correspondence, *Playboy,* September 1968, p. 224.

83. *Look, op. cit.,* p. 72.

84. "Mixing Pot with Gunpowder," correspondence, *Playboy,* July 1969, p. 46.

85. *Look, op. cit.,* p. 72.

86. "Eyewitness Report on Drugs, Race Problems and Boredom," *U.S. News & World Report,* January 25, 1971, p. 33.

87. "U.S. Army Says Marijuana Can Damage Your Mind," *Los Angeles Free Press,* December 12, 1969, p. 17.

88. Stuart Auerbach, "Excess of Viet Killing Blamed on Marijuana," *Los Angeles Times,* May 11, 1970.

89. *U.S. News & World Report, op. cit.,* p. 32.

90. *Los Angeles Times, op. cit.*

91. "Pot Seems to Be Big Vietnam Problem," *Listen Magazine,* April 1969.

92. Harry L. Freedman and Myron J. Rockmore, "Marijuana: A Factor in Personality Evaluation and Army Maladjustment," *Clinical Psychopathology,* October 1946, p. 235.

93. *Medical World News, op. cit.*

94. William Braden, "Today's Angry GI, Does He Enjoy Killing?" *Los Angeles Times,* December 4, 1969.

95. *Ibid.*

96. *Ibid.*

97. Ted Sell, "3 More GIs Charged in My Lai Investigation," *Los Angeles Times,* March 26, 1970, p. 7.

98. Ted Sell, "GIs Smoked Marijuana Night before My Lai, Senators Told," *Los Angeles Times,* May 25, 1970.

99. *Los Angeles Times,* December 4, 1969, *op. cit.*

100. "GIs and Drugs," *Behaviour Today,* August 31, 1970.

101. *Los Angeles Times,* March 26, 1970, *op. cit.*

102. "Fresh Disclosures on Drugs and GIs," *U.S. News & World Report,* April 6, 1970, p. 32.

103. *Los Angeles Times,* December 4, 1969, *op. cit.*

104. "Most Viet GIs Held Drug Users," *Los Angeles Times,* August 16, 1970.

105. "GIs: 1 in 5 Go to Pot, Army Says," *Los Angeles Herald Examiner,* April 4, 1970, p. 1.

106. "Is the Army Going to Pot?" *Medical World News,* February 2, 1969.

107. "GI Drug Deaths Rising in Vietnam, Army Says," *Los Angeles Times,* October 31, 1970.

108. "The Addict in Vietnam," *Medical World News,* May 8, 1970.

9. the literature of cannabis use

1. Oliver Byrd, personal communication.

2. James R. Gamage and Edmund L. Zerkin, *A Comprehensive Guide to the English-Language Literature on Cannabis* (Beloit, Wisc.: Stash Press, 1969).

3. *Indian Hemp Drugs Commission Report,* Government Printing Office, 1893–1894.

4. J. F. Siler et al, "Marijuana Smoking in Panama," *Milit. Surg.,* 1933, pp. 269–280.

5. New York City Mayor's Committee on Marijuana, *The Marijuana Problem in the City of New York* (Lancaster, Pa.: Jacques Cattell Press, 1944).

6. *Marijuana and Health,* a Report of the Secretary, Department of Health, Education and Welfare to Congress, January 31, 1971.

7. Lester Grinspoon, "Marijuana," *Scientific American,* December 1969, pp. 17–25.

8. John A. Talbott and James W. Teague, "Marijuana Psychosis," *J.A.M.A.,* October 13, 1969, pp. 299–302.

9. Lester Grinspoon, quoted in *Drugs and Drug Abuse Education Newsletter,* January 1970, p. 7.

10. Peter B. Dews, "The Pharmacologist's Dilemma," *Pediatrics,* January 1970, pp. 2–3.

11. H. Dobell, "On Some Effects of Cannabis Indica," *Med. Times Gaz.,* Vol. 2, 1863, pp. 245–246.

12. J. Aulde, "Studies in Therapeutics—Cannabis Indica," *Ther. Gaz.,* August 15, 1890, pp. 523–526.

13. J. R. Lynch, "A Case of Accidental Poisoning by Seven Minims and a Half of Tincture of Cannabis Indica. Recovery," *Lancet,* September 30, 1871, p. 493.

14. A. J. Manasseh, "Symptoms of Poisoning from a Small Dose of Tincture of Cannabis Indica," *Lancet,* March 11, 1899, p. 723.

15. J. C. McWalter, "Concerning Cannabis Indica Poisoning," *Pharm. J.,* November 3, 1900, p. 498.

16. L. J. Minter, "Indian Hemp Poisoning," *Brit. Med. J.,* December 19, 1896, pp. 1773–1774.

17. E. F. Palgrave, "A Case of Poisoning by Cannabis Indica," *St. Barth. Hosp. J.,* Vol. 7, 1900, p. 76.

18. B. Walker, "Indian Hemp Poisoning," *Brit. Med. J.,* November 7, 1896, p. 1382.

19. H. S. Williams, "An Overdose of Cannabis Indica," *Ther. Gaz.,* January 15, 1885, pp. 18–19.

20. F. H. Brown, "Case of Poisoning by Cannabis Indica," *Boston Med. Surg. J.,* Vol. 67, 1862–1863, pp. 291–292.

21. W. W. Campbell, "Report of an Experiment with Cannabis Indica," *Med. Times Gaz.,* Vol. 2, 1863, pp. 194–195.

22. D. W. Prentiss, "Report of Cases of Poisoning from Exalgine, Cannabis Indica, Arsenic and Camphor," *Ther. Gaz.,* February 15, 1892, pp. 103–106.

23. A. Roche, "Symptoms of Poisoning from a Small Dose of Tincture of Cannabis Indica," *Lancet,* December 24, 1898, p. 1701.

24. P. A. Simpson, "Native Poisons of India," *Pharm. J.,* February 3, 1872, pp. 626–627.

25. "Indian Hemp Poisoning," *Brit. Med. J.,* November 28, 1896, p. 1619.

26. H. Fisher, "Case of Cannabis Indica Poisoning," *Cincinnati Lancet-Clinic,* Vol. 37, 1896, p. 405.

27. A. Dallas, "Ganja and

Aphonia," *Indian Med. Rec.*, Vol. 11, 1896, p. 76.

28. P. B. Bentlif, "A Case of Poisoning by Extract of Cannabis Indica," *Clin. Sketches*, Vol. 3, 1896, p. 70.

29. R. C. Bicknell, "Some Effects of Cannabis Indica in Large Doses," *Ther. Gaz.*, January 15, 1898, pp. 13–15.

30. J. Foulis, "Two Cases of Poisoning by Cannabis Indica," *Edinburgh Med. J.*, Vol. 8, 1900, pp. 201–210.

31. W. Strange, "Cannabis Indica. As a Medicine and As a Poison," *Brit. Med. J.*, July 7, 1883, p. 14.

32. G. G. Fischlowitz, "Poisoning by Cannabis Indica," *Med. Rec.*, August 22, 1896, pp. 280–281.

33. C. C. Baxter-Tyrie, "A Case of Poisoning by Cannabis Indica," *Lancet*, December 4, 1897, p. 1452.

34. J. Attlee, "Case of Poisoning by Cannabis Indica," *Lancet*, October 17, 1896, p. 1078.

35. M. L. Geiser, "Poisoning by Cannabis Indica," *Med. Rec.*, October 10, 1896, p. 519.

36. S. E. Hamaker, "A Case of Overdose of Cannabis Indica," *Ther. Gaz.*, December 15, 1891, p. 808.

37. T. Ireland, "Insanity from the Abuse of Indian Hemp," *Alienist & Neurol.*, Vol. 14, 1893, pp. 622–630.

38. T. E. Saxby, "Poisoning by Cannabis Indica. Recovery," *Brit. Med. J.*, October 15, 1898, p. 1160.

39. H. C. Wood and R. M. Smith, "Poisoning by Cannabis Indica," *Ther. Gaz.*, November 15, 1884, pp. 514–515.

40. R. Robertson, "Toxic Symptoms from Tincture of Indian Hemp in Official Doses," *Med. Times Gaz.*, Vol. 1, 1885, pp. 817–819.

41. N. Tirard, "Toxic Effects of Cannabis Indica," *Lancet*, March 29, 1890, p. 723.

42. C. R. Marshall, "The Active Principle of Indian Hemp: A Preliminary Communication," *Lancet*, June 23, 1897, pp. 235–238.

43. "Toxic Effects of Cannabis Indica," *Lancet*, March 15, 1890, p. 621.

44. A. M. Fielde, "An Experience in Hasheesh-Smoking," *Ther. Gaz.*, July 16, 1888, pp. 449–451.

45. V. Dinshaw, "Complete Aphonia after Ganja-Smoking; Recovery," *Indian Med. Rec.*, Vol. 11, 1896, p. 14.

46. W. M. Kelley, "Cannabis Indica," *Brit. Med. J.*, June 30, 1883, p. 1281.

47. J. Laurance, "On the Prevalence of, and Ill Effects Resulting from, the Use of Bhang and Other Narcotic Drugs in the Native Army," *Madras Quart. Med. J.*, Vol. 6, 1884, pp. 274–278.

48. C. R. Marshall, "Note on the Pharmacological Action of Cannabis Resin," *Proc. Cambridge Philos. Soc.*, Vol. 9, 1897, pp. 149–150.

49. J. Bell, "On the Haschisch or Cannabis Indica," *Boston Med. Surg. J.*, April 16, 1857, pp. 209–216, and April 23, 1857, pp. 229–236.

50. J. H. Tull-Walsh, "On Insanity Produced by the Abuse of Ganja and Other Preparations of Indian Hemp, with Notes of Cases," *Indian Med. Gaz.*, Vol. 29, 1894, pp. 333–334, pp. 369–372, and pp. 446–451.

51. A. B. Clarke, "On the Cannabis Indica," *Boston Med. Surg. J.*, May 21, 1857, pp. 315-316.

52. H. C. Wood, "On the Medical Activity of the Hemp Plant, as Grown in North America," *Proc. Amer. Philosophical Soc.*, November 19, 1869, pp. 226–232.

53. H. W. Sawtelle, "A Case Presenting Peculiar Susceptibility to the Action of Cannabis Indica Administered for Neuralgia; Re-

covery," *Amer. Lancet,* Vol. *18,* 1894, p. 2.

54. W. B. Rushin, "Two Cases of Acute Poisoning from Solid Extract of Cannabis Indica," *Southern Med. Rec.,* Vol. 20, 1890, pp. 363–364.

55. T. S. Clouston, "The Cairo Asylum—Dr. Warnock on Hasheesh Insanity," *J. Ment. Sci.,* October 1896, pp. 790–795.

56. J. H. Tull-Walsh, "Hemp Drugs and Insanity," *J. Ment. Sci.,* January 1894, pp. 21–36.

57. C. R. Marshall, "A Review of Recent Work on Cannabis Indica," *Pharm. J.,* August 16, 1902, pp. 131–132.

58. J. Warnock, "Insanity from Hasheesh," *J. Ment. Sci.,* January 1903, pp. 96–110.

59. G. F. W. Ewens, "Insanity Following the Use of Indian Hemp," *Indian Med. Gaz.,* Vol. 39, 1904, pp. 401–413.

60. H. E. Gowers, "Haschisch Hallucinations," *Amer. Physician,* Vol. 32, 1906, pp. 72–76.

61. C. J. Robertson-Milne, "Notes on Insanity with Illustrative Cases," *Indian Med. Gaz.,* Vol. 41, 1906, pp. 129–132.

62. G. F. W. Ewens, "Insanity Following the Use of Indian Hemp," in *Insanity in India* (Calcutta, 1908), pp. 129–142.

63. A. S. M. Peebles and H. W. Mann, "Ganja as a Cause of Insanity and Crime in Bengal," *Indian Med. Gaz.,* Vol. 491, 1914, pp. 395–396.

64. L. J. Bragman, "The Weed of Insanity," *Med. J. Rec.,* October 7, 1925, pp. 416–418.

65. A. Schneider, "The Effects of Large Doses of Cannabis Indica. (Subjective Experiment)," *J. Amer. Pharm. Assoc.,* March 1923, pp. 208–214.

66. W. S. J. Shaw, "Cannabis Indica. A Dangerous Drug," *Brit. Med. J.,* September 29, 1923, p. 586.

67. J. E. Dhunjibhoy, "The Role of Indian Hemp in Causation of Insanity in India," in J. Cunningham (Ed.), *Far Eastern Association of Tropical Medicine, Transactions of the 7th Congress* (Calcutta: Thacker's Press, 1928), pp. 400–407.

68. J. E. Dhunjibhoy, "A Brief Resume of the Types of Insanity Commonly Met With in India, with a Full Description of Indian Hemp Insanity Peculiar to the Country," *J. Ment. Sci.,* Vol. 76, 1930, pp. 254–264.

69. G. C. Burns, "Neurosine Poisoning," *J.A.M.A.,* April 11, 1931, pp. 1225–1226.

70. G. T. Harding, "Neurosine Poisoning," *J.A.M.A.,* June 13, 1931, p. 2054.

71. "Effects of Cannabis," *J.A.M.A.,* February 25, 1933, p. 601.

72. W. Bromberg, "Marihuana Intoxication. A Clinical Study of Cannabis Sativa Intoxication," *Amer. J. Psychiat.,* September 1934, pp. 303–330.

73. E. Lindemann and W. Malamud, "Experimental Analysis of the Psychopathological Effects of Intoxicating Drugs," *Amer. J. Psychiat.,* January 1934, pp. 853–881.

74. E. T. Baker-Bates, "A Case of Cannabis Indica Intoxication," *Lancet,* April 6, 1935, p. 811.

75. W. A. J. Fleming, "A Case of Cannabis Indica Intoxication," *Lancet,* June 1, 1935, pp. 1301–1302.

76. V. Lewitus, "Mariajuana," *Amer. J. Nurs.,* July 1936, pp. 677–678.

77. P. H. Drewry, "Some Psychiatric Aspects of Marijuana Intoxication," *Psychiat. Quart.,* April 1936, pp. 232–242.

78. C. R. McCormack, "Marihuana," *Hygeia,* October 1937, pp. 898–899.

79. W. Russell and the Medical Staff of Pretoria Mental Hospital,

"Mental Symptoms Associated with the Smoking of Dagga," *S. Afr. Med. J.*, Vol. 12, 1938, pp. 85–88.

80. W. Bromberg, "Marihuana. A Psychiatric Study," *J.A.M.A.*, July 1, 1939, pp. 4–12.

81. J. L. Frew, "Cannabis Indica Poisoning," *Royal Melbourne Hosp. Clin. Rep.*, Vol. 10, 1939, pp. 93–94.

82. W. Bromberg, "The Effects of Marihuana," *Proc. Assoc. Res. Nerv. Ment. Dis.*, Vol. 19, 1939, pp. 180–189.

83. H. C. Curtis, and J. R. Wolfe, "Psychosis Following the Use of Marijuana with Report of Cases," *J. Kansas Med. Soc.*, December 1939, pp. 515–517.

84. M. Nesbitt, "Psychosis Due to Exogenous Toxins–Marihuana," *Illinois Med. J.*, March 1940, pp. 278–282.

85. W. Bromberg, "Marihuana Addiction," in *Practitioners Library of Medicine and Surgery* (New York, 1941), Supplement, pp. 255–262.

86. J. M. Henninger, "Marijuana Intoxication," *J. Crim. Psychopath.*, Vol. 2, 1941, p. 360.

87. R. N. Chopra, G. S. Chopra and I. C. Chopra, "Cannabis Sativa in Relation to Mental Diseases and Crime in India," *Indian J. Med. Res.*, January 1942, pp. 155–171.

88. S. Allentuck and K. M. Bowman, "The Psychiatric Aspects of Marihuana Intoxication," *Amer. J. Psychiat.*, September 1942, pp. 248–251.

89. W. C. Fowler, "Cannabis Indica," *Lancet*, September 18, 1943, p. 368.

90. H. J. Anslinger, "Psychiatric Aspects of Marihuana Intoxication," *J.A.M.A.*, January 16, 1943, pp. 212–213.

91. K. M. Bowman, "Psychiatric Aspects of Marihuana Intoxication," *J.A.M.A.*, June 3, 1944, p. 376.

92. R. J. Bouquet, "Marihuana Intoxication," *J.A.M.A.*, April 1, 1944, pp. 1010–1011.

93. H. S. Gaskill, "Marihuana, an Intoxicant," *Amer. J. Psychiat.*, September 1945, pp. 202–204.

94. H. C. Mookerjee, "Hemp Drug Addiction and Physical Damage," *Calcutta Rev.*, November 1948, pp. 84–96.

95. H. C. Mookerjee, "Hemp Drug Addiction and Mental Derangement," *Calcutta Rev.*, December 1948, pp. 147–160.

96. H. C. Mookerjee, "The Problem of Hemp Drugs Addiction in India," *New Rev.*, December 1948, pp. 401–414, and January 1949, pp. 48–60.

97. P. O. Wolff, "Problems of Drug Addiction in South America," *Brit. J. Addict.*, Vol. 46, 1949, pp. 66–78.

98. D. M. Johnson, "The Effects of Cannabis Indica," in D. M. Johnson, *Indian Hemp. A Social Menace* (London: Christopher Johnson, 1952), pp. 53–65.

99. D. M. Johnson, "Matters for Conjecture," in D. M. Johnson, *Indian Hemp. A Social Menace* (London: Christopher Johnson, 1952), pp. 88–104.

100. D. M. Johnson, "A Menace within a Menace," in D. M. Johnson, *Indian Hemp. A Social Menace* (London: Christopher Johnson, 1952), pp. 105–110.

101. D. M. Johnson, "The Social, and Other, Importance of Indian Hemp," in D. M. Johnson, *Indian Hemp. A Social Menace* (London: Christopher Johnson, 1952), pp. 66–75.

102. D. M. Johnson, *The Hallucinogenic Drugs (The Insanity-producing Drugs: Indian Hemp and Datura)* (London: Christopher Johnson, 1953).

103. C. G. F. Smartt, "Mental Maladjustment in the East African," *J. Ment. Sci.*, July 1956, pp. 441–466.

104. H. C. Mookerjee, *Our*

Hemp Drug Problem (Calcutta: Book House, 1956).

105. A. Benabud, "Psychopathological Aspects of the Cannabis Situation in Morocco. Statistical Data for 1956," *Bull. Narc.*, October-December 1957, pp. 1–16.

106. F. Ames, "A Clinical and Metabolic Study of Acute Intoxication with Cannabis Sativa and Its Role in the Model Psychosis," *J. Ment. Sci.*, October 1958, pp. 972–999.

107. H. B. M. Murphy, "The Cannabis Habit. A Review of Recent Psychiatric Literature," *Bull. Narc.*, January-March 1963, pp. 15–23.

108. H. Mohan and G. C. Sood, "Conjugate Deviation of the Eyes after Cannabis Indica Intoxication," *Brit. J. Ophthal.*, March 1964, pp. 160–161.

109. C. Christozov, "The Moroccan Aspect of Cannabis Intoxication Based on Studies of Chronic Mental Patients. II," *Maroc-Med.*, December 1965, pp. 866–889.

110. G. S. Chopra and P. S. Chopra, "Studies on 300 Indian Drug Addicts with Special Reference to Psychosociological Aspects, Etiology and Treatment," *Bull. Narc.*, April-June 1965, pp. 1–9.

111. S. C. McMorris, "What Price Euphoria. The Case against Marijuana," *Medicoleg. J.*, Vol. 34, 1966, pp. 74–79.

112. A. Boroffka, "Mental Illness and Indian Hemp in Lagos," *E. Afr. Med. J.*, September 1966, pp. 377–384.

113. E. G. Wilkins, "Undesirable Effects of Marijuana," *Brit. Med. J.*, August 19, 1967, pp. 496–497.

114. E. Robbins, L. Robbins, W. A. Frosch and M. Stern, "Implications of Untoward Reactions to Hallucinogens," *Bull. N.Y. Acad. Med.*, November 1967, pp. 985–999.

115. W. Modell, "Mass Drug Catastrophes and the Roles of Science and Technology," *Science*, April 21, 1967, pp. 346–351.

116. "Marihuana," *Med. Lett. Drugs Ther.*, September 22, 1967, pp. 73–74.

117. P. Dally, "Undesirable Effects of Marijuana," *Brit. Med. J.*, August 5, 1967, p. 367.

118. H. S. Becker, "History, Culture and Subjective Experience. An Exploration of the Social Basis of Drug-induced Experiences," *J. Health Soc. Behav.*, September 1967, pp. 163–176.

119. E. Tylden, "A Case for Cannabis?" *Brit. Med. J.*, August 26, 1967, p. 556.

120. M. H. Keeler and C. B. Reifler, "Grand Mal Convulsions Subsequent to Marijuana Use," *Dis. Nerv. Syst.*, July 1967, pp. 474–475.

121. M. H. Keeler, "Adverse Reaction to Marihuana," *Amer. J. Psychiat.*, November 1967, pp. 674–677.

122. L. J. Hekimian and S. Gershon, "Characteristics of Drug Abusers Admitted to a Psychiatric Hospital," *J.A.M.A.*, July 15, 1968, pp. 125–130.

123. M. H. Keeler, C. B. Reifler and M. B. Liptzin, "Spontaneous Recurrence of Marihuana Effect," *Amer. J. Psychiat.*, September 1968, pp. 384–386.

124. D. E. Smith, "Acute and Chronic Toxicity of Marijuana," *J. Psychedelic Drugs*, Fall 1968, pp. 37–47.

125. American Medical Association, Council on Mental Health, "Marihuana and Society," *J.A.M.A.*, June 24, 1968, pp. 1181–1182.

126. W. D. Alsever, "An Evaluation of Marihuana for School Physicians, Nurses and Educators," *J. Sch. Health*, December 1968, pp. 629–638.

127. F. Jorgensen, "Abuse of Psychotomimetics," *Acta Psychiat.*

Scand., Supplement 203, 1968, pp. 205–216.

128. V. A. Dohner, "LSD and Marihuana. Where Are the Answers?" *Science,* June 7, 1968, pp. 1061–1062.

129. M. H. Keeler, "Marihuana Induced Hallucinations," *Dis. Nerv. Sist.,* May 1968, pp. 314–315.

130. W. Keup, "Marihuana," *Science,* March 14, 1969, p. 1144.

131. L. N. Robins, H. S. Darvish and G. E. Murphy, "The Long-term Outcome for Adolescent Drug Users. A Follow-up Study of 76 Users and 146 Non-users," presented at the American Psycopathological Association's Symposium, "Psychopathology of Adolescence," New York City, February 1969, Mimeo.

132. H. Graff, "Marihuana and Scopolamine High," *Amer. J. Psychiat.,* March 1969, pp. 1258–1259.

133. B. E. Leonard, "Cannabis. A Short Review of Its Effects and the Possible Dangers of Its Use," *Brit. J. Addict.,* May 1969, pp. 121–130.

134. W. Grossman, "Adverse Reactions Associated with Cannabis Products in India," *Ann. Intern. Med.,* March 1969, pp. 529–533.

135. A. A. Baker and E. G. Lucas, "Some Hospital Admissions Associated with Cannabis," *Lancet,* January 18, 1969, p. 148.

136. M. M. Glatt, "Is It All Right to Smoke Pot?" *Brit. J. Addict.,* May 1969, pp. 109–114.

137. "The Effects of Marijuana on Consciousness," in C. T. Tart (Ed.), *Altered States of Consciousness* (New York: John Wiley and Sons, 1969), pp. 335–355.

138. D. Perna, "Psychotogenic Effects of Marihuana," *J.A.M.A.,* August 18, 1969, pp. 1085–1086.

139. J. A. Talbott and J. W. Teague, "Marihuana Psychosis. Acute Psychosis Associated with the Use of Cannabis Derivatives," *J.A.M.A.,* October 13, 1969, pp. 299–302.

140. International Narcotic Education Assoc., *Marijuana or Indian Hemp and Its Preparation* (Los Angeles, 1936).

141. New York City Mayor's Committee on Marijuana, *op. cit.*

142. David Solomon (Ed.), *The Marijuana Papers* (Indianapolis: Bobbs-Merrill Co., 1966).

143. Frank R. Gomila, "Present Status of the Marijuana Vice in the United States," in Robert P. Walton, *Marijuana: America's New Drug Problem* (Philadelphia: J. B. Lippincott, 1938), pp. 27–40.

144. *Ibid.,* p. 30.

145. Mayor La Guardia's Committee on Marijuana, "The Marijuana Problem in the City of New York," in David Solomon (Ed.), *The Marijuana Papers* (Indianapolis: Bobbs-Merrill Co., 1966), pp. 245–250.

146. *Ibid.,* p. 250.

147. *Ibid.*

148. *Ibid.,* pp. 259–260.

149. *Ibid.,* p. 252.

150. *Ibid.,* pp. 254–259.

151. *Ibid.,* p. 259.

152. *Ibid.,* p. 261.

153. *Ibid.,* p. 265.

154. *Ibid.,* pp. 269–284.

155. *Ibid.,* p. 272.

156. *Ibid.,* p. 276.

157. *Ibid.,* p. 283.

158. *Ibid.,* p. 289.

159. *Ibid.,* p. 312.

160. *Ibid.,* p. 335.

161. *Ibid.,* p. 341.

162. William Paton, quoted in "Worldwide," *AMA News,* April 12, 1971, p. 2.

163. Harold Kolansky and William T. Moore, "Effects of Marijuana on Adolescents and Young Adults," *J.A.M.A.,* April 19, 1971, pp. 486–492.

164. Walter Wolman, quoted in "Marijuana Perils Shown in Study," *AMA News,* April 19, 1971.

165. "Study Disputed: Psychi-

atrists Find Hazard in Marijuana," *Los Angeles Times*, April 19, 1971.

166. Robert Wallerstein, quoted in David Perlman, "The Pot Report Is Questioned," *San Francisco Chronicle*, April 27, 1971, p. 20.

167. Leo Hollister, quoted in *ibid.*

168. Norman Zinberg, quoted in *ibid.*

169. Leo Hollister, quoted in *ibid.*

10. the law and mary jane

1. John Rosevear, *Pot: A Handbook of Marijuana* (New York: University Books, 1967), p. 122.

2. *Ibid.*, p. 124.

3. *Ibid.*, p. 126.

4. *Ibid.*, p. 117.

5. *Ibid.*, p. 104.

6. *Ibid.*, p. 95.

7. People of Colorado *vs.* David H. Stark (1965), 400 P. 2d., 923, No. 21394.

8. "Marijuana: Millions of Turned-on Users," *Life*, July 7, 1967, pp. 16–23.

9. John Glenn, "Narcotics Conviction Can Hurt Job Chances Students Warned," *Los Angeles Times*, November 29, 1967.

10. Lloyd Shearer, "Why Students Take Pot," *Parade*, October 15, 1967.

11. George B. McClellan, "Canada's Mounties: Focus on a Famous Force," *Pace*, February 1966, p. 41.

12. Holland *vs.* Missouri, 252 US 416, 1920.

13. *Single Convention on Narcotic Drugs of the United Nations, 1961*, art. 28, par. 1; art. 49, par. 2(f).

14. Boris Yaro, "Legalize Marijuana for Adults, Judge Urges," *Los Angeles Times*, September 24, 1967.

15. Rudy Villasenor, "Judge Who Urged Legal Marijuana Relieved of Post," *Los Angeles Times*, October 5, 1967.

16. Donald Louria, *Nightmare Drugs* (New York: Pocket Books, 1966), p. 36.

17. Gene R. Haislip, "Current Issues in the Prevention and Control of Marijuana Abuse," paper presented to the First National Conference on Student Drug Involvement at the University of Maryland, August 16, 1967.

18. Ferdinand Mount, "The Wild Grass Chase," *National Review*, January 20, 1968, p. 84.

19. Jerry Cohen, "Marijuana: Views Collide," *Los Angeles Times*, December 4, 1967.

20. Antoni Gollan, "The Great Marijuana Problem," *National Review*, January 20, 1968, p. 75.

21. Joseph Oteri, quoted by Cohen, *op. cit.*

22. Commonwealth of Massachusetts *vs.* Joseph D. Leis and Ivan Weiss, Superior Court Nos. 28841–2, 28844–5, and 28864–5.

23. Mount, *op. cit.*

24. Pete Wilson, "Juvenile Drug Abuse as a Legislative Problem" (unpublished paper).

25. Joe Reichman, testimony given before the Senate Public Health and Safety Committee, Los Angeles, California, October 18, 1967.

26. Wilbur F. Littlefield, *ibid.*

27. Gollan, *op. cit.*

28. Mount, *op. cit.*

29. Gene Blake, "Peace Officers and DAs Back Bill on Marijuana," *Los Angeles Times*, April 16, 1968.

30. "Leary Tosses Head into

the Ring," *Los Angeles Free Press,* May 23, 1969, p. 2.

31. *Playboy,* November 1970, p. 67.

32. Jean Strouse, *Up against the Law* (New York: New American Library, 1970), pp. 101–102.

33. Rudolph Chelminski, "Open Season on Drug Smugglers," *Life,* June 26, 1970, pp. 28–35.

34. "The Perils of Pot," *Playboy,* April 1967, p. 170.

35. "Rigid Controls Curbing Japan Drug Problem," *Los Angeles Times,* December 6, 1970, p. 4.

36. "Americans in Spain Get Stiff Drug Penalties," *Los Angeles Times,* May 20, 1970.

37. "Americans Sentenced in Crete on Smuggling," *Los Angeles Times,* December 20, 1970, p. 8.

38. "Sweden Will Expel GI Drug Offenders," *Los Angeles Times,* October 14, 1970.

39. "Overseas Drug Arrests," *Playboy,* August 1970, p. 49.

40. William Tuohy, "Sands Prison–Throwback to Middle Ages," *Los Angeles Times,* February 15, 1970.

41. "Soviet Press Warns of Pot Use by Teens," *Los Angeles Times,* December 17, 1970, p. 6.

42. "Israel Worried about Rising Use of Hashish," *Los Angeles Times,* May 17, 1970.

43. William Tuohy, "Istanbul Where Penalty for Pot Is a Long Trip," *Los Angeles Times,* April 9, 1970.

44. Dial Torgerson, "Mexico's Harsh Message: Hippies Not Wanted," *Los Angeles Times,* March 30, 1969.

45. Don Cook, "France a Bad Trip for Pot Prone Americans," *Los Angeles Times,* March 23, 1970.

46. Alfred Lindesmith, *The Addict and the Law* (Bloomington: Indiana University Press, 1965), p. 241.

47. *Proceedings, White House Conference on Narcotic and Drug Abuse* (Washington, D.C.: U.S. Government Printing Office, 1962), p. 286.

48. Abraham Lincoln, address before the Young Men's Lyceum, Springfield, Ill., January 27, 1838.

11. the non-drug aspects of pot

1. "What's Wrong with Drug Education?" *Time,* February 15, 1971, p. 46.

2. *Ibid.*

3. *Ibid.*

4. "The Pot Report: Still Inconclusive," *Time,* February 15, 1971, p. 46.

5. John Kaplan, *Marijuana, The New Prohibition* (New York: World Publishing Co., 1970), pp. 5–6.

6. Michael Aldrich, in Harold Hart (Ed.), *Drugs For and Against* (New York: Hart Publishing Co., 1970), p. 77.

7. *Ibid.*

8. Ed Bear, "Dream a Little Dream of Me," *Queens Quarterly,* Summer 1970, p. 10.

9. Barbara Lewis, *The Sexual Power of Marijuana* (New York: World Publishing Co., 1970), pp. 5–6.

10. "Stanford Law Professor Opposes Marijuana Law," *Monterey Peninsula Herald,* October 1, 1970.

11. Kaplan, *op. cit.,* pp. 314–315.

12. *The Book of Acts,* Chapter 26.

13. Maitland Zane, "Getting High in Society," *San Francisco Chronicle*, October 27, 1970, p. 8.

14. Kaplan, *op. cit.*, p. 314.

15. Rudy Villasenor, "Judges Study Appeal on Contempt," *Los Angeles Times*, October 30, 1970, p. 31.

16. "The Nation," *Los Angeles Times*, November 22, 1970.

17. Kaplan, *op. cit.*, p. 318.

18. *Ibid.*, p. 321.

19. *Monterey Peninsula Herald, op. cit.*

20. Kaplan, *op. cit.*, p. 321.

21. *Ibid.*, p. 329.

22. *Ibid.*, p. 330.

23. Kaplan, *op. cit.*, p. 332.

24. *Monterey Peninsula Herald, op. cit.*

25. *Ibid.*

26. Kaplan, *op. cit.*, p. 333.

27. *Ibid.*, p. 334.

28. *Ibid.*, p. 332.

29. *Ibid.*, p. 334.

30. *Ibid.*, p. 317

31. *Ibid.*, p. 334.

32. *Ibid.*, p. 335.

33. "Crime Expense," *U.S. News & World Report*, October 26, 1970, p. 30.

34. Kaplan, *op. cit.*, p. 341.

35. *Ibid.*, p. 342.

36. *Ibid.*, p. 342.

37. *Ibid.*, p. 343.

38. *Ibid.*, p. 344.

39. "The Pot Report," *Time*, February 15, 1971, p. 46.

40. Kaplan, *op. cit.*, p. 343.

41. *Ibid.*, p. 343.

42. *Ibid.*, p. 346.

43. *Ibid.*, p. 346.

44. *Ibid.*, p. 346.

45. *Ibid.*, p. 346.

46. Peter B. Dews, "The Pharmacologist's Dilemma," *Pediatrics*, January 1970, pp. 3–4.

47. *Ibid.*, pp. 5–6.

48. *Ibid.*, p. 5.

49. *Ibid.*, p. 6.

appendix

1. "The Pot Problem," *Time*, March 11, 1965, p. 49.

2. Arthur Alarcon, quoted in Jerry Cohen, "Marijuana: Views Collide," *Los Angeles Times*, December 4, 1967.

3. David W. Mauer and Victor H. Vogel, *Narcotics and Narcotic Addiction* (Springfield, Ill.: C. C. Thomas, 1954), p. 238.

4. "The Marijuana Problem," *Newsweek*, July 24, 1967, p. 48.

5. A. Benabud, "Psychopathological Aspects of the Cannabis Situation in Morocco, Statistical Data for 1956," *Bull. Narc.*, Vol. 9, 1957, p. 4.

6. Shana Alexander, "The Case of the Pot-Smoking School Principal," *Life*, November 17, 1967, p. 25.

7. John Kendall, "Mother Warns of Drugs after Son's Death," *Los Angeles Times*, July 31, 1967.

8. Walton, *op. cit.*, p. 122.

9. Maurer and Vogel, *op. cit.*, p. 244.

10. Ausubel, *op. cit.*, pp. 102–103.

11. Samuel Allentuck, "Medical Aspects: The Marijuana Problem in the City of New York," in David Solomon (Ed.), *The Marijuana Papers* (Indianapolis: Bobbs-Merrill Co., 1966), p. 283.

12. David Smith, testimony given before California Assemblyman Pete Wilson, Los Angeles, March 1, 1968.

13. "Traditional: The Hodja," in Andrews (Ed.)., *op. cit.*, pp. 25–26.

14. Henri Michaux, "Light Through Darkness," in George Andrews (Ed.), *The Book of Grass* (New York: Grove Press, 1967), p. 102.

15. Walton, *op. cit.*, p. 121.

16. Gerard Piel, "Narcotics," *Life*, July 19, 1943.

17. C. Knight Aldrich, "The Effect of a Synthetic Marijuana-like Compound on Musical Talent as Measured by the Seashore Test," *Pub. Health Report*, 59(13), pp. 431–433.

18. Walton, *op. cit.*, p. 121.

19. William Burroughs, "Cannabis and Opiates," in Andrews (Ed.), *op. cit.*, p. 207.

20. Goode, *op. cit.*, p. 173.

21. William Burroughs, quoted in Donald Louria, *The Drug Scene* (New York: McGraw-Hill, 1968), pp. 102–103.

22. Ausubel, *op. cit.*, pp. 98–99.

23. James L. Goddard, letter to John J. Bellizzi, printed in *INOAE Newsletter*, November 1967.

24. "Opposed to Marijuana Use, FDA Chief Says," *Los Angeles Times*, November 9, 1967.

25. Transcript of WCCO tape of Goddard Press Conference, University of Minnesota, Minneapolis, October 7, 1967, in *INOAE Newsletter*, November 1967.

26. *Los Angeles Times, op. cit.*

27. Rosevear, *op. cit.*, p. 93.

28. Judge Charles Wyzanski, *Harvard Alumni Bulletin*, 11, 1967, quoted in Ferdinand Mount, "The Wild Grass Chase," *National Review*, January 30, 1968, p. 83.

29. American Medical Association, *The Crutch that Cripples* (Chicago: American Medical Association, 1967).

30. S. Charen and L. Perlman, "Personality Studies of Marijuana Addicts," *Amer. J. Psychiat.*, 1946, pp. 674–682.

31. F. T. Merrill, *Marijuana the New Dangerous Drug* (Washington, D.C.: Opium Research Committee, 1950).

32. Ausubel, *op. cit.*, p. 105.

33. Martin H. Keeler, "Adverse Reactions to Marijuana," paper presented at the 1967 meeting of the American Psychiatric Association, Detroit, Michigan, May 11, 1967.

34. Allentuck, *op. cit.*, pp. 269–283.

35. Frances Ames, "A Clinical and Metabolic Study of Acute Intoxication with Cannabis Sativa and Its Role in the Model Psychoses," *J. Mental Sci.*, 1958, pp. 972–999.

36. Cordeiro De Farias, "Use of Moconha (Cannabis Sativa L.) in Brazil," *Bull. Narc.*, Vol. 7, 1955, pp. 5–19.

37. Leary and Alpert, *op. cit.*, p. 209.

38. Rosevear, *op. cit.*, pp. 136–137.

39. Ron Einstoss, "Hippie 'Priest' Tells of Drug Use during Trial but Plea Fails," *Los Angeles Times*, January 26, 1968.

40. Rosevear, *op. cit.*, p. 136.

41. Jerry Cohen, "Hippie High Priest Convicted, Jailed for Marijuana Possession," *Los Angeles Times*, October 19, 1967.

42. Ron Einstoss, "Ex-Hippie High Priest Vows to Quit Drugs," *Los Angeles Times*, June 6, 1969.

43. Gene R. Haislip, "Current Issues in the Prevention and Control of Marijuana Abuse," paper presented to the First National Conference on Student Drug Involvement, University of Maryland, College Park, Md., August 16, 1967.

44. United States *vs.* Reynolds (1878), 98 US 145.

45. People *vs.* Woody (1964), 394 P. 2d, 813.

46. Sherbert *vs.* Verner (1963), 374 US 83 1790.

47. Stephen Abrams, "The Oxford Scene and the Law," in Andrews (Ed.), *op. cit.*, p. 236.

48. *Restriction of Research on Marijuana, Annual Report,* Drug Abuse Information Project, University of California Medical Center, San Francisco, p. 10.

49. "Pinning Down the Weed," *Science News,* September 27, 1969, p. 263.

50. *Ibid.*, p. 264.

51. *Ibid.*, p. 264.

52. *Ibid.*, p. 264.

53. "Pot Facing Stringent Scientific Examination," *Science News,* January 24, 1970, p. 103.

54. *Ibid.*, p. 104.

55. *Ibid.*, p. 105.

56. Timothy Leary and Richard Alpert, "The Politics of Consciousness Expansion," in Andrews (Ed.), *op. cit.*, pp. 209–210.

57. Rosevear, *op. cit.*, pp. 114–115.

58. *Ibid.*, p. 127.

59. *Ibid.*, pp. 135–136.

60. Farnsworth and Prout, *op. cit.*

61. Pablo Osvaldo Wolff, *Marijuana in Latin America: The Threat It Constitutes* (Washington, D.C.: Linacre Press, 1949), p. 31.

62. *Statement by the French Delegation,* May 14, 1963, U.N. Doc. E/CN 7/L 268.

63. Alfred R. Lindesmith, *The Addict and the Law* (Bloomington, Ind.: Indiana University Press, 1965), p. 234.

64. John Kaplan, *Marijuana, The New Prohibition* (New York: World Publishing Co., 1970), pp. 278–279.

65. *Ibid.*, p. 279.

66. *Ibid.*, p. 279.

67. J. Waller, "Chronic Medical Conditions and Traffic Safety,"

New England Journal of Medicine, Vol. 273, 1965, pp. 1413–1420.

68. Melvin L. Selzer and Sue Weiss, "Alcoholism and Fatal Traffic Accidents: A Study of Futility," *Municipal Court Review,* 1965, pp. 15–20.

69. Alcohol and Highway Safety, quoted in Kaplan, *op. cit.*, p. 276.

70. Kaplan, *op. cit.*, p. 285.

71. Kaplan, *op. cit.*, p. 277.

72. Alfred Crancer et al, "A Comparison of the Effects of Marijuana and Alcohol on Simulated Driving Performance," *Science,* October 31, 1969, pp. 851–854.

73. "Marijuana Fails to Mar Driving in Simulator," *Los Angeles Times,* June 4, 1969, p. 4.

74. H. Kalant, "Marijuana and Simulated Driving," *Science,* October 31, 1969, pp. 640–641.

75. D. F. Caldwell et al, quoted in "Marijuana Effects Turned Off," *Science News,* February 21, 1970, p. 197.

76. Kaplan, *op. cit.*, p. 282.

77. Crancer, *op. cit.*, p. 854.

78. Theodore James, "Dagga and Driving," *S.A. Medical Journal,* May 10, 1970, pp. 580–581.

79. *Ibid.*, p. 581.

80. W. H. McGlothlin et al, "Marijuana Use among Adults 1969;" Alfred Crancer et al, "Driving Records of Persons Arrested for Illegal Drug Use;" and J. Waller, "Chronic Medical Conditions and Traffic Safety," *N. E. J. of Med.*, 1965, pp. 1413–1420, quoted in Kaplan, *op. cit.*, p. 309.

81. Kaplan, *op. cit.*, p. 285.

82. Andrew T. Weil, Norman E. Zinberg and Judith Nelsen, "Clinical and Psychological Effects of Marijuana in Man," *Science,* December 13, 1968, pp. 1234–1242.

index